Phototriangulation

Phototriangulation

Sanjib K. Ghosh
The Ohio State University

Lexington Books
D.C. Heath and Company
Lexington, Massachusetts
Toronto   London

Library of Congress Cataloging in Publication Data

Ghosh, Sanjib Kumar, 1925-
    Phototriangulation.

    Bibliography: p. 229.
    Includes index.
    1. Aerial triangulation. 2. Astronautics in geodesy. I. Title.
QB311.G52   526.3'3   74-32494
ISBN 0-669-98210-5

Published simultaneously in Canada.

Printed in the United States of America.

International Standard Book Number: 0-669-98210-5

Library of Congress Catalog Card Number: 74-32494

To Dolly

Contents

List of Figures

List of Tables

Preface

Phototriangulation, or *spatial triangulation,* is the process for the extension and provision of control information (as may be necessary for topographic or similar mapping) by which the measurements of coordinates, angles, or distances on overlapping photographs are related to spatial solutions by using perspective principles. Generally, this process involves the use of aerial photographs and is called "Aerotriangulation" or "aerial triangulation."

As a teacher in photogrammetry, specifically while teaching phototriangulation, I have always felt the need for a book—a book which could be considered as a coherent picture of facts and ideas significant to the specific subject matter. This could not be done without research. The author's consolation is that he is not merely collecting others' work, but adding some of his own also, however modest and insignificant it may be.

There is a tendency in teaching to be extremely theoretical in approach, going too much into various abstract concepts and ideas. Photogrammetry is an applied science—the practical side must not be ignored. In this book I have attempted a blending of the theories and their applications in practice.

It is the purpose of this book to give a rigorous treatment to phototriangulation as a self contained subject. I will also try to describe its empirical background and to develop a feeling for its numerous applications. A number of special approaches have been included in order to exhibit the various general concepts and to increase the usefulness of the book even to specialists in various agencies and countries.

A serious attempt has been made to present various methods in a unified manner. The specialist may find many simplifications of existing proofs, and also new results. Several previously developed methods show that the apparent difficulties in problems may become almost trite once they are presented in a natural way and put into proper context.

The relevant references and/or sources have been listed in the Bibliography. They are indicated by numerical references in brackets in the text. The interested reader may sometimes obtain more information from these sources than has been presented herein. It is correct that the basic contents of most sections are available in specialized works (publications) streamlined for particular needs. However, the consolidation of ideas offering chances of comparative studies (in view of different available cameras, restitution instruments, computer and other facilities as well as various mathematical models and conceptual approaches) is something that would be lacking in such fragmentary studies. On the other hand, it can be stated with emphasis that one cannot become an overnight expert in phototriangulation by merely reading this book (or reading some journal articles or attending some lectures). The student should devote some time and effort to practice also.

Prerequisites

The use of this book presupposes some knowledge of elementary college-level mathematics: linear, matrix, and vector algebra; trigonometry; and projective geometry. For a greater appreciation, the reader should also understand the principles of least squares, propagation of variance, and their current symbology as used in the fields of engineering in general, and surveying and mapping in particular.

If this book is used as a basic (background) text in phototriangulation, the student will be aided by having taken several introductory college-level mathematics and general physics courses (particularly optics), followed by courses dealing with elementary photogrammetry, stereo photogrammetry, and adjustment computations.

Organization of the Book

The book is divided into thirteen chapters, which are divided into sections. The decimal numbering system has been used for major heading values. Figures and equations are also numbered according to chapter.

Chapter 1 deals with a brief history of phototriangulation and presents some fundamental concepts. The second chapter discusses the single-model method as applicable with high-flown photography to provide control for low-flown models. Chapter 3 presents a complete discussion of the aeropolygon method of strip triangulation, which is the method in maximum use today. The reader must understand this concept fully because various other methods (aeroleveling, independent models, computational sequential, independent geodetic control) are nothing but extensions of the basic concepts of the aeropolygon method. For this reason, the topics related to error sources (chapter 4) and error types (chapter 5) are discussed with primary references to aeropolygon. In view of this, a separate section (chapter 6) is presented on the adjustment of strips, also with a direct bias on aeropolygon. The adjustment concepts of other methods and formations are given in other chapters. Since the uses of auxiliary data are on the increase, it was felt that without some introductory ideas on various auxiliary data, the book would be incomplete. Therefore, chapter 11 deals with auxiliary data.

Accuracy and economic considerations are discussed rather broadly in chapter 13 to emphasize its importance in planning for triangulation jobs and in deciding which equipment and method would be suitable for the job. It is felt that enough has not been discussed here; but then, this book was not meant only for the planner or the working executive who wants more in this area. He also draws considerably from his own experience and requirements.

With the idea of enriching this presentation for the student, the researcher, and the practitioner, I have decided to present in the appendixes some relevant developments and explanations—the forms of matrices in the coplanarity condition as directly used in the independent models or sequential triangulation (Appendix A), the computer programs for simultaneous blocks (Appendix B), and the computer programs for Independent Blocks (Appendix C).

Perhaps some of the points in this book could have been made a little more clearly with the aid of well constructed elaborate examples from actual cases. This is a task for the future; time limitations did not permit this in some cases, while, in other cases, it was felt that the general flow of reading would have been disturbed.

Acknowledgments

The author acknowledges a great debt to his students, colleagues, and the members of the photogrammetry profession (particularly those within the American and International Societies of Photogrammetry). Concepts, innovations, and the like are to a greater or lesser degree based on work of others, and to sort out each contribution will be impossible here. However, special appreciation is expressed for the assistance obtained from Dr. Arthur J. Brandenberger, Director of the Department of Photogrammetry, Laval University, Quebec, Canada. He read the entire manuscript and made many useful suggestions. Dr. Henry J. Steward of the Ohio State University Department of Geodetic Science assisted in revising the manuscript with respect to technical English. I am grateful to Mrs. Jacqueline A. Orwig for her careful typing of the final manuscript and to Mr. Prabhakar Misra for his help in proofreading.

The number of people directly and indirectly involved in the publication-production of this book was considerable. They include the publisher, typists, editors, draftsmen, and many others. Finally my wife, Dolly, was also involved directly. They were all indispensable and I depended so much on their help. Nevertheless, the contents of the book are my responsibility.

If a professor thinks what matters most
Is to have gained an academic post
Where he can earn a livelihood, and then
Neglect research, let controversy rest,
He's but a petty tradesman at the best
Selling retail the work of other men.

KĀLIDĀSA, ~400 AD
in Mālavikāgnimitra i.17

1 Introduction

At the present time, about 90 percent of all new topographic maps in the world are compiled by aerial photogrammetry. The provision of control for such compilation is a huge task. Phototriangulation in one form or the other is used almost everywhere to supplement the already existing basic geodetic control as may be necessary. Compared to the purely geodetic ground-control methods (e.g., triangulation, trilateration, traversing, etc.) the methods of phototriangulation seem to be more economical, faster in operation, and ultimately yield more satisfactory results.

The information (data) obtained from phototriangulation is two-fold: primarily, the coordinates of the control points to be used in orienting the stereomodels as required for map compilation, and secondarily, the orientation elements to facilitate such orientations. The type of phototriangulation providing such complete information may be termed "total" or "global" (see Chap. 6). In most cases, however, phototriangulation involves coordinates of control points, either complete coordinates (X, Y, Z, that is, trivariate) or partial (planimetry or elevation, that is, univariate or bivariate). Examples of partial phototriangulation are:

1. Radial, principal point triangulation
2. Isocenter triangulation
3. Nadir-point triangulation
4. Stereo-templet triangulation

These partial methods will not be discussed in this book and reference can be made to the *Manual of Photogrammetry* [5].

1.1 History

J.H. Lambert of Switzerland may be considered to be the founder of space resection, which is the basis of aerial phototriangulation. In 1759 he discussed the geometrical properties of a perspective image and the procedure of finding the point in space from which a photograph was exposed. R. Sturm and G. Hauck, both of Germany, established the relationship between projective geometry and photography in 1833.

However, the real foundation of aerial triangulation was established and considerable progress made only during the twentieth century. The development of stereoplotting instruments and comparators in various European countries advanced the field further. Various methods of triangulation also evolved because necessary equipment became available, standard accuracy was required, and some other factors. However, most of these methods were empirical and adjustments were graphical or semicomputational. In the 1920s and afterwards, O. von Gruber and many others following him developed these techniques further. From the 1950s onwards, computational methods were increasingly encouraged as the facilities of more sophisticated computers became available. E. Church of the United States and other scientists following him developed computational (analytical) methods. Also in this area, the contributions of the U. S. Coast and Geodetic Survey (the National Oceanic and Atmospheric Administration) and the Canadian National Research Council have been significant.

Because of the costs involved, however, the computational methods almost exclude their use in the private sector. Among other reasons, this has led to the most recent (1960s) developments of the semianalytical methods (Chap. 8) and the development of analog stereoinstruments.

The efforts of the International Society of Photogrammetry (especially Commission III), with considerable support from the European Organization for Photogrammetric Research (OEEPE) and several national societies (particularly the American Society of Photogrammetry), have been instrumental in developing the science to its present state.

1.2 Various Classifications

In the existing literature and in scientific communications, phototriangulation is classified according to different criteria:

1. With respect to the *unit* analyzed
   a. *Single model* used, for example, to provide control for several low-flown stereomodels from one high-flown model, or to determine information on boundary points in cadastral work
   b. *Strip triangulation,* consisting of several models in one strip
   c. *Block triangulation,* consisting of several strips with or without crossing (tie) strips
2. With respect to the *ground control*
   a. Complete geodetic (ground) control
   b. Independent geodetic (ground) control
3. With respect to the *data acquisition* and *data processing* devices and methods

a. *Analog triangulation,* using analogical stereo-instruments
b. *Computational* (analytical) *triangulation,* using comparators for photocoordinates and high-speed electronic computers for numerical solutions
c. *Semianalytical* (or semianalog) *triangulation,* which is, broadly, a combination of analog and computational triangulation

4. With respect to *auxiliary devices*
   a. *Without* auxiliary devices and data
   b. *With* data obtained from auxiliary (airborne or other) devices

1.3 Instruments

Various instruments may be required in performing a phototriangulation. The specific instrument and its use depends on various factors such as availability, desired precision, time and funds available, and the experience and education of the workers. Some of the instrumentation which may be used is listed as follows:

1. For analog, computational, (analytical) or semianalog (semi-analytical) methods:
   a. *First-order (universal) type stereoinstruments,* for example, Wild A7, A10; Zeiss C5, C8; Nistri Beta; Galeleo-Santoni Model IV: Poivilliers Model B
   b. *Second-order stereoplotters,* for example, Wild A8, B8; Zeiss Planimat; Galeleo-Santoni Models III, II; Kern PG3, PG2; Poivilliers Model D; Thompson-Watts plotter; Kelsh plotter
   c. *Analytical plotters,* for example, Nistri-Bendix AP/C
   d. *Radial triangulators,* for example, Wild RT1
   e. Equipment for slotted-templet triangulation

2. For purely computational methods:
   a. *Stereocomparators,* for example, Zeiss PSK, Wild STK, Nistri TA3
   b. *Monocomparators,* for example, Mann (several models) and Brown multilaterative

3. For computation and adjustment work:
   a. *Computers* (high-speed electronic), for example, IBM 360 or 7094 systems
   b. *Desk calculators, slide rules,* etc.

4. For aid in preparation, photo inspection, etc.:
   a. *Stereoscopes* for example, Old Delft Scanning, Fairchild, Wild ST10, Zeiss OV

b. *Point-transferring devices,* for example, Wild PUG, Zeiss Snap Marker, Bausch & Lomb Variscale

c. *Drafting instruments and tools*

1.4 Operational Phases

All phototriangulation jobs can be divided into three distinct phases:

1. *Preparation* with respect to material, equipment, control data, etc.
2. *Data acquisition* involving instrument work, observation, card punching, etc.
3. *Data processing* involving computation and adjustment of the data as well as final evaluation and analysis

The details of each phase depend on the method of triangulation, the instrument used, accuracy requirements, and other factors. These will be discussed fully in the appropriate sections of this book.

In instrumental (analog) strip triangulation, one must pay special attention to the instrument used, that is, whether or not the instrument has a Zeiss parallelogram[a] or, whether or not the instrument is being used with a base-in or base-out[b] setting.

As an example of the base-in or base-out principle, if the first photograph of a strip is placed in the left plotting camera and the second in the right one in which it is to remain unaltered, the third photograph would have to be inserted in a plotting camera placed still further to the right. This problem may be solved mechanically by inserting the third photograph in the left plotting camera in place of the first one and by resetting the base, which had been set for the first pair of photographs, by displacement of the space-rod sleeves toward one another (base-inside, Figure 1-1) by opposite displacement of the space-rod sleeves away from one another (base-outside, Figure 1-2). The distance of the space-rod sleeves is then larger than that of the two projection centers. The space rods diverge downward, and it can be seen that this arrangement corresponds geometrically to an interchanging of the two plotting cameras.

---

[a]Zeiss parallelogram is a special design in most precision stereoinstruments. It involves the placement of cameras at fixed positions (perspective centers are separated by a constant distance). This permits the operation of the linear translation elements (bx, by, and bz) without actually moving the cameras (projectors), gives some freedom in the choice of the scale of the stereomodel, and some other advantages.

[b]Base-in and base-out are permissible settings in some instrument systems. With alternate base-in and base-out settings, it is possible to perform strip triangulation in an instrument with only two cameras.

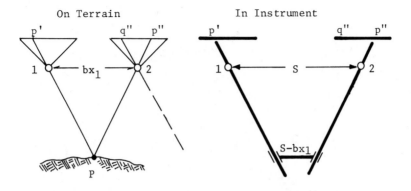

Figure 1-1. Base-in (schematic)

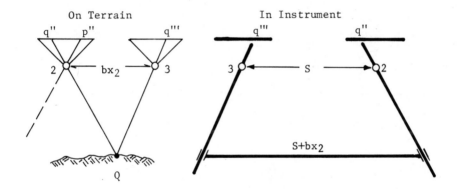

Figure 1-2. Base-out (schematic)

2

Single Model

This method, outlined first by Zeller in 1934 (see also Brandenberger [14]), is extremely helpful in determining control points for several low-altitude models from one high-altitude model. This method can be profitably used particularly in the photogrammetric determination of supplementary ground control and of boundary points in cadastral mapping. Both vertical and convergent photography can be used in this method.

2.1 Preparation and Observation

The preparation and instrument work phases in this method are similar to those of the first model in a strip triangulation. In order to avoid duplication, therefore, reference is made here to Chap. 3, where details for such models are discussed. However, since scale transfer is not required in the case of single models, steps 1g and 1h of Sec. 3.2 are not necessary.

2.2 Computation and Adjustment

New control points are determined from pairs of photographs adjusted at a precision stereoplotting instrument by reference of given fixed points. This can be done in one of several ways:

1. Graphically: Points plotted directly on a plotsheet are considered (elevations read off the instrument counter). The data can then be used directly for setting up in any plotter with a lower order precision.
2. Seminumerically: All coordinates of the points (X, Y, and H) are read off the instrument counters, misclosures adjusted graphically, and the points finally plotted separately at a coordinatograph. The data can then be used in subsequent plotting or simply for keeping a record.
3. Numerically: All coordinates (X, Y, and H) of the points read off the instrument are adjusted completely numerically (analytically).

   For a numerical or seminumerical adjustment the steps are as follows.

1. *Transformation* of the instrument planimetric coordinates (X, Y) to the ground system. This requires at least two, but preferably more, known ground control points.

2. *Adjustment* of the misclosures (closing errors) of each coordinate separately or simultaneously either graphically (seminumerically) or analytically (numerically).

3. *Assessment* of the accuracy. This is done by computing the standard errors (separately in X or Y or in planimetry) based on the residual errors for each coordinate at all the known points. This third step is optional and is taken only when an indication of the obtained accuracy is desired.

Transformation

Transformation of the planimetric coordinates is only permissible after the model has been levelled (see also Ghosh [35]). Otherwise, for purely numerical work, a three-dimensional spatial transformation must be performed. Here the working equations are

$$\left. \begin{array}{l} X^t = X_0 + aX - bY \\ \\ Y^t = Y_0 + bX + aY \end{array} \right\} \tag{2.1}$$

where a = a constant = $k \cos \theta$

b = a constant = $k \sin \theta$

θ = the angle between the two systems on the XY plane

X^t, Y^t = the transformed (ground) coordinates

X, Y = the instrument coordinates

X_0, Y_0 = the ground coordinates of the origin of the instrument system (that is, the shift components)

A form (see Fig. 2-1) has been developed for the purpose of transformation which has been extremely helpful.

In case an affine deformation is suspected (that is, the scales along X and Y are different), Equation (2.1) takes the form:

$$\left. \begin{array}{l} X^t = X_0 + aX - bY \\ \\ X^t = Y_0 + cX + dY \end{array} \right\} \tag{2.1a}$$

where a = $k' \cos \theta$ = constant

b = $k'' \sin \theta$ = constant

The working equations are:
$$\begin{cases} X^t = X_o + ax - by \\ Y^t = Y_o + bx + ay \end{cases}$$

Points	x	X^g	X^t	U	UU	Remarks
[ ]						
[ ]/n						

Points	y	Y^g	Y^t	V	VV	
[ ]						
[ ]/n						

Points	$x-x_s=x'$	$X^g-X^g_s=X'$	$y-y_s=y'$	$Y^g-Y^g_s=Y'$

$[x'x']+[y'y'] = I =$

$[x'X']+[y'Y'] = II=$

$[x'Y']-[y'X'] =III=$

$II \div I = a =$

$III \div I = b =$

$X_o = X^g_s-ax_s+by_s =$

$Y_o = Y^g_s-ay_s-bx_s =$

$m_p = \pm\sqrt{\{[UU]+[VV]\}\div(n-2)} =$

x,y : Machine coordinates

X^g,Y^g : Ground(given) coordinates

X^t,Y^t : Transformed coordinates

Note : Subscript s stands for the centroid of the used points

$U = X^g-X^t$ and $V = Y^g-Y^t$

Figure 2-1. Linear Transformation of Plan-Coordinates with Two or More Points

$$c = k' \sin \theta = \text{constant}$$

$$d = k'' \cos \theta = \text{constant}$$

k' and k" are the scale factors along X and Y, respectively.

Adjustment of Data

The aforementioned transformation yields the coordinates of both the given (known) points as well as the new points (meant to provide control for the low-altitude models, for example) in the ground system (X^t, Y^t), from the instrument system (X, Y). The ground coordinates (X^g, Y^g) of the given points may not exactly agree with the corresponding transformed coordinates. The differences $(\Delta X = X^g - X^t$ and $\Delta Y = Y^g - Y^t)$ are the results of the residual deformation present in the model because of various reasons. Differences in the elevations $(\Delta H = H^g - H)$ are directly obtained, i.e., known ground elevation minus the elevation read in the model after absolute orientation. These corrections, closing errors with changed signs $(\Delta X, \Delta Y, \text{and } \Delta H)$, at the given fixed points have to be used for determining the corrections that are to be applied next to each of the observed (transformed) coordinates and elevations of the new points. This can be done in two ways: graphically or analytically (numerically).

Graphical Adjustment. All the given (fixed) points and the new points are plotted graphically using a suitable scale. This is usually done at the plotting table while the points are read in the oriented model. Based on the differences of the transformed coordinates $(\Delta X, \Delta Y, \text{and } \Delta H)$ from the given values of the known points, curves of equal X, Y and H corrections are constructed by interpolation. An example is given in Fig. 2-2 where curves of equal Y corrections at intervals of 10 cm are constructed for a model.

Here points I through V are the given ground-control points and points 1 through 20 are the new points to supply control for the low-altitude models. With the aid of these curves of equal corrections (separately drawn for X, Y, and H) the corrections to the corresponding coordinates of the new points can be determined by interpolation. As a result, the final corrected ground coordinates of these new points are determined and are used to orient the low-altitude models.

Numerical (Analytical) Adjustment. The corrections, as assumed according to the laws of propagation of errors for a model, are expressed by the three following equations (see also model-deformation formulas in Ghosh [35]):

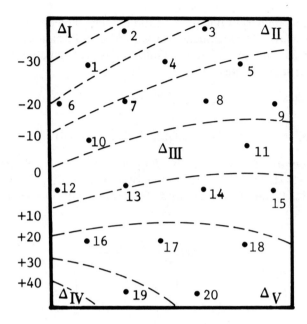

Figure 2-2. Curves of Equal Y- Corrections with Intervals of 10 cm

$$\Delta X = a_1 + a_2 \cdot X + a_3 \cdot Y + a_4 \cdot X^2 + a_5 \cdot Y^2$$

$$\Delta Y = b_1 + b_2 \cdot X + b_3 \cdot Y + b_4 \cdot X^2 + b_5 \cdot Y^2 \qquad (2.2)$$

$$\Delta H = c_1 + c_2 \cdot X + c_3 \cdot Y + c_4 \cdot X^2 + c_5 \cdot Y^2$$

where X, Y, and H are the coordinates and $a_1 \ldots a_5$, $b_1 \ldots b_5$, and $c_1 \ldots c_5$ are certain constants. ΔX, ΔY, and ΔH are each determined as explained earlier for at least five given points. The constants $a_1 \ldots a_5$ are obtained by solving the five corresponding linear equations in ΔX. Similarly $b_1 \ldots b_5$ and $c_1 \ldots c_5$ are obtained from the sets of linear equations in ΔY and ΔH, respectively. Next the corrections (ΔX, ΔY, and ΔH) to the coordinates of the new points are obtained by inserting their respective X and Y coordinates into the above equations.

This method of adjusting the coordinates proves to be very effective in practice. In case there are more than the minimum number of known ground control points in the model (five), an adjustment may be made using the least-squares principle to solve for the constants.

2.3 Example of Single-Model Triangulation

Given below is an example of determination of control points for four low-altitude models from one high-altitude model. The photographs were taken on a test area. The technical details are: Fairchild camera; $f = 150$ mm; format 23×23 cm; vertical aerial photography; triangulation at Wild A7 using compensation plates.

Flying altitudes: $h_{high} = 6000$m

                              $h_{low} = 2000$m

Model scale: 1:20,000 (high-flown model)

Ground control data are available for points W_1, W_3, U_2, S_1, and S_3 (see Figs. 2-3 and 2-4). The coordinates of all other points, i.e., W_2, V_1, V_2, V_3, U_1, U_3, T_1, T_2, T_3, and S_2 are required. The ground data and the instrument (observational) data are given in Table 2-1.

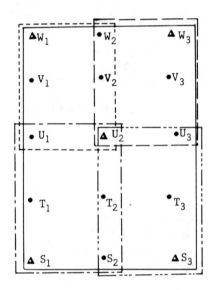

Figure 2-3. Schematic Location of Control Points and Models

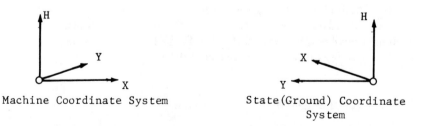

Machine Coordinate System   State(Ground) Coordinate System

Figure 2-4. Systems of Coordinates

Table 2-1
Ground and Observation Data

Points	Readings at A7 x(mm)	y(mm)	H(m)	Given Ground Coordinates and Elevation Y^g (m)	X^g (m)	H^g (m)
ΔW_1	123.26	522.20	377.6	6316.0	17,226.7	378.6
W_2	204.17	521.22	371.7			
ΔW_3	285.59	519.35	370.5	3068.2	17,172.3	371.2
V_1	123.17	442.58	376.4			
V_2	203.76	441.11	372.0			
V_3	282.96	438.83	370.3			
U_1	121.71	361.17	383.8			
ΔU_2	202.69	361.40	375.5	4726.7	14,015.0	376.4
U_3	283.92	358.58	374.3			
T_1	121.99	282.78	390.6			
T_2	202.93	284.33	386.5			
T_3	273.94	278.31	394.6			
ΔS_1	123.06	201.24	388.9	6319.7	10,808.4	388.3
S_2	200.01	199.99	382.1			
ΔS_3	284.92	202.36	391.8	3082.8	10,833.9	391.4

Procedure: The different steps are:

Step 1: The machine coordinates (x and y) are reduced to one system homologous (similar) to the state coordinate system by subtracting all the x values (machine) from a higher value (300.00 mm considered). Then the two systems become:

<pre>
        Y   X

        ↑   ↑
        | |
 X ←————'   Y ←————'

   In Machine   On Ground
</pre>

Step 2: Transformation of the machine coordinates is then performed from the x-y system to the Y-X system with the help of two points only (W_1 and S_3).

Step 3: Graphical adjustment is performed separately for the X'_a, Y'_a, and H'_a coordinates.

The general transformation equations in this case are:

$$Y = Y^0 + ax - by$$

$$X = X^0 + bx + ay$$

(Also see Eq. (2.1)).

After Step 1 we obtain the reduced (without transformation or adjustment) instrument coordinates (see Table 2-2). The constants of transformation (X^0, Y^0, a, and b) are then computed:

$$Y_1 = Y^0 + ax_1 - by_1$$

$$Y_2 = Y^0 + ax_2 - by_2$$

$$X_1 = X^0 + bx_1 + ay_1$$

$$X_2 = X^0 + bx_2 + ay_2$$

$$Y_1 - Y_2 = a(x_1 - x_2) - b(y_1 - y_2)$$

that is,

$$Y' = ax' - by'$$

Similarly,

$$X' = bx' + ay'$$

Therefore

$$a = \frac{Y' + by'}{x'} \; .$$

Now substituting this value in $X' = bx' + ay'$ we obtain

$$X' = bx' + \frac{y'Y' + by'y'}{x'} = \frac{bx'x' + y'Y' + by'y'}{x'}$$

$$b = \frac{x'X' - y'Y'}{x'x' + y'y'} = \frac{III}{I}$$

$$a = \frac{Y'}{x'} + \frac{x'X' - y'Y'}{x'x' + y'y'} \cdot \frac{y'}{x'}$$

$$= \frac{Y'x'x' + x'X'y'}{(x'x' + y'y')x'}$$

$$= \frac{(x'Y' + y'X')}{(x'x' + y'y')} = \frac{II}{I}$$

Table 2-2
Reduced A7 Readings

| Points | Reduced A7 Readings | | |
	x(mm)	y(mm)	H(m)
W_1	176.74	522.20	377.6
W_2	95.83	521.22	371.7
W_3	14.41	519.35	370.5
V_1	176.83	442.58	376.4
V_2	96.24	441.11	372.0
V_3	17.04	438.83	370.3
U_1	178.29	361.17	383.8
U_2	97.31	361.40	375.5
U_3	16.08	358.58	374.3
T_1	178.01	282.78	390.6
T_2	97.07	284.33	386.5
T_3	26.06	278.31	394.6
S_1	176.94	201.24	388.9
S_2	99.99	199.99	382.1
S_3	15.08	202.36	391.8

In our case, considering the two points W_1 and S_3

$$x_1 = 176.74 \quad x_2 = 15.08 \quad x' = 161.66 \text{ mm}$$
$$y_1 = 522.20 \quad y_2 = 202.36 \quad y' = 319.84 \text{ mm}$$
$$Y_1 = 6{,}316.0 \quad Y_2 = 3{,}082.8 \quad Y' = 3233.2 \text{ m}$$
$$X_1 = 17{,}266.7 \quad X_2 = 10{,}833.9 \quad X' = 6392.8 \text{ m}$$

$$Y = Y^0 + ax - by$$
$$X = X^0 + bx + ay$$
$$x_1 - x_2 = x' = 161.66; \ x'x' = 26{,}133.9556$$
$$Y_1 - Y_2 = Y' = 3233.2$$
$$y_1 - y_2 = y' = 319.84; \ y'y' = 102{,}297.6256$$
$$X_1 - X_2 = X' = 6392.8$$

$$x'x' + y'y' = I = 128{,}431.5812$$
$$x'Y' = 522{,}679.1120$$
$$y'X' =$$
$$x'Y' + y'X' = II = 2{,}567{,}352.2640$$
$$x'X' = 1{,}033{,}460.0480$$
$$y'Y' =$$
$$x'X' - y'Y = III = -646.6400$$

$$\text{II} \div \text{I} = a = 19.99003858$$

$$\text{III} \div \text{I} = b = -0.00503490$$

$$Y^0 = Y_1 - ax_1 + by_1 = 2780.33$$

$$X^0 = X_1 - ay_1 - bx_1 = 6788.79$$

All points are now transformed using the computed constants (see X'_a, Y'_a, and H'_a in Table 2-3). The correction graphs are then drawn (see Fig. 2-5). The corrections obtained from these graphs (δX, δY, and δH in Table 2-3) are now applied to obtain the final corrected (adjusted) coordinates (see X_a, Y_a, and H_a in Table 2-3).

From these are obtained the standard errors:

$$m_X = \pm \sqrt{\Sigma (e_x \cdot e_x)/n} \qquad (2.3)$$

and similarly for m_Y and m_H where n is the number of new points.

In this case the values are:

$$\left. \begin{array}{l} m_X = \pm 0.3 \text{ ft} \\ m_Y = \pm 0.7 \text{ ft} \\ m_H = \pm 0.4 \text{ ft} \end{array} \right\} \qquad (2.4)$$

2.4 Results from a Test

The following information obtained from a test conducted in the Department of Geodetic Science of Ohio State University is indicative of the requirements and results in similar applications of this method.

The test (Ohio State University Research Foundation Project No. 647) involved 41 models; vertical photography; standard cameras (i.e., focal length 6 in. and format 9 × 9 in.); flying height approximately 6000 m; overlap approximately 60 percent; model scale: 1:20,000 at Wild Autograph A7. Each model had at least four control points. The operators were moderately experienced (i.e., each having experience of more than 1 yr at the stereoplotting instruments).

The tests indicated:

1. Standard residual Y parallaxes in the instrument: ±0.02 mm (i.e., reduced to the picture, it is ±0.01 mm)
2. Standard error of scale determination of the models: ±0.02 percent
3. Standard planimetric errors: $m_X = m_Y = \pm 0.02$ mm in the model
4. Standard residual elevation error in the model after adjustment: $m_H = \pm 0.0001 \cdot h$ where h is the flying height
5. Standard pointing error of X and Y coordinates in the model: ±0.01 mm

17

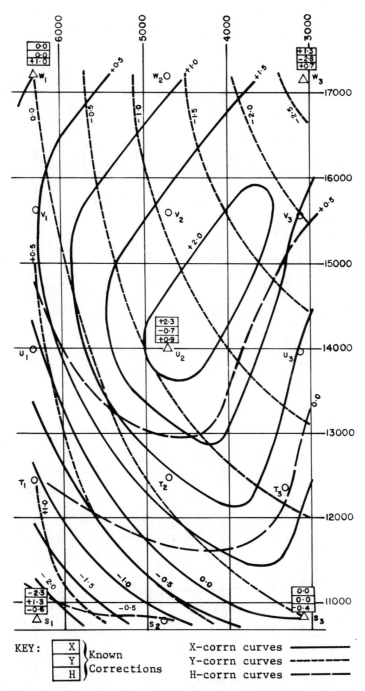

KEY:

X	}Known
Y	
H	}Corrections

X-corrn curves ————
Y-corrn curves − − − −
H-corrn curves —·—·—

Figure 2-5. Correction Graph

Table 2-3
Adjustment of Coordinates[a]

Points	Transformed Coordinates			Corrections from Graph (see Step 3)			Corrected Coordinates		
	X'_a	Y'_a	H'_a	δX	δY	δH	X_a	Y_a	H_a
ΔW_1	17,226.7	6316.0	377.6	0.0	0.0	+1.0	17,226.7	6316.0	378.6
W_2	17,207.5	4698.6	371.7	+0.9	-1.4	-0.8	17,208.4	4697.2	372.5
ΔW_3	17,170.5	3071.0	370.5	+1.8	-2.8	+0.7	17,172.3	3068.2	371.2
V_1	15,635.1	6317.4	376.4	+0.5	+0.3	+0.7	15,635.6	6317.7	377.1
V_2	15,606.1	4706.4	372.0	+1.6	-1.1	+0.8	15,607.7	4705.3	372.8
V_3	15,560.9	3123.2	270.3	+1.5	-2.0	+0.5	15,562.4	3121.2	370.8
U_1	14,007.7	6346.2	383.8	0.0	+0.6	+0.3	14,007.7	6346.8	384.1
ΔU_2	14,012.7	4727.4	375.5	+2.3	-0.7	+0.9	14,015.0	4726.7	376.4
U_3	13,956.7	3103.6	374.3	+1.0	-1.3	+0.2	13,957.7	3102.3	374.5
T_1	12,440.7	6340.2	390.6	-1.1	+1.0	0.0	12,439.6	6341.2	390.6
T_2	12,472.1	4722.2	386.5	+0.9	-0.2	+0.3	12,473.0	4722.0	386.8
T_3	12,352.1	3302.7	394.6	+0.7	-0.6	0.0	12,352.8	3302.1	394.6
ΔS_1	10,810.7	6318.4	388.9	-2.3	+1.3	-0.6	10,808.4	6319.7	388.3
S_2	10,786.1	4780.1	382.1	-1.2	+0.7	-0.5	10,784.9	4780.8	381.6
ΔS_3	10,833.9	3082.8	391.8	0.0	0.0	-0.4	10,833.9	3082.8	391.4

[a]This being over a test area, the ground coordinates of the new (assumed unknown data) points were available and were used to obtain the residual errors: $e_X = X_a - X_g$; $e_Y = Y_a - Y_g$ and $e_H = H_a - H_g$.

6. Standard pointing error in elevation: $\pm 0.00005 \cdot h$
7. Average time required at the instrument: 4 hr per model
8. Average time required for coordinate transformation with a desk calculator: 4 hr per model
9. Average time required in graphical adjustment: 4 hr per model

From the above results, the following conclusions may be drawn. Taking into consideration the general graphic limits on line thicknesses in mapping, a standard planimetric error of $\leq \pm 0.25$ mm is acceptable. This means that for the standard planimetric errors given above, if the instrument Wild A7 were used for map compilation, a transmission enlargement from autograph to coordinatograph scales up to eight times may be permissible.

The permissible graphical plotting accuracy of contours in precision topographical mapping with photogrammetric procedures is $\pm 0.0002 \cdot h$. This means that considering the standard pointing error in elevation shown above, one can easily use high-altitude photographs for providing control for about three times (somewhat more) enlarged low-altitude photographs.

3 Aeropolygon

The aeropolygon method (French *Cheminement aerien*) may be defined as one in which the geometry of exposure for the strip as a whole is reproduced (at the restitution instrument or through computation). This is done by using the principle of coorientation of the individual photographs in the strip. Aeropolygon is one of two methods of empirical (analogical) strip triangulation, the other being aeroleveling (see Chap. 7).

A first-order stereoplotting instrument (i.e., instruments of highest precision and versatility such as the Wild Autograph A7 or the Zeiss Stereoplanigraph C8 is generally used for precise strip triangulation with this method. Depending on the camera, the relative flying height, and the mechanical limitations of the stereoinstrument, a suitable scale is chosen for the instrument (model) coordinate system.

The relative orientation of pictures 1 and 2 is carried out after the correct principal distance, the interior orientation of the cameras, and the known approximate value of the base have been introduced. The model is then scaled, and absolute orientation performed. This is done with reference to a sufficient number of given ground-control points (at least three noncollinear ground-control points; or a distance, an azimuth, the longitudinal and lateral slopes between points in the model, and one vertical control point). The coorientation of the subsequent photos, 3, 4, 5, etc., (i.e., relative orientation with by, bz, ω, ϕ, and κ movements of the new photograph) is performed without the use of any auxiliary data. By such orientation and by scale transfer between the subsequent models, the oriented and scaled strip surface is reconstructed. The strip adjustment (correction for propagated errors) based on the errors (misclosures) at the given ground-control points is performed next. This can be done graphically, semigraphically, or analytically.

The entire operation may be divided into three distinct phases:

1. Preparation
2. Observation, etc. at the instrument
3. Computation and adjustment of the coordinates of all points in the strip

3.1 Preparation

To obtain maximum efficiency from the instrument there is a need for good systematic sequential preparation. This enables the entire job to be done with optimum speed, economy, and precision. The following preparatory steps are necessary:

1. Collection of data: As an example, trigonometric data, field sketches to help identify the control points, photographs along with the photoindices, charts, computation and other relevant forms, diapositives, and camera calibration data may be collected as the initial part of the preparation.

2. Selection of photos: Photos should be selected so that the least number of models (in the block and individual strips), as well as the least number of control points, are handled in subsequent operations. If photography has, for example, 80 percent fore-and-aft overlap, working models may be chosen so that models in one strip are made to appear squarely opposite those in adjacent strips. This will also facilitate block adjustment afterwards.

3. Decision on model and plotting scales: The model and plotting scales must be decided upon with respect to the camera focal length, the flying height, limitations in the stereoplotting instrument, accuracy requirements, etc.

4. Selection of control points: The available ground-control points are first identified and located on the photographs with the help of all available information. In addition to these, two types of pass (minor control) points are necessary: (a) transfer points (between models) and (b) tie or wing points (between strips).

   a. Transfer points (see Fig. 3-1): Points connecting models in the same strip [U (upper), C (central), and L (lower)] in the area common to two adjacent models, are selected. The C points along with two auxiliary points (call them a and b, good for elevation readings only, chosen very close to the nadir or principal point), are used for analogical transfer of scale from one model to the next. The C point also serves as the planimetric (X and Y coordinates) connection between the successive models. It is at this point that the X and Y counters at the stereoinstrument are set in the new model to the readings from the previous model. The U and L points are wing points near the upper and lower edges of the area common to two adjacent models. These transfer points have to be indicated with the utmost precision as they determine, among other things, the precision of the strip triangulation. The a, b, and C points should be as close as possible to the nadir point.

   b. Tie or wing points: Points connecting different strips (adjacent or crossing strips) where the required precision for the transference of

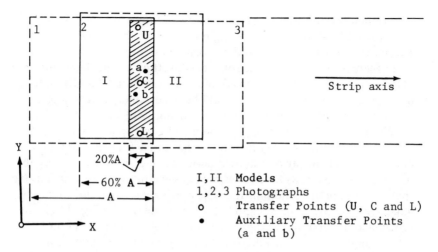

I,II   Models
1,2,3   Photographs
o   Transfer Points (U, C and L)
•   Auxiliary Transfer Points
        (a and b)

Figure 3-1. Location of Transfer Points Between Models

these points from one strip to the other need not be higher than the propagated precision obtained in the triangulation of a single strip. Tie points are not as decisive for the precision of triangulation as transfer points. They only determine the precision of the connection between the adjacent or crossing strips.

After selecting the location of the control points, these should be properly indicated by sketching or marking on the reference photo, diapositive, or negative in use. This is done better with a point marking and transferring device such as the Wild PUG or Zeiss Snap Marker.

Sketching of the points facilitates their identification at the instrument. When a point and its neighborhood are sketched, no marking is necessary on the photograph; only the area should be indicated with a circle and a reference number.

Marking on the emulsion of the diapositive or negative, and stereoscopic transference of such marked points, may be resorted to in an area where it is difficult to choose a point as in thickly wooded areas or desert areas. This ensures independence from the topography. The mark should be only on one photo of each strip which will avoid ambiguity and possible confusion.

5. Schematic diagram: A schematic diagram is prepared to show all the points to be read at the instrument. This is of great help to the instrument operator during observation as well as to the computer (adjuster) afterwards. The sequence of observation of the points may be indicated in this diagram.

6. Determination of initial κ, by, ϕ, and bz settings (for the first model): This should be done so that during observation, the operator does not exceed the limits of the by and bz scales in the instrument. For short strips there is usually no chance of exceeding the bz scale, but in the case of long strips this should be considered also. The initial ϕ and bz settings to be given to the first model should be ascertained at this stage.

A method of computing initial κ (swing) will be described here, which in view of its accuracy, recommends itself particularly for long strips. The essence of this method is that in each of the first and last photographs of the strip, a known point is selected in such a way that these two points are as far as possible equidistant from the strip axis (so that the straight line adjoining them is approximately parallel to the strip axis; see Fig. 3-2, points 1 and 83). A third point (2 in Fig. 3-2) is then selected in the first photograph at a sufficient distance from point 1. The ground angle α is determined from known ground coordinates. If line 1 to 83 is parallel to the axis of the strip, this angle α can be adequately regarded as the azimuth of the straight line 1 to 2. The first photograph is then inserted in the autograph camera in its zero position and the instrument coordinates of points 1 and 2 are read off in this photograph. The azimuth α' determined from the instrument coordinates differs from α by κ_1, that is, $\kappa_1 = \alpha - \alpha'$.

The angle κ_1, being the initial swing, is then introduced into the instrument camera. In case the line 1 to 83 is not approximately parallel to the strip axis, the strip axis should be determined first with the aid of the difference between the distances e_1 to e_{83} and the distances 1 to 83 between the two points. With the aid of this angle and the angle α, the azimuth of the line 1 to 83 in the instrument coordinate system and, subsequently, the initial swing can be determined. This initial swing is now introduced in the instrument camera carrying the first picture.

To help understand the above, consider the following problem (see Fig. 3-2).

Problem: Determine the initial swing κ_1 of a strip where the flight direction is east to west, the camera used is a Zeiss RMK (f = 21 cm; 18 × 18 cm), the photographs are vertical, the flying height is 3000 m, the model scale is 1:7500, and where four points are given. Ground coordinates are given in meters.

	X	Y
1	+2100.4	1470.4
2	2808.5	3555.9
83	18,157.2	528.7
84	18,250.1	2099.3

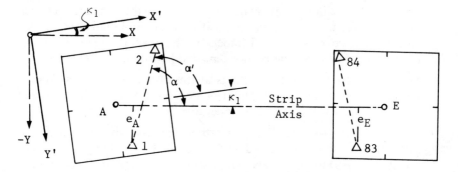

Figure 3-2. Determination of Initial Swing (κ_1)

The distances measured on the picture are:

1-2	153.4 mm
83-84	110.8 mm
e_A	75.0 mm
e_E	36.8 mm

Initial $\kappa_1 = 0$ gives instrument coordinates in millimeters

	X'	Y'
1	61.41	347.65
2	172.84	75.45

Suggested Procedure:

a. Compute α' from the instrument coordinates of points 1 and 2.
b. Find the average picture scale (determine separately from 1 to 2 and 83 to 84).
c. Find the distance l between 1 and 83 in the picture scale.
d. Find the angle θ between line 1 to 83 and the strip axis.

$$\frac{e_A - e_E}{l} = \theta$$

e. Find angle θ' (angle at 1 between 2 and 83) from ground coordinates.
f. $\alpha = \theta + \theta'$.
g. $\kappa_1 = \alpha - \alpha'$.

7. Determination of the effective principal distance. This will be used afterwards at the instrument (and should be done after properly consid-

ering the distortions, if any, in the film). For this, the distances between fiducial marks appearing in the diapositive/negative should be compared against their corresponding distances in the "taking" camera (as obtained from the camera calibration data or other sources of information).

8. Determination of all other settings at the instrument. Gears, knobs, levers, Dove prisms, etc., should be decided upon at this stage and should be recorded to guide the operator.

9. Testing the instrument. Before starting with the observation at the instrument, it should be tested with a model of precision grid plates to see if the instrument is capable of giving the desired observational precision in the strip triangulation.

3.2 Observation, etc., at the Instrument (Data Acquisition)

For an aerial triangulation by the aeropolygon method at any precision stereoinstrument, the following steps are necessary.

1. For the first model:
   a. Place the pictures on the plate carriers with emulsion side down. Check if the compensating plates were necessary.
   b. Place the plate carriers in their proper places in the instrument.
   c. Ensure proper settings of the principal distances (calibrated focal length); all gears; Dove prisms; diapositive lever; triangulation lever; sense of rotation of the hand wheels; Y-Z changeover knob; sense of rotation of the X, Y, and Z(H) counters; order of transmission to the plotting table; approximate base (bx, in or out, see explanation at the end of Chap. 1).
   d. Perform a satisfactory relative orientation.
   e. Perform a satisfactory absolute orientation (i.e., scaling and leveling of the model) with respect to the available ground-control data.
   f. Record the instrumental coordinates (X, Y, and elevation) of all the control points in the model from the instrument counters.
   g. Record the instrumental elevations of a, b, and C (and wing points if more precision is required) for the purpose of scale transfer. For example, read the elevations under stereovision at a, at b, and at C; and under pseudovision at a, at b, and at C.

   Note the elevations and the average of the stereo (normal) and pseudovisions at these points (respectively H_a, H_b, and H_C).
   h. Bring the measuring mark at 2C and disconnect the coordinate printer at this point.

2. For the second and all following models:
   a. Place the new picture properly on the picture carrier. Leave the picture common with the previous model at the instrument and replace the other picture with the new one.
   b. Change the Dove prisms and the triangulation lever.
   c. Introduce approximate base (bx) by changing "in" to "out" or vice versa (see end of Chap. 1).
   d. Perform a satisfactory coorientation (relative orientation) of the new picture with respect to the old one (common with the previous model).
   e. Transfer the scale with the help of the instrumental elevations read in this model at the a, b, and C points. This may be done by moving the Z foot disc and setting the elevation counter to read H_a of the previous model. At this point (a) bring the measuring mark to touch the ground by moving bx once under stereo (normal) vision and once under pseudovision. Repeat such settings of bx for H_b and H_C and eventually set bx to the average of such settings. Consider the wing points also for the scale transfer if more precision is required. This operation corresponds to the scale-restraint condition imposed in computational photogrammetry, (see Chap. 9).
   f. Check the relative orientation and scale transfer.
   g. Set the X and Y counters at the C point (common with the previous model) to their corresponding values read in the previous model.
   h. Record the coordinates (instrumental X, Y, and H) of all the control points in the model.
   i. Record the instrumental elevations of the forward a, b, and C points for the purpose of scale transfer to the following model.

Extreme care should be taken in the coorientation and scale transfer to the new models. All three points (a, b, and C) should be read twice for the instrumental elevations in the previous model. In the new model bx should be read at least twice for each point corresponding to its elevation (as read in the previous model). Finally bx should be set at the average value.

Instrumental backlash should be avoided in the setting of each element by having the last movement against some force (e.g., gravity or a spring). It is further suggested that two rounds of observations in opposite directions be made with a view to avoiding the effects of certain mechanical errors and any gross error in recording.

The recording of the instrument coordinates of all control points and the elements of orientation can best be done by using the scheme indicated in Tables 3-1 and 3-2.

Table 3-1
Instrument Data

PICTURE SCALE:			MODEL SCALE:		
Pair	bx (mm)	by' (mm)	by" (mm)	bz' (mm)	bz" (mm)
1-2	221.46, I	00.00	00.04	00.02	00.40
3-2	220.77, O	00.32	00.04	00.89	00.40
3-4	220.03, I	00.32	01.14	00.89	01.59

Table 3-2
Original Readings of Instrument Coordinates and Heights

	Model i									
	X(mm)			Y(mm)			H(m)			
Pair	I	II	Average	I	II	Average	I	II	Average	Point
1-2	0.00	0	0.00	100.00	0	100.00	425.0	4.8	424.9	12
	111.20	20	111.20	96.80	79	96.80	415.2	4.6	414.9	13
	166.37	37	166.37	267.39	40	267.40	471.8	1.6	471.7	2
	29.70	68	29.69	308.75	68	308.72	443.3	3.3	443.3	1
	128.54	57	128.56	185.91	93	185.92	434.1	3.9	434.0	101m'

3.3 Computation and Refinement (Data Processing)

The different steps are:

1. Averaging the instrument coordinates for two rounds of observations and correcting for model connection errors.
2. Transformation of the instrument coordinates to the ground system with the help of at least two (possibly all) of the known control points in the first model.
3. Adjustment of the coordinates, each separately, either graphically, semigraphically, or analytically.
4. Obtaining residual errors for each coordinate at all known points in the strip and computing the standard error. This step is optional and is taken only when an indication of the obtained accuracy is desired.

GEAR-SETTINGS:						
ω' (g)	ω'' (g)	ϕ' (g)	ϕ'' (g)	κ' (g)	κ'' (g)	Remarks
102.27	98.29	98.08	100.02	388.97	389.76	
97.43	98.29	100.37	100.02	391.72	389.76	
97.43	99.03	100.37	101.79	319.72	391.01	

Model i+1										
X(mm)			Y(mm)			H(m)				
I	II	Average	I	II	Average	I	II	Average	Pair	Remarks
111.22	25	111.24	96.76	78	96.77	412.6	3.2	412.9	3-2	
166.42	42	166.42	267.48	48	267.48	468.2	8.1	468.2		
128.56	55	128.56	185.94	93	185.94	434.0	4.7	434.4		

Averaging and Correcting for Model Connection Errors

The coordinate readings to a point from different rounds in the same model must first be averaged and the values rounded up according to the normal practice.

Considerable differences may occur between the instrument coordinates (X, Y, and H) read in a model (N) and those which result from the following model (N + 1) for the same points, especially for marginal pass points. These differences arise from imperfections in the relative orientations (for various reasons), instrumental errors (imperfect counter settings, changing of base inwards to outwards or vice versa, etc.), and errors in pointing. In practice, these errors are eliminated by connecting model N + 1 with model N mathematically such that the sum of the deviations of the instrument coordinates found in model N + 1, from the corresponding

Table 3-3
Final Model Connection

	Model i				Model i+1			
Pair	X(mm)	Y(mm)	H(m)	Point	X(mm)	Y(mm)	H(m)	Pair
1-2	0.00	100.00	424.9	12				
	111.20	96.80	414.9	13	111.21	96.75	414.6	3-2
	166.37	267.40	471.7	2	166.39	267.46	469.9	
	29.69	308.72	443.3	1				
	128.56	185.92	434.0	101m'	128.53	185.92	436.1	

values in model N (for X, Y, and H), becomes zero. This correction corresponds basically to accumulative linear shifts to the model as a whole, given separately for each coordinate (see Table 3-3). This correction takes care of the dissimilarities between adjacent models.

Even after the final model connection, differences still occur between the resulting instrument coordinates in models N and N+1 for the same points. These differences can be attributed to the accidental dissimilarity of the errors as already mentioned. Now the different values of the instrument coordinates resulting for the same points from adjacent models are averaged in order to obtain the final (unadjusted) values. A suggested recording scheme is presented in Table 3-4.

Transformation of the Instrument Planimetric
Coordinates to the Ground System

For this purpose the ground control points given in the first model are used. At least two (but possibly all) of the available ground-control points in the first model are needed for this. The transformation constants are determined in the same way as was discussed in Chap. 2 (see Eq. (2.1) and Fig. 2-1; also see Ghosh [35]). Since the elevations H are already read at the instrument in terms of the ground units, only X and Y coordinates are transformed for all points in the strip.

3.4 Adjustment of the Coordinates

The differences between the transformed instrument coordinates resulting from the triangulation at the instrument and the given ground coordinates

Table 3-4
Averaging of Instrument Coordinates

Point	X(mm)	Y(mm)	H(m)	Remarks
12	0.00	100.00	424.9	
13	111.21	96.77	414.8	
2	166.38	267.43	470.8	
1	29.69	308.72	443.3	
101m'	128.55	185.92	435.0	

of the given fixed points represent the errors (misclosures) ΔX, ΔY, and ΔH in these points which are conditioned by the triangulation. These errors are due to the effects of various sources (see Chap. 4). The data are corrected by using any method suitable for the purpose (see Chap. 6).

4

Sources of Error

Each component part of the working system in aerotriangulation contributes to the error and its subsequent propagation through the strip and block. While the errors due to approximations in the mathematics applied in various stages may be significant at times, it is beyond the scope of this section. Only the physical sources that are inherent in the system and the component parts will be discussed here. Analogical (empirical) corrections and/or computational data refinements should correct for these errors before or during the triangulation procedure.

4.1 Emulsion Carrier

The carrier of emulsion (film or glass, negative or diapositive) may be subject to dimensional or other errors which are functions of the material (film or glass type), time (aging), temperature and its variations, humidity variations, and also the treatment (both physical and chemical) of the material during, before or after processing. The effect on each picture may be complicated. However, for photogrammetric evaluations, they may be categorized as in the following subsections:

Dimensional Distortion

A distinction can be made between systematic and irregular distortions:

1. *Systematic (uniform) distortion*—Expansion or shrinkage may be considered as radial from any point in the photograph (e.g., fiducial center, see *Manual of Photogrammetry* [5]) and it produces a scale error, $dl_s:l =$ constant, for any length l measured on the photograph in any direction. It is known from experience that this error can reach an amount of 1/500 with film base. This causes an error in the interior orientation of the projected bundle of rays and can be eliminated by an appropriate proportional change in the principal distance (f) of the instrument camera or by a linear transformation (as in computational approaches) of the photo coordinates of points. In a limited sense, in some cases, this error can be eliminated by correct scaling of the stereomodel. The observed lengths between marks (fiducial or shrinkage—see Fig. 4-1) are compared with

33

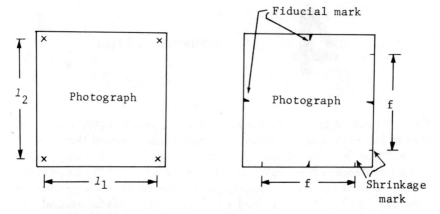

Figure 4-1. Information on Distortion in Different Cameras

their corresponding correct lengths (obtained from camera calibration data) to obtain information on the systematic distortion.

2. Systematic differential distortion, of a different nature, is often noticed in the film base, with one systematic distortion along the length of the film and a different systematic distortion along the width of the film, the errors being linear in each direction. Due to their complexity and the fact that the difference between the two linear scale errors are generally negligible for all practical purposes, in practice, no effort is made to correct for such errors in instrumental (analog) phototriangulation. In computational approaches, this error may be corrected by performing an affine transformation of the photo coordinates (see Ghosh [35]). In the instrumental approaches, an average of the scale errors is considered for the appropriate change in the focal length (principal distance).

3. Irregular distortion is conditioned by varying elastic properties of the material and can easily result in the displacement of the photo point by $\pm 10 - \pm 20 \ \mu$m. Such errors can be complex and do not usually follow a normal distribution pattern. As such, no effort is generally made in practice to correct for their occurrence.

In the analytical (numerical-computational) approach, the effects of such distortions can be, to a great extent, compensated by using correction equations as below (see Keller and Tewinkel [52]):

$$
\left.
\begin{aligned}
x' &= x + a_1 + b_1 x + c_1 y + d_1 xy \\
y' &= y + a_2 + b_2 x + c_2 y + d_2 xy
\end{aligned}
\right\}
\tag{4.1}
$$

where x', y' are the corrected coordinates of photo points x, y are the observed (uncorrected) values

$a_1, b_1 \ldots c_2, d_2$ are certain coefficients to be determined

The four fiducial marks yield four sets of such equations. Keller and Tewinkel point out that these two equations correct for several influences at the same time.

1. a_1 and a_2 provide translations to the origin from the comparator system to the principal point (fiducial center) of the photograph.

2. $b_1, b_2, c_1,$ and c_2
   a. Accomplish the rotation of the observed system.
   b. Account for the nonperpendicularity of the comparator axes.
   c. Correct for skewness of axes caused by film distortion.
   d. Correct for scale differences in x and y regardless of whether the error is caused by differential film distortion or errors in the comparator.

3. d_1 and d_2 provide a quadratic or curvilinear correction for film distortion.

Note: Similar corrections may be easily applied by using Réseau photography.[a]

Lack of Flatness

For good metric work it is necessary that the image surface defined by the surface of the emulsion be absolutely flat. Lack of flatness may cause unsharpness or deviation or both. The deviation should not exceed $\pm 20 \mu m$, for normal analog work. This is particularly important in case an optical-projection-type instrument is used for the triangulation. This is never a very serious problem in stereoplotting instruments or comparators with orthogonal (to the photo surface) viewing. On the other hand, lack of sufficient flatness of the image surface during the exposure (in the taking camera) is an error, which may considerably affect the quality of the subsequent triangulation.

This problem is overcome greatly by using Réseau photography. In computational work this can be done by performing a separate transformation for each image point by using preferably the four surrounding Réseau points [5]. In analog (instrumental) approach corrections can be applied based on precalibration of the stereomodel containing the Réseau grid [5].

---

[a]Réseau (focal-plane grid plate) photography is usable to correct for any kind of film deformation.

36

Image Unsharpness

Image unsharpness may occur as a result of limited resolving power of the emulsion, limited and varied resolving power of the camera lens, and the optics of the measuring instrument. Note that resolution is indicated in lines per mm. The optical resolution is a function of the radial distance (from the photo center). The image unsharpness may also be caused by the movement of the camera during the opening of the shutter (exposure) in flight. Although in many modern cameras the latter effect is compensated greatly by using the IMC (Image Motion Compensation) devices, the final resulting unsharpness could be considerable. Deviations due to unsharpness of the image should not exceed $\pm 20\mu$m for normal work. Sharpness differences in the two corresponding images yielding stereoscopic models may contribute towards varying pointing accuracies. Generally this is seldom a cause of concern. However, in jobs demanding very high accuracy, this is worth considering.

4.2 Camera

The photograph used in phototriangulation must, theoretically, fulfill the condition of being a central projection. This condition is not completely obtained due to mechanical and optical errors of the photographing camera or the projecting camera of the instrument. The resulting errors can be categorized as follows.

Interior Orientation

The deviations in the projected bundle of rays (during phototriangulation) from the corresponding bundle in the object space (during photographing) can be considered in terms of six errors of interior orientation.

$d\bar{x}$, $d\bar{y}$: Two translation errors of the photograph with reference to the perspective (projection) center, 0.

df : Translation error of the photograph, along the camera axis, with respect to the perspective center, 0. This corresponds to a focal-length error.

$d\bar{\omega}$, $d\bar{\phi}$, $d\bar{\kappa}$: Rotation errors, the first two defining the nonperpendicularity of the image plane to the camera axis and the last one defining the rotation around the camera axis.

With approximately vertical photography and relatively flat terrain, the procedures of relative orientation, scaling and absolute orientation of the stereomodel largely compensate the errors of interior orientation (see Brandenberger [14]). In the case of convergent, normal-convergent, or tilted photography, or photographs on mountainous terrain, such compensation is only partially possible, and such errors can be critical.

For an understanding of this and derivations see Ghosh [35].

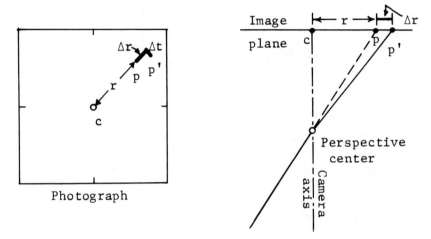

Figure 4-2. Objective (lens) Distortion

Objective (Lens) Distortion

The image point is displaced and the central projection is disturbed by objective distortion (lens distortion). With reference to the picture plane, usually a distinction is made between radial (Δr) and tangential (Δt) distortions. Systematic radial distortion may be represented by the distortion curve (obtained from camera calibration). To some extent, for many modern cameras, such distortions may be ignored for all practical purposes. Excessive systematic radial distortion is usually eliminated either by using compensation devices in the system (e.g., compensation plates, cams, or lenses similar to that of the taking camera in the instrument [Porro Koppe principle] or the reproduction system) or by computational procedures. Conventionally, the radial distortion is considered positive when it is in the direction away from the center of the field (see also *Manual of Photogrammetry* [5]). The radial distortion can be considered in terms of two components (Δx and Δy), as in Fig. 4-3.

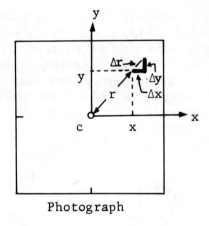

Photograph

Figure 4-3. Components of Radial Distortion

The radial distance (r) is given by the formula:

$$r = \sqrt{x^2 + y^2} \tag{4.2}$$

The distortions and their components are related to each other through the expressions

$$\frac{\Delta r}{r} = \frac{\Delta x}{x} = \frac{\Delta y}{y} \tag{4.3}$$

From this one can obtain the required correction formulas:

$$\left. \begin{aligned} -\Delta x &= -\frac{x \cdot \Delta r}{\sqrt{x^2 + y^2}} \\[2ex] -\Delta y &= -\frac{y \cdot \Delta r}{\sqrt{x^2 + y^2}} \end{aligned} \right\} \tag{4.4}$$

The corrected photo coordinates will be given by:

$$\left. \begin{aligned} x' &= x - \Delta x = x\left(1 - \frac{\Delta r}{r}\right) \\[2ex] y' &= y - \Delta y = y\left(1 - \frac{\Delta r}{r}\right) \end{aligned} \right\} \tag{4.5}$$

An alternative method is to fit a polynominal to the distortion curve, e.g.,

$$\Delta r = a_0 r + a_1 r^3 + a_2 r^5 + a_3 r^7 + \ldots \qquad (4.6)$$

in which at least five to six terms are taken to express the curve adequately. This finally gives

$$\left. \begin{array}{l} x' = x(1 - a_0 - a_1 r^2 - a_2 r^4 - \ldots) \\[2mm] y' = y(1 - a_0 - a_1 r^2 - a_2 r^4 - \ldots) \end{array} \right\} \qquad (4.7)$$

Due to the complex nature of the asymmetry of radial distortion, in practice generally no effort is made to compensate for the irregular part of such errors. This is particularly true of the tangential distortion.

4.3 Instrument

Several different types of instruments are used in phototriangulation. The instrument (analog stereoplotter, analytical plotter, or comparator) is never perfect. Such instrumental errors generate systematic and irregular observational errors of photo (or model) coordinates or operational errors of relative and absolute orientations or scale transfer between models. The magnitude of these errors can only be reduced to the level of observational errors (of the coordinates). The systematic errors of phototriangulation caused by systematic instrumental errors can be compensated with relative ease. However, elimination of the irregular parts of such errors is virtually impossible. Such irregular instrument errors follow a distribution, which is generally different from a normal distribution and may, after propagation, tend to appear as systematic (see quasisystematic errors in Chap. 5).

4.4 Operator (Observer)

The so-called "personal (observational) errors" caused by the instrument operator must be accounted for. Partly these are contributive to the *operational errors* (discussed in Chap. 5) and partly they are *interpretational*, resulting in *pointing errors*. Blunders due to carelessness of the operator or misinterpretation or misidentification of points cannot be totally avoided but must be kept to a minimum by providing adequate checks at various stages. Personal errors are generally irregular and follow a more or less random distribution pattern; however, there are systematic differences between individual operators and sometimes a systematic trend occurring due to physiological (e.g., eye fatigue) or psychological causes may be noticed. It has been noticed that personal errors tend to reduce with the experience of the operator. A combination of high-quality instrument, photographs, and ground control worked upon by an experienced operator is capable of giving top quality results from phototriangulation.

4.5 Earth's Curvature

If the triangulation is performed in a true rectangular three-dimensional space-coordinate system (e.g., universal geocentric, local-space-rectangular, etc.) the earth-curvature effect is automatically taken into consideration.

If, however, the work is performed in a geodetic system with respect to a reference surface it is advisable to consider the earth's curvature effect.

The aerial photograph is a central projection on a plane, but the geodetic positioning of points on the earth's surface is based on one (or the other) of the following reference surfaces (see also Clark and Clendinning [22]):

1. Geoid (every point is horizontal, by definition, on the geoid—spirit leveling refers to geoid).
2. Any reference ellipsoid (a regular geometrical shape of ellipsoid of revolution, different according to different experts' ideas).
3. Earth sphere (approximated, best fitting sphere).

None of these reference (curved) surfaces can be portrayed by the photograph without distortion. However, for a single photograph covering a limited part of the earth's surface, the reference surface may be assumed to be a sphere, for all practical purposes. The situation is, however, different in a stereomodel, a strip, or a block.

The correction may be applied either to the individual photos or the stereomodels (strip or block). The former approach seems to be more convenient in computational work whereas the latter is traditionally used in analog work.

In a purely computational approach (e.g., with comparator measurements or with an analytical plotter) this correction may be added to the corrections due to lens distortion and refraction. Earth-curvature correction may be sizable sometimes (see Table 4-1). The error (in the amount of the computed correction) due to nonverticality of the photograph may exceed other image errors. For this reason, for precision work, earth-curvature correction is not always favored. In the analog approach corrections may be applied at various stages: with correction plates at the diapositive printer or at mechanical correction cams in the plotting instrument (e.g., Kern PG instruments or Wild A10).

Table 4-1
Radial Distortion Effect Due to Earth's Curvature[a]

At r (mm)	For Flight Height (km)						
	0.5	1	2	4	6	8	10
10	0	0	0	0	0	0	0
20	0	0	0.1	0.1	0.2	0.2	0.3
40	0.1	0.2	0.4	0.9	1.3	1.8	2.2
60	0.4	0.8	1.5	3.0	4.5	6.0	7.6
80	0.9	1.8	3.6	7.2	10.8	14.3	17.9
100	1.8	3.5	7.0	14.0	21.0	28.0	35.0
120	3.1	6.0	12.1	24.2	36.3	48.4	60.5
140	4.9	9.6	19.2	38.4	57.6	76.8	96.0

[a]Vertical photograph; f = 15 cm. Negative radial distortions are given in micrometers.

On Single Photographs

The situation is shown in Fig. 4-4 where a perfectly vertical photograph and a spherical reference surface is assumed. With an ellipsoid or other reference figure of the earth, the situation is somewhat different.

If we consider the geodetic distance S of a ground point P from the nadir point N, the correct location of the image point should be p′ and not p where it is photographed. This displacement ds (p′p) is always negative (towards the photograph nadir point n) and increases with the third power of S. The amount of displacement ds is

$$ds = \frac{h \cdot s^3}{2R \cdot f^2} = \frac{fS^3}{2Rh^2} \tag{4.8}$$

On Stereomodel, Strip or Block

In stereophotogrammetry with model point P obtained by intersection of two conjugate rays from the two photographs, the terrain being recreated is in the desired scale and in proper orientation and the earth's curvature has little effect upon a single model. However, strip and block formation would yield misclosures in rectangular coordinates (the origin of the measuring system of coordinates being in the first or starting model).

Misclosure in Elevations. After the starting model is properly oriented, the elevations are referenced to the tangent plane through the center (M) of this

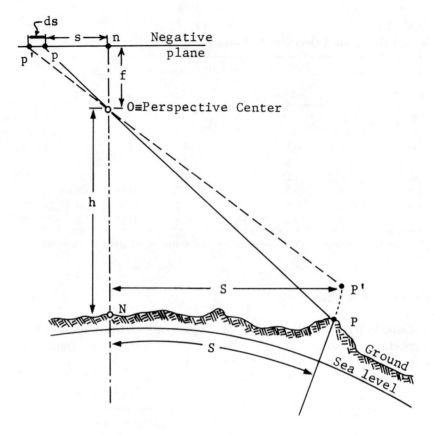

Figure 4-4. Earth Curvature Effect on a Photograph

model (see Fig. 4-5). This means that during triangulation, H′ is read as the elevation difference instead of the correct value H. The difference between H and H′ increases as the distance of the point from M increases.

This elevation error (misclosure):

$$\Delta H = H' - H \approx R - \sqrt{R^2 + X^2} = R\{1 - \sqrt{(1 + X^2/R^2)}\} \quad (4.9)$$

where R is the radius of the earth sphere. Since X is small compared to R, this expression can be expanded into a series:

$$\Delta H \approx - \frac{X^2}{2R} + \frac{X^4}{8R^3} - \dots \quad (4.9a)$$

In short strips, depending on the accuracy requirements, it may be sufficient to consider the first term only.

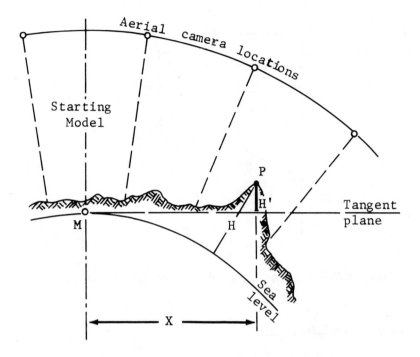

Figure 4-5. Earth Curvature Effect on Elevation

Misclosure in the Planimetric Distance. The recorded distance (planimetric) of a point P from the point M corresponds to the projection of the distance S (see Fig. 4-6) onto the tangent plane through M. Accordingly, the distance error (misclosure) is

$$\Delta S = D - S = R \sin \beta - R\beta$$

where S is the geodetic distance, D is the recorded distance, and β is the subtended angle (at the center of the earth sphere) corresponding to S.

Expanding $\sin \beta$ into a series,

$$\Delta S = R\left(\beta - \frac{\beta^3}{6} + \ldots - \beta \right) \tag{4.10}$$

Neglecting higher order terms,

$$\Delta S \approx - \frac{R\beta^3}{6}$$

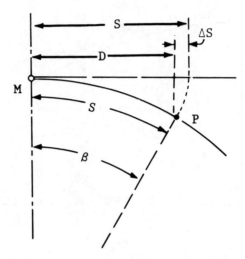

Figure 4-6. Earth Curvature Effect on Planimetric Distance

Also because $\beta = S/R$ we get

$$\Delta S \approx - \frac{S^3}{6R^2} \qquad (4.10a)$$

or approximately, $S = D$

$$\Delta S \approx - \frac{D^3}{6R^2} \qquad (4.10b)$$

This effect may be neglected in many practical cases, e.g., with $D = 100$ km, $\Delta D = \Delta S \approx -5m$.

With Elevation, Affecting Bridging

In aeropolygon techniques the first model is practically unaffected because its scale is determined by means of given coordinates with respect to the sea level. It is, however, necessary to reduce to sea level datum the instrument X and Y coordinates of points determined by the triangulation. The distance S between two points A and B shows a small error dS (see Fig. 4-7) with respect to the corresponding distance on the level of control used in the first model. This becomes more of a problem in super-wide-angle photography on highly mountainous terrain. The amount dS depends on the elevations H_A and H_B of the points A and B, and is given by:

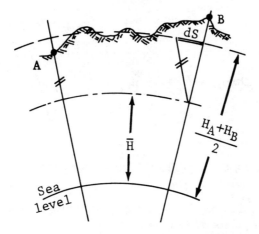

Figure 4-7. Reduction of Instrument Distance to Sea Level

$$dS = \left(\frac{H_A + H_B}{2} - \overline{H} \right) \frac{S}{R} \qquad (4.11)$$

where $\overline{H}$ indicates the mean elevation of the given ground-control points in the first (initial) model.

R is the radius of the earth sphere.

As an extreme example consider wide-angle (standard) photography, i.e., f = 150 mm; format 230 × 230 mm; flying height h = 13,000 m. Consider two points L(A) and U(B) at the lower and upper edges of the strip such that

$$\Delta Y_{L,U} = S \approx 17,000 \text{ m}$$

$$\overline{H} = 1000 \text{ m}; \quad \frac{H_L + H_U}{2} = 4000 \text{ m}$$

In this case, using Eq. (4.11),

$$dS = d\Delta Y_{L,U} = 8 \text{ m}$$

Generally, this error dS is negligible in the Y coordinates (width) of the strip. This is, however, different in the X coordinates (length) of the strip, because of an accumulation of the errors in the models during the strip formation.

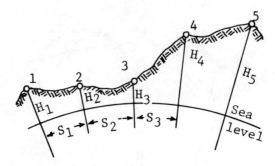

Figure 4-8. Strip Profile Along Transfer (Nadir) Points

Consider errors dS_i for the distance S_i between successive (close to nadir) transfer points (see Fig. 4-8), i.e.,

$$\text{for} \quad S_1 \approx \Delta X_{1,2} \quad \text{giving} \quad dS_1 = \left(\frac{H_1 + H_2}{2} - \overline{H} \right) \frac{S_1}{R} \approx 0$$

$$S_2 \approx \Delta X_{2,3} \qquad dS_2 = \left(\frac{H_2 + H_3}{2} - \overline{H} \right) \frac{S_2}{R}$$

$$\vdots \qquad\qquad \vdots$$

$$S_N \approx \Delta X_{N,N+1} \qquad dS_N = \left(\frac{H_N + H_{N+1}}{2} - \overline{H} \right) \frac{S_N}{R}$$

For a transfer point at the end of model N the total closure error is

$$\Delta S = dS_1 + dS_2 + \ldots + dS_N \tag{4.12}$$

and, further,

$$\Delta S \approx \Delta X = \frac{F}{R} \tag{4.13}$$

where   F is the area (shown in Fig. 4-9), the algebraic sum of the vertical plane areas bounded by the straight lines connecting points 1, 2 ... N, the normals at points 1, 2 ... N and the line of equal sea-level elevation $\overline{H}$.

R is the radius of the earth sphere.

For long strips in mountainous areas this error can attain a significant amount. For example, if $F = 50$ km², ΔX becomes 8 m. The functional curve of ΔX is a purely empirical one (see also Brandenberger [14] and *Manual of Photogrammetry* [5]), according to the different ground forms.

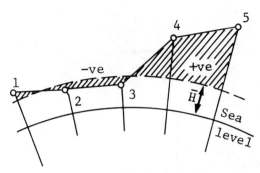

Figure 4-9. Explanation of F

It has to be decided for each case as to what extent this error should be considered. In the case of extermely rugged terrain, it is advisable to reduce each model to sea level.

Such corrections should always be considered in graphically plotted planimetric aerial triangulation. In purely numerical work, particularly when the retangular universal coordinates system is used, this is automatically taken care of during or before the adjustment phase.

4.6 Atmospheric Refraction

The atmospheric refraction causes a radial displacement (see dr in Fig. 4-10) of image due to the bending of the optical rays between the ground points and the image points.

The atmosphere may be considered in terms of a certain number of layers with refractive indices decreasing from sea level upwards. Considering the surface of contact between two layers of atmosphere (see Fig. 4-11), one gets the following relationship according to Snell's law:

$$(n + dn)\sin\beta_i = n \cdot \sin(\beta_i + d\alpha) \tag{4.14}$$

where $n, n + dn$ are the refractive indices of the upper and lower layers, respectively.

$\beta_i, \beta_i + d\alpha$ are the angles of incidence and refraction, respectively, at the surface of contact.

This gives:

$$\frac{n + dn}{n} = \frac{\sin \beta_i \cdot \cos d\alpha + \cos \beta_i \cdot \sin d\alpha}{\sin \beta_i}$$

The angle $d\alpha$ being very small, $\sin d\alpha \approx d\alpha$ and $\cos d\alpha \approx 1$, that is,

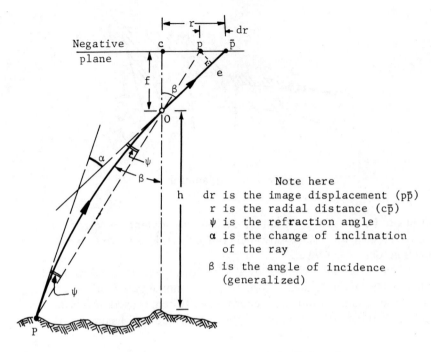

Figure 4-10. Effect of Atmospheric Refraction

$$\frac{n + dn}{n} = 1 + \frac{dn}{n} = 1 + d\alpha \cdot \cot \beta_i$$

and

$$d\alpha = \frac{dn}{n} \tan \beta_i \qquad (4.15)$$

We can generalize, without any appreciable error, for the entire ray path with $\beta_i = \beta$. Next, integrating Eq. (4.15),

$$\alpha = \int_{\alpha_p}^{\alpha_0} d\alpha = \tan \beta \int_{n_p}^{n_0} \frac{dn}{n} = \tan \beta \cdot \ln (n) \Big/_{n_p}^{n_0} \qquad (4.16)$$

This requires the values of the refraction coefficients, n's, which can be obtained from simple expressions or standard tables used in practice (e.g., the Smithsonian Institute physical tables [90]):

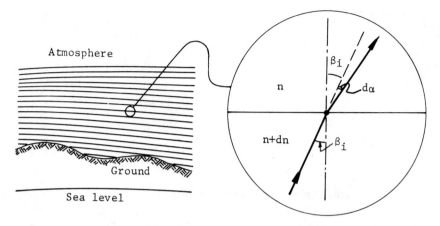

Figure 4-11. Refraction of Light Ray

$$n = 1 + \frac{n' - 1}{1 + at} \cdot \frac{B}{760} \qquad (4.17)$$

where n' = refraction index at 0°C and 760 mm air pressure = 1.0002926

   a = expansion coefficient of air due to temperature

   t = temperature (°C) at the location in question

   B = air pressure (mm) at the location in question

For all practical purposes we can assume the path of light to be circular and, therefore (see Fig. 4-10),

$$\Psi = \alpha/2 \qquad (4.18)$$

Now, combining Eqs. (4.18) and (4.16).

$$\psi = \frac{\tan \beta}{2} \cdot \ln (n) \bigg/ \begin{matrix} n_0 \\ n_p \end{matrix} \qquad (4.19)$$

Considering Fig. 4-10

   $pe = Op \cdot \psi \approx f \cdot \sec \beta \cdot \psi$ and $dr = p\bar{p} = pe \sec \beta = f \cdot \sec^2 \beta \cdot \psi$

that is

$$dr = f \cdot \sec^2 \beta \cdot \frac{\tan \beta}{2} \cdot \ln (n) \bigg/ \begin{matrix} n_0 \\ n_p \end{matrix} \qquad (4.20)$$

This can be modified by considering

$$\tan \beta = r/f \text{ and } \sec \beta = \frac{\sqrt{r^2 + f^2}}{f}$$

This gives

$$dr = \frac{(r^2 + f^2)r}{2f^2} \cdot \ln (n) \Big/ \begin{matrix} {}^{no} \\ {}_{np} \end{matrix}$$

$$= \frac{(r^2 + f^2)r}{2f^2} [\ln (n_o) - \ln (n_p)] \qquad (4.20a)$$

This expression also indicates that very inclined rays are critically dangerous as dr increases with the third power in r and this effect is somewhat comparable to that caused by the earth's curvature (although in the opposite direction). This error is considered positive (radially away from the nadir point on the vertical aerial photograph).

Further, according to Eq. (4.17), we obtain, respectively, at O and P

$$n_o = 1 + \frac{n' - 1}{1 + at_o} \cdot \frac{B_o}{760}$$

and

$$n_p = 1 + \frac{n' - 1}{1 + at_p} \cdot \frac{B_p}{760}$$

where n_o and n_p are the refraction indices at O and P, respectively

       t_o and t_p are the air temperatures (°C) at O and P, respectively

       B_o and B_p are the air pressures (mm) at O and P respectively

In normal practice (e.g., in U.S. National Oceanic Survey[b] [52]) a standard atmosphere is assumed. No attempt is made to account for temperature, pressure, or humidity variations. Equation (4.20a) is adopted as a power series

$$dr = k_1 r + k_2 r^3 + \ldots \qquad (4.21)$$

where k_1, k_2, etc., are constants. The series is considered up to two terms in practice. dr, k_1 and k_2 are pretabulated for the standard atmosphere with respect to the particular camera used for the specific job.

In this respect, also see Schut [88], Bertram [13], and U.S. Government Publication [103].

[b]At the time of publication, the survey was known as the U.S. Coast and Geodetic Survey.

4.7 Geodetic—Cartographic System

Basically the measurements in stereotriangulation for the determination of new points need to be made in the particular system of reference. They have to be finally expressed in terms of the map projection (or reference grid) system used for the area in question. Generally, the given coordinates are available in the particular reference system, and are consequently affected by the distortions of that system (e.g., the distances determined from the coordinates, X, Y, H of the map projection system are not quite identical with the corresponding ground distances). The misclosures (discrepancies) in the aerial (photo) triangulation would involve such distortions.

Consequent to the above, one has to apply the projection function to the observation data (of the phototriangulation) in order to bring the instrument coordinates to include the appropriate projection deformations. Usually conformal systems of projection are used in topographic mapping and in most of such conformal systems the errors are limited to third-order polynomials in X and/or Y coordinates, i.e.,

$$\Delta X = f(X^3) \text{ or } f(Y^3)$$

$$\Delta Y = f(X^3) \text{ or } f(Y^3).$$

This means that correct projection coordinates for the points determined by stereotriangulation are obtained by including terms with X^3 or Y^3 in the formulas for the adjustments (along with first- and second-order terms in X or Y). In practice, however, for strips with length less than about 100 km, the consideration of second-order deformations yields satisfactory results.

5

Propagation of Errors

The following operations are affected by errors during a strip triangulation (except the computational N-photo solution in the simultaneous mode, which is discussed in Sec. 9.2):

In each photograph: interior orientation (see Sec. 4.2)

In the first model: relative and absolute orientations

In the second and subsequent models: coorientation (dependent relative orientation), scale transfer, and model connections

In all models: recording of instrument data

The errors may be considered primarily as systematic and irregular.

5.1 Systematic Errors (also see *Manual of Photogrammetry*[5])

It is normal to define the systematic errors of a strip triangulation as errors of constant amounts and signs occurring in each unit (photo, model, triplet, or sub-block)—systematic errors of the first order. There are, however, systematic errors which follow more complicated laws. These can be more or less complicated mathematical functions of parameters such as distance, time, temperature, etc. The consideration of such (second and higher order) systematic errors would complicate the mathematical formulations in strip triangulation, thereby giving lengthy adjustment formulas whose application may be impracticable for economic and efficiency reasons.

Systematic errors of the first order known to us are the results of image errors, instrument errors, and observation (operational) errors. Systematic errors generate a systematic falsification of the strip's form and can be related to the involved operations and elements (see Brandenberger [14]):

1. Seven initial errors of the first model:
   a. Scale error $\quad\quad\quad\quad\quad\quad\quad$ dS_0
   b. X, Y, and Z translation errors $\quad$ dX_0, dY_0, and dZ_0
   c. X-tilt error $\quad\quad\quad\quad\quad\quad\quad$ $d\Omega_0$
   d. Y-tilt error $\quad\quad\quad\quad\quad\quad\quad$ $d\Phi_0$
   e. Rotation (swing) error $\quad\quad\quad$ dK_0

53

2. Five coorientation errors in the second and subsequent models:
   a. Systematic by error dby_s
   b. Systematic bz error dbz_s
   c. Systematic X-tilt error $d\omega_s$
   d. Systematic Y-tilt error $d\phi_s$
   e. Systematic swing error $d\kappa_s$

3. The scale-transfer error in second and subsequent models:
   a. Systematic bx error dbx_s

4. Three model connection errors in second and subsequent models:
   a. Systematic model connection error in X dX_s
   b. Systematic model connection error in Y dY_s
   c. Systematic model connection error in Z dZ_s

A right-handed rectangular (X, Y, Z) coordinate system will be considered in this section for the derivations of the expressions. This will correspond to similar systems used in land surveying and geodesy (i.e., eastings, northings, and elevations). However, in order to bring this into agreement with the general practices in photogrammetry, the system proposed and adopted by the International Society of Photogrammetry (see Ghosh [35]) will be considered for the rotations Ω, Φ, and K (see Fig. 5-1, where positive directions are indicated by arrowheads).

Errors in the First Model

Scale Error: dS_0. The effect of this error on the strip, as represented in Fig. 5-2, may be expressed in terms of errors in the strip coordinates of points as follows:

$$\left. \begin{array}{l} \Delta X = (X - X_M)\, dS_0 \\ \Delta Y = (Y - Y_M)\, dS_0 \\ \Delta Z = (Z - Z_M)\, dS_0 \end{array} \right\} \qquad (5.1)$$

where $\Delta X, \Delta Y, \Delta Z$ are the errors in the strip coordinates

   X, Y, Z are the strip coordinates of points

   X_M, Y_M, Z_M are the strip coordinates of the center of the first model

X-Translation Error: dX_0. The effect of this error on the strip is translation of the entire strip in X by an amount dX_0 (see Fig. 5-3), with no error in Y or Z.

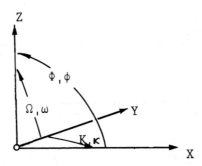

Figure 5-1. System of Coordinates and Rotations

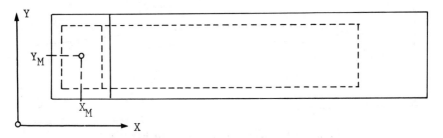

Figure 5-2. Effect of Scale Error in First Model

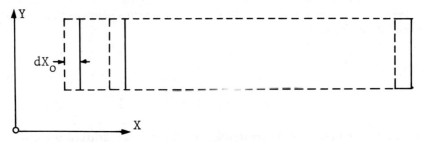

Figure 5-3. Effect of Translation Error dX_0

Y-Translation Error: dY_0. The effect of this error on the strip is translation of the entire strip in Y by an amount dY_0 (see Fig. 5-4) and no error in X or Z.

Z-Translation Error: dZ_0. The effect of this error on the entire strip in Z by an amount dZ_0 (see Fig. 5-5) while there is no error in X or Y.

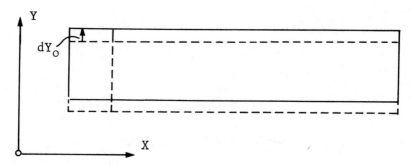

Figure 5-4. Effect of Translation Error dY_0

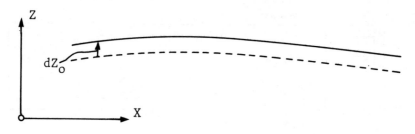

Figure 5-5. Effect of Translation Error dZ_0

X-Tilt (or Lateral-tilt) Error: $d\Omega_0$. The effect of this error on the strip is represented in Fig. 5-6, and may be expressed in terms of errors in the strip coordinates of points as follows:

$$\left.\begin{array}{l} \Delta X = 0 \\ \Delta Y = -(Z - Z_M)d\Omega_0 \\ \Delta Z = (Y - Y_M)d\Omega_0 \end{array}\right\} \tag{5.2}$$

Y-Tilt (or Longitudinal-tilt) Error: $d\Phi_0$. Its effect on the strip is represented in Fig. 5-7 and may be expressed as follows:

$$\left.\begin{array}{l} \Delta X = -(Z - Z_M)d\Phi_0 \\ \Delta Y = 0 \\ \Delta Z = (X - X_M)d\Phi_0 \end{array}\right\} \tag{5.3}$$

Rotation (or Swing) Error: dK_0. Its effects may be expressed in the following formulas and represented in Fig. 5-8.

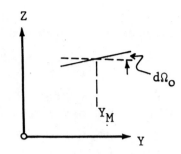

Figure 5-6. Effect of X-tilt Error $d\Omega_o$

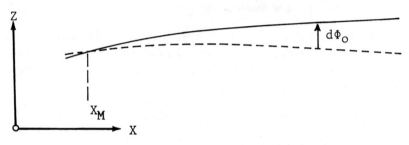

Figure 5-7. Effect of Y-tilt Error $d\Phi_o$

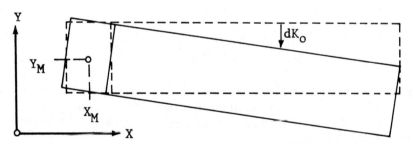

Figure 5-8. Effect of Rotation Error dK_o

$$\left.\begin{array}{l}
\Delta X = (Y - Y_M)dK_o \\
\Delta Y = -(X - X_M)dK_o \\
\Delta Z = 0
\end{array}\right\} \qquad (5.4)$$

By considering the origin of the system of the strip coordinates to be at the center of the first model (i.e., $X_M = Y_M = Z_M = 0$), the combined effect of all the errors of the first model may be expressed in the following:

$$\left.\begin{aligned}
\Delta X &= dX_0 + X \cdot dS_0 + Y \cdot dK_0 - Z \cdot d\Phi_0 \\
&= a_0 + a_1 \cdot X + a_2 \cdot Y + a_3 \cdot Z \\[4pt]
\Delta Y &= dY_0 - X \cdot dK_0 + Y \cdot dS_0 - Z \cdot d\Omega_0 \\
&= b_0 + b_1 \cdot X + b_1 \cdot Y + b_3 \cdot Z \\[4pt]
\Delta Z &= dZ_0 + X \cdot d\Phi_0 + Y \cdot d\Omega_0 + Z \cdot dS_0 \\
&= c_0 + c_1 \cdot X + c_2 \cdot Y + c_3 \cdot Z
\end{aligned}\right\} \qquad (5.5)$$

Errors in the Second and Subsequent Models

Systematic by Error of Coorientation: dby_s. The effect of this error on the strip is represented in Fig. 5-9. Whereas it has no effect on the misclosures in X and Z strip coordinates, its effect on Y may be expressed for points in the ith model as

$$\Delta Y = (i - 1)dby_s \approx \alpha_0 + \frac{X}{b} \, dby_s = \alpha_0 + \alpha_1 \cdot X \qquad (5.6)$$

where α_0 and α_1 are constants

   X is the strip coordinate

   b is the average base (length)

   This error causes an indirect (and apparent) rotation error in the strip

$$d\kappa_r = dby_s/b \qquad (5.7)$$

Systematic bz error of Coorientation: dbz_s. The effect of this error is represented in Fig. 5-10. It has no effect on the misclosures of the X and Y strip coordinates but the effect on Z may be expressed in a way similar to that of dby_s by the following:

$$\Delta Z = (i - 1)dbz_s \approx \beta_0 + \beta_1 \cdot X \qquad (5.8)$$

where β_0 and β_1 are constants.

   Further, this error causes an apparent (and indirect) inclination error in the strip:

$$d\phi_i = dbz_s/b \qquad (5.9)$$

Systematic X-Tilt Error of Coorientation: $d\omega_s$. This error yields an effect of torsion in the strip and generates the following errors at a point P of the strip (see Fig. 5-11) in the ith model, the total closure in ω being $\Delta\omega = (i-1)d\omega_s$:

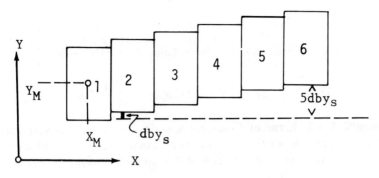

Figure 5-9. Effect of Systematic by-Error dby_s

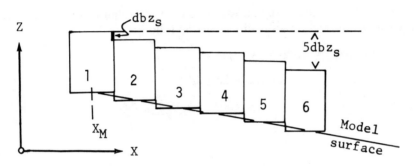

Figure 5-10. Effect of Systematic bz-Error dbz_s

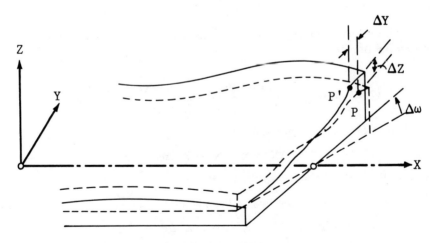

Figure 5-11. Effect of Systematic X-tilt Error $d\omega_s$

$$\left.\begin{aligned}
\Delta X &= 0 \\[4pt]
\Delta Y &= -Z \cdot \Delta\omega = -Z(i - 1)d\omega_s \approx -\frac{Z \cdot X}{b}d\omega_s \\[4pt]
\Delta Z &= Y \cdot \Delta\omega = Y(i - 1)d\omega_s \approx \frac{Y \cdot X}{b}d\omega_s
\end{aligned}\right\} \quad (5.10)$$

Systematic Y-Tilt Error of Coorientation: $d\phi_s$. This error has an effect similar to that of the earth's curvature and causes misclosures in X and Z coordinates. At the $(i + 1)$th exposure station, one obtains the closure error

$$\Delta\phi = i \cdot d\phi_s \approx \frac{X}{b}d\phi_s$$

The effect of this error on the strip is represented in Fig. 5-12. The systematic $d\phi_s$ error causes dbz errors as follows:

$$-dbz_3 \quad = \quad b \cdot d\phi_s$$
$$-dbz_4 \quad = \quad b \cdot d\phi_s + 2b \cdot d\phi_s$$
$$-dbz_5 \quad = \quad b \cdot d\phi_s + 2b \cdot d\phi_s + 3b \cdot d\phi_s$$

$$\vdots \qquad\qquad \vdots$$

$$-dbz_{i+1} \quad = \quad b \cdot d\phi_s + 2b \cdot d\phi_s + 3b \cdot d\phi_s + \ldots + b(i - 1)d\phi_s$$
$$= \quad \frac{i(i - 1)b}{2}d\phi_s$$

This dbz error corresponds to the Z error directly, i.e., at the end of the ith model one gets

$$\Delta Z = -dbz_{i+1} = \frac{i(i - 1)b}{2}d\phi_s \approx \frac{X(X - b)}{2b}d\phi_s .$$

The error in X is expressed by

$$\Delta X = X - S' - Z \cdot \Delta\phi$$

where $S' = R' \cdot \Delta\phi$ and also $S' = i \cdot b$

$R' = $ Radius of the falsified sea level

This gives: $\Delta X = R' \sin \Delta\phi - R' \cdot \Delta\phi - Z \cdot \Delta\phi$

Expanding $\sin \Delta\phi$ into a series:

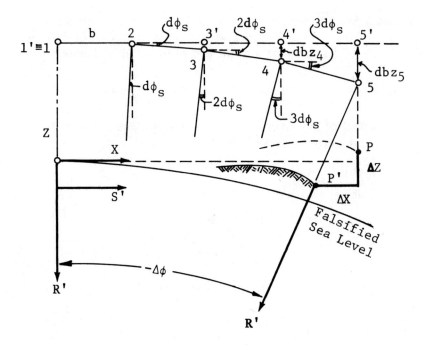

Figure 5-12. Effect of Systematic Y-tilt Error $d\phi_s$

$$\Delta X \approx R'\left(\Delta\phi - \frac{\Delta\phi^3}{6} + \ldots - \Delta\phi\right) - Z \cdot \Delta\phi$$

$$\approx -R'\frac{\Delta\phi^3}{6} - Z \cdot \Delta\phi$$

Further

$$\Delta\phi = i \cdot d\phi_s \approx \frac{X}{b}\,d\phi_s \quad \text{and} \quad R' \approx \frac{b}{d\phi_s}$$

Substituting, one obtains

$$\left.\begin{aligned}
\Delta X &= -\frac{X^3}{6b^2}\,d\phi_s^2 - \frac{XZ}{b}\,d\phi_s \\[1mm]
\Delta Y &= 0 \\[1mm]
\Delta Z &= \frac{X(X-b)}{2b}\,d\phi_s
\end{aligned}\right\} \tag{5.11}$$

Systematic Swing Error of Coorientation: $d\kappa_s$. This error causes a parabolic warping of the strip in Y direction and causes misclosures in Y and X coordinates. The swing error at the end of the ith model amounts to

$$\Delta\kappa = (i - 1) \cdot d\kappa_s \approx \frac{X}{b} d\kappa_s$$

The effect of this error on the strip is represented in Fig. 5-13. The systematic $d\kappa_s$ error causes dby error as follows:

$$dby_3 = b \cdot d\kappa_s$$
$$dby_4 = b \cdot d\kappa_s + b \cdot 2d\kappa_s$$
$$dby_5 = b \cdot d\kappa_s + b \cdot 2d\kappa_s + b \cdot 3d\kappa_s$$

$$\begin{array}{cc} \vdots & \vdots \\ \vdots & \vdots \end{array}$$

$$dby_{i+1} = b \cdot d\kappa_s + 2b \cdot d\kappa_s + 3b \cdot d\kappa_s + \ldots + (i - 1)b \cdot d\kappa_s$$
$$= \frac{i(i - 1)b}{2} d\kappa_s$$

This dby error corresponds directly to the Y error. Therefore, at the end of the ith model one obtains

$$\Delta Y = dby_{i+1} = \frac{i(i - 1)b}{2} d\kappa_s \approx \frac{X(X - b)}{2b} d\kappa_s \ .$$

In this case the X error can be expressed by

$$\Delta X = X - S'' - Y \cdot \Delta\kappa$$

where $S'' = R'' \cdot \Delta\kappa$ and $S'' = i \cdot b$

R'' is the radius of curvature of the strip deformation in planimetry

that is, $\Delta X = R'' \cdot \sin\Delta\kappa - R'' \cdot \Delta\kappa - Y \cdot \Delta\kappa$

In a way similar to the case of $d\phi_s$, one obtains:

$$\left. \begin{array}{l} \Delta X \approx -\dfrac{X^3}{6b^2} d\kappa_s^2 - \dfrac{XY}{b} d\kappa_s \\[2ex] \Delta Y = \dfrac{X(X - b)}{2b} d\kappa_s \\[2ex] Z = 0 \end{array} \right\} \qquad (5.12)$$

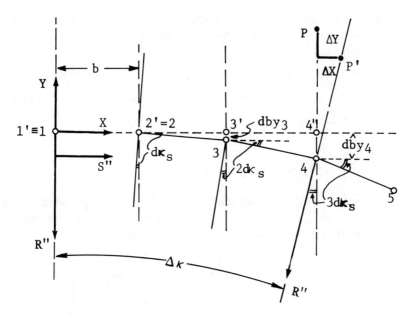

Figure 5-13. Effect of Systematic Swing Error $d\kappa_s$

Scale-transfer Error: dbx_s

Considering that dbx is constant, $dbx_2 = dbx_3 = \ldots = dbx_i = dbx_s$. Furthermore, in the ith model, the total-scale error

$$\Delta S \approx \frac{(i - 1)dbx_s}{b} = \frac{X - b}{b^2} dbx_s$$

Its effect on the misclosures of the three coordinates are:

$$\left.\begin{aligned}
\Delta X &= dbx_s + 2dbx_s + 3dbx_s + \ldots + (i - 1)dbx_s \\
&= \frac{i(i - 1)}{2} dbx_s = \frac{X(X - b)}{2b^2} dbx_s \\
\Delta Y &= Y \cdot \Delta S = \frac{(X - b)Y}{b^2} dbx_s \\
\Delta Z &= Z \cdot \Delta S = \frac{(X - b)Z}{b^2} dbx_s
\end{aligned}\right\} \quad (5.13)$$

Apparently, the scale error itself is linear but its effect on the X coordinates is of the second order.

By considering the origin of the system of the strip coordinates to be at the center of the first model, the combined primary effect of all the systematic errors in the second and subsequent models may be expressed by general expressions as:

$$\left.\begin{aligned}
\Delta X &= \lambda_0 + \lambda_1 \cdot X + \lambda_2 \cdot X^2 + \lambda_3 \cdot X^3 + \lambda_4 \cdot XY + \lambda_5 \cdot XZ \\
\Delta Y &= \mu_0 + \mu_1 \cdot X + \mu_2 \cdot X^2 + \mu_3 \cdot XY + \mu_4 \cdot XZ \\
\Delta Z &= \nu_0 + \nu_1 \cdot X + \nu_2 \cdot X^2 + \nu_3 \cdot XY + \nu_4 \cdot XZ
\end{aligned}\right\} \quad (5.14)$$

Model Connection Errors

The errors are translatory and may be considered in terms of the three components, dX_s, dY_s, and dZ_s. These errors give, in the ith model, misclosures that may be expressed by the following:

$$\left.\begin{aligned}
\Delta X &= (i-1)dX_s = \frac{X-b}{b} dX_s \\
\Delta Y &= (i-1)dY_s = \frac{X-b}{b} dY_s \\
\Delta Z &= (i-1)dZ_s = \frac{X-b}{b} dZ_s
\end{aligned}\right\} \quad (5.15)$$

5.2 Irregular Errors

The errors remaining after the systematic errors are subtracted from the total errors occurring during a triangulation are the irregular errors. They have the general property that their size and sign vary from photograph to photograph, or from model to model, or from strip to strip, or from block to block. Such errors originate from various sources, mostly physical, for example, irregular image errors, irregular instrument errors, irregular observation errors, and irregular adjustment errors.

Irregular errors may follow various types of distributions. Their mathematical treatment requires that some mathematical assumptions are made about their natures. The usual assumption is that such irregular errors have a normal distribution i.e., they are treated as accidental (random) errors. It must, however, be kept in mind that accidental errors are really abstract—deduced mathematically—whereas irregular errors are physical. The law of probability is common to both. The greatest weakness of this conception is that the "standard error" conception is based on an "abstract error" conception. This conception means that

1. The error of zero magnitude has the highest probability.
2. Positive and negative errors are equally probable.
3. Theoretically even an error of magnitude $\pm\infty$ can occur.

The mathematical treatment of such errors on the basis of the mathematical probability yields an error frequency diagram which is the famous bell-shaped curve of Gauss. This is expressed by an exponential function of the type $e^{-a\epsilon^2}$

where   e = base of natural logarithm

      a = a constant

      ϵ = the error

It may be questionable if irregular errors are predictable so as to be put under the theory of probability.

In phototriangulation, the approximation of irregular (concrete physical) errors by accidental (abstract, mathematically designed) errors is reasonable. However, the quality of this approximation depends on the remaining systematic errors of the higher orders. If most of the systematic errors of the higher orders have been previously eliminated, the remaining errors will more nearly approach a normal distribution. There are limitations with regard to the application of such a procedure. The degree of approximation varies from case to case.

The size of accidental errors is usually indicated by the standard error m where (without going into the problem of weighting)

$$m = \pm\sqrt{\frac{\Sigma\epsilon^2}{n}} \quad \text{and also m} = \pm\sqrt{\frac{\Sigma v^2}{n-1}} \qquad (5.16)$$

where   n is the number of observations (data)

      ϵ are the true accidental errors

      v are the accidental errors referred to the arithmetic mean of n observations (the true errors ϵ being unknown)

Due to the inadequacy of approximating irregular errors by accidental errors, the standard error m has to be interpreted judiciously when used to indicate the accuracy in a particular case.

The effects of the propagation of irregular errors may often appear as systematic. Such errors, in strip triangulation, are caused by correlation of irregular coorientation errors and by the accumulation of various irregular errors. Some errors being functions of other errors, their effects can not be properly interpreted as accidental. Such errors are termed "*quasi-systematic*" or "*pseudoaccidental*," according to their interpretations.

Quasi-systematic Errors Associated with dbx

An irregular dbx error (scale-transfer error) generates a quasi-systematic X-error (see Fig. 5-14). In analogical strip triangulation the scale transfer is usually performed by means of the elevation Z (see Sec. 3.2). The elevation error dZ_2 (in model 2), dZ_3 (in model 3), etc., generate dbx errors, which in turn, cause ΔX errors. For the various ΔX errors at the right exposure stations of the models or the corresponding model-transfer point one gets (see Fig. 5-14):

$$\Delta X_3 = dbx_2$$

$$\Delta X_4 = 2dbx_2 + dbx_3$$

$$\Delta X_5 = 3dbx_2 + 2dbx_3 + dbx_4$$

$$\vdots \qquad\qquad \vdots$$

$$\Delta X_{n+1} = (n-1)dbx_2 + (n-2)dbx_3 + \ldots + dbx_n \qquad (5.17)$$

Assuming equal standard errors m_{bx} and m_z in various models, with the help of Eq. (5.17), one obtains for the standard error M_x of X at the farthest edge of model n (by applying the Gaussian law of error propagation and summation of the square numbers):

$$M_x = \pm\sqrt{\left\{\frac{n(n-1)(2n-1)}{6}m_{bx}^2\right\}} \qquad (5.18a)$$

This represents a 3/2 power function of X (since $n \approx X/b$). Further, one can obtain expressions of errors in Y and Z (with respect to irregular errors in bx):

$$\left.\begin{array}{l} M_Y = \pm\dfrac{Y}{b}\sqrt{n \cdot m_{bx}} \\[2em] M_Z = \pm\dfrac{Z}{b}\sqrt{n \cdot m_{bx}} \end{array}\right\} \qquad (5.18b)$$

Quasi-systematic Error Associated with dby

Irregular dby, $d\omega$, or $d\kappa$ errors may generate a quasi-systematic dby error, even though the models individually may be free from Y parallax, etc.

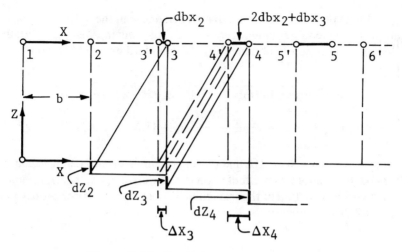

Figure 5-14. Quasi-Systematic X-Error

The total dby error at the nadir points 2, 3 ... (n + 1) result from the summation of the errors, for example,

$$\Delta by_i = dby_i + dby_{\omega i} + dby_{\kappa i} \qquad (5.19)$$

where Δby_i is the total effect expressed in terms of dby

dby_i is the part contributed by irregular dby error

$dby_{\omega i}$ is the part contributed by irregular ω error

$dby_{\kappa i}$ is the part contributed by irregular κ error.

Using Eq. (5.19) and considering the geometry of the stereomodels:

$$\Delta by_2 = dby_2 + \bar{Z} \cdot d\omega_2 + b \cdot d\kappa_1$$

$$\Delta by_3 = (dby_2 + dby_3) + \bar{Z}(d\omega_2 + d\omega_3) + b(2d\kappa_1 + d\kappa_2)$$

$$\Delta by_4 = (dby_2 + dby_3 + dby_4) + \bar{Z}(d\omega_2 + d\omega_3 + d\omega_4) + b(3d\kappa_1 + 2d\kappa_2 + d\kappa_3)$$

$$\vdots \qquad\qquad\qquad \vdots$$

$$\Delta by_{n+1} = \sum_{r=2}^{r=n+1} dby_r + \bar{Z} \sum_{r=2}^{r=n+1} d\omega_r + b\{n \cdot d\kappa_1 + \ldots + d\kappa_n\} \qquad (5.20)$$

Here $\bar{Z} = \dfrac{3Z^2 + 2d^2}{3Z}$.   (See Ghosh [35].)

From this expression, assuming that by, ω, and κ in the various exposure stations have the same standard errors (m_{by}, m_ω, and m_κ, respectively), the following expression is obtained for the standard error of the combined effect.

$$M_Y = \pm\sqrt{\{n \cdot m_{by}^2 + n\overline{Z}^2 m_\omega^2 + b^2(1^2+2^2+3^2+ \ldots +n^2)m_\kappa^2\}}$$

$$= \pm\sqrt{n} \cdot \sqrt{\left\{ m_{by}^2 + \overline{Z}^2 m_\omega^2 + \frac{b^2}{6}(n + 1)(2n + 1)m_\kappa^2 \right\}} \qquad (5.21)$$

Here also, as before, n $\approx$ X/b and this expression indicates that irregular dκ errors have a predominant effect upon the dby errors and, therefore, upon the Y error propagation of the triangulated strip. Such Y error propagates with a 3/2 power function of X, as revealed in Eq. (5.21).

Quasi-systematic Error Associated with dbz

In a way similar to the foregoing subsections, it can be shown that an irregular dϕ error may combine with dbz errors to generate a quasi-systematic Z error:

$$M_Z = \pm\sqrt{n} \cdot \sqrt{\left\{ m_{bz}^2 + \frac{b^2}{6} (n + 1)(2n + 1) m_\phi^2 \right\}} \qquad (5.22)$$

This also indicates that the irregular dϕ errors have a predominant effect upon dbz errors and, therefore, upon the elevation (Z) error propagation in the strip. This error propagates with a 3/2 power function of X.

Irregular Model Connection Errors

The propagation of irregular model connection errors may be expressed in the following equation.

$$\left. \begin{array}{l} \Delta X = dX_{1,2} + dX_{2,3} + \ldots + dX_{n-1,n} \\[4pt] \Delta Y = dY_{1,2} + dY_{2,3} + \ldots + dY_{n-1,n} \\[4pt] \Delta Z = dZ_{1,2} + dZ_{2,3} + \ldots + dZ_{n-1,n} \end{array} \right\} \qquad (5.23)$$

Assuming equal (standard) errors m_X, m_Y, m_Z for each model connection

$$M_X = \pm \sqrt{(n-1)} \cdot m_x \approx \sqrt{n} \cdot m_x$$
$$M_Y = \pm \sqrt{(n-1)} \cdot m_Y \approx \sqrt{n} \cdot m_Y \qquad\qquad (5.24)$$
$$M_Z = \pm \sqrt{(n-1)} \cdot m_Z \approx \sqrt{n} \cdot m_Z$$

Equations (5.24) indicate that the propagation of accidental (irregular) model connection error increases with the square root of n (or, thereby, of X).

5.3 Total Effect of All Errors

If all systematic and quasi-systematic errors are combined, one obtains the following expressions for error propagations:

$$\Delta X = a_0 + a_1 X + a_2 Y + a_3 Z + a_4 XY + a_5 XZ + a_6 X^2 + a_7 X^3$$
$$\Delta Y = b_0 + b_1 X + b_2 Y + b_3 Z + b_4 XY + b_5 XZ + b_6 X^2 \qquad (5.25)$$
$$\Delta Z = c_0 + c_1 X + c_2 Y + c_3 Z + c_4 XY + c_5 XZ + c_6 X^2$$

where a_0, a_1, $a_2 \ldots$, b_0, $b_1 \ldots$, c_0, $c_1 \ldots$ are constants

It must, however, be kept in mind that inadequately corrected objective (lens) distortion, film shrinkage, earth's curvature, etc., may give parabolic deformations in all directions and, in view of this, a more generalized set of expressions for error propagation would be

$$\Delta X = a_0 + a_1 X + a_2 Y + a_3 Z + a_4 XY + a_5 XZ + a_6 YZ$$

$$+ a_7 X^2 + a_8 Y^2 + a_9 Z^2 + a_{10} XY^2 + a_{11} X^2 Y + a_{12} XZ^2$$

$$+ a_{13} YZ^2 + a_{14} X^2 Z + a_{15} Y^2 Z + a_{16} XYZ + a_{17} X^3 \qquad (5.26)$$

Similar expressions for ΔY and ΔZ will also be expected.

In recent literature a variety of formulas in use are given. Many of them are known to offer adequate results, although not all of them may be justified from a theoretical point of view. Some examples are given below:

1. The set of polynomials used by the U.S., NOAA (Coast and Geodetic Survey) as presented by Keller and Tewinkel [51]:

$$X = x - \Delta Z \cdot (3hx^2 + 2ix + j) + ax^3 + bx^2 + cx - 2dxy - ey - f$$

$$Y = y - \Delta Z \cdot (kx^2 + 1x + m) + 3ax^2y + 2bxy + cy + dx^2 + ex + g$$

$$Z = z[1 + (3hx^2 + 2ix + j)^2 + (kx^2 + 1x + m)^2]^{1/2}$$
$$+ hx^3 + ix^2 + jx + kx^2y + 1xy + my + n$$

$$(5.27)$$

2. The set of polynomials presented by Schut [85] for the National Research Council of Canada:

$$X = a_1 + a_3x + a_4y + a_5(x^2 - y^2) + 2a_6xy + a_7(x^3 - 3xy^2)$$
$$- a_8(3x^2y - y^3) + \ldots$$

$$Y = a_2 + a_4x + a_3y + a_6(x^2 - y^2) + 2a_5xy + a_7(3x^2y - y^3)$$
$$+ a_8(x^3 - 3xy^2) + \ldots$$

$$(5.28)$$

3. The set of polynomials suggested in the *Manual of Photogrammetry* by the American Society of Photogrammetry [5]:

$$\Delta X = a_0 + a_1x + a_2y + a_3xy + a_4xz + a_5x^2 + a_6x^3$$
$$\Delta Y = b_0 + b_1x + b_2y + b_3xy + b_4xz + b_5x^2$$
$$\Delta Z = c_0 + c_1x + c_2y + c_3z + c_4xy + c_5xz + c_6x^2$$

$$(5.29)$$

4. The set of polynomials suggested by Mikhail [70]:

$$X = a_0 + ax + by - cz + e(x^2 - y^2 - z^2) + 2gzx + 2fxy + \ldots$$
$$Y = b_0 - bx + ay + dz + f(-x^2 + y^2 - z^2) + 2gyz + 2exy + \ldots$$
$$Z = c_0 + cx - dy + az + g(-x^2 - y^2 + z^2) + 2fyz + 2ezx + \ldots$$

$$(5.30)$$

Acceptable results have been claimed by each of the above, using them under normal working conditions. In the above, X, Y, Z are the ground coordinates (given); x, y, z are the strip-model coordinates (observed); ΔX, ΔY, ΔZ are the corrections necessary to transform the model coordinates into ground coordinates; and the rest are constants (polynomial coefficients).

The graphical strip adjustment is usually based on the error propagation along longitudinal sections where Y = constant. Considering this, in such cases, one can use (for Y = constant sections and Z = constant, i.e., with flat terrain):

$$\Delta X = a_0 + a_1X + a_2X^2 + a_3X^3$$
$$\Delta Y = b_0 + b_1X + b_2X^2 + b_3X^3$$
$$\Delta Z = c_0 + c_1X + c_2X^2 + c_3X^3$$

$$(5.31)$$

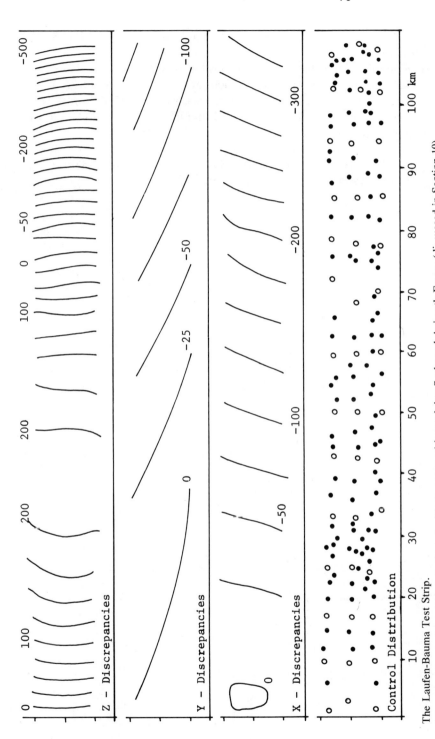

The Laufen-Bauma Test Strip.
Discrepancies are in m. Points indicated with ∘ are used in studying Scale and Azimuth Errors (discussed in Section 10).

Figure 5-15. An Example of Error Propagation in Strip Triangulation

For shorter strips and for most aeroleveling cases one can neglect X^3, at least for ΔY and ΔZ.

An example of such error propagations through a strip is shown in Fig. 5-15. Here the photo-scale was 1:60,000, and the model-scale (at Wild Autograph A7) was 1:15,000. The camera used was a Wild RC7a on a test area in Switzerland (Courtesy of OEEPE, the European Organization for Photogrammetric Research Studies).

In this respect one may remember the research performed by Bachmann [11]. He was the first to discover that the correction formulas for the strip coordinates involve third-order terms in X.

6 Adjustment Methods

The compensation for misclosures (errors) in a strip triangulation may be done by one of the following adjustment methods:

1. Graphical
2. Numerical (analytical)
3. Mechanical

Often the practicing photogrammetrist-adjuster uses a method which may be a combination of two or more of the above. The aim of such an adjustment is the elimination of systematic and quasi-systematic errors (see Chaps. 4 and 5). Both graphical and numerical methods require a sufficient number of known ground-control (given) points. The mechanical methods are applicable in cases with control inadequate for other methods. The graphical and mechanical methods have their limitations as imposed by the material and equipment used in such adjustments.

It has been established by working photogrammetrists, see Brandenberger [14], that for strips of moderate lengths on a fairly flat terrain (as occurring in practice) the falsification of any longitudinal section ($Y =$ constant) through the strip is subject to the laws of propagation of errors in accordance with Eq. (5.25). Strictly speaking, these are valid only for strips on flat and horizontal ground in the level of the first model. The application of these formulas produce very satisfactory results in case the relative elevation difference on the ground (throughout the whole strip) are not more than 5 percent of the average flying height and the strip does not have more than 30 models. Furthermore, when the strip is not too long, i.e., if the number of models is less than 20 and the total length of the strip on ground is less than about 60 miles, one can neglect the third-order term in Eq. (5.25) and still obtain satisfactory results.

In order to take into account in practice the falsification of the triangulated strip, the coefficients a_0, $a_1 \ldots c_3$ must be known in Eq. (5.25). These coefficients are obtained when there is a sufficient number of given fixed points within the strip. For example, to be able to solve for a_0, a_1, a_2, and a_3 for a certain longitudinal section ($Y =$ constant) one should have at least four evenly spaced control points lying along the section.

In practice, apart from the group of fixed ground-control points in the first model, three other groups of fixed points have to be given (see Fig. 6-1). These points are often geodetically determined in the field after the strip has been flown. In such cases they can serve as transfer or tie pass points provided they are suitably located.

6.1 Graphical (Strip) Adjustment

Generally speaking, the graphical method of adjustment is used when no high-speed computer is available. Its greatest advantage is that the existing blunders are easily detectable. With sufficient ground control available, the graphical method can give more than satisfactory results in practically all cases of aero (photo) triangulation. Equation (5.25) is relevant in this case. Each of the equations in Eq. (5.25) separately represents a section through the error surface. For practical use, one may replace the error surface by three (or two) longitudinal sections (profiles) (see Fig. 6-2).

The errors ΔX, ΔY, and ΔZ at all the given points within the strip are determined from the differences between the transformed instrument coordinates (X^t, Y^t) and elevations (Z_r) and their corresponding true ground values (X^g, Y^g, Z^g) $(\Delta X = X^t - X^g, \Delta Y = Y^t - Y^g$ and $\Delta Z = Z_r - Z^g)$. When these errors are known, the longitudinal sections of the strip's error surface (see Fig. 6-2) are constructed with the help of the transverse profile planes P_1, P_2, P_3 and P_4 (note in Fig. 6-1).

The longitudinal sections are graphs of third (or second) degree. Hence one requires four (or three) points along each section (U, C, or L). To facilitate further construction consider sections $X = $ constant at four (or three) locations of the strip. On the basis of such transverse profiles, then, three longitudinal profiles may be drawn parallel to the strip X axis. These three profiles are drawn such that one is placed in the axis of the strip (see profile C in Fig. 6-1) and the other two at equal distances from profile C on either side and close to the margins of the strip (see profiles U and L in Fig. 6-1). A set of three such longitudinal error profiles are constructed for each of the coordinates X, Y, and Z (see Fig. 6-4).

Ideally, the error surface cross-section (transverse profile) is a straight line. The irregularities (see Fig. 6-3) may be due to the errors in the ground coordinates, in the observations, in identification, etc. It is justified to approximate such a cross-profile by a straight line (e.g., see Fig. 6-3b) or a flat second-order curve, which is finally considered for the errors to be considered for such adjustment.

These sets of longitudinal profiles define the error surface in the strip for the particular coordinate. Note that error profiles are nothing but the correction profiles with changed signs. Thereby the corrections to be applied to the observation data (the transformed instrument coordinates X, Y, and the elevation Z) at any point can be easily obtained by simple graphical interpolation from the set of longitudinal profiles. This has to be done with proper consideration of the location of the point in question in the

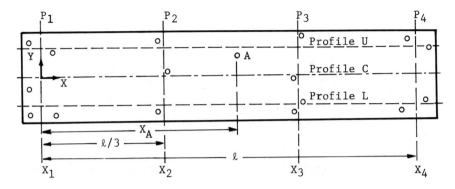

Figure 6-1. Location of Fixed Control Points and Profiles

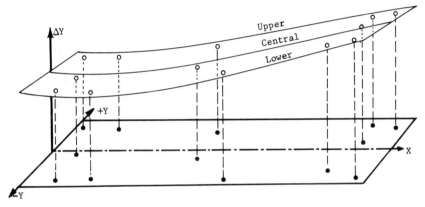

Figure 6-2. Representation of the Error Surface for Y Errors in a Strip

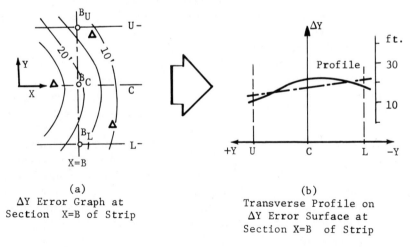

(a)	(b)
ΔY Error Graph at	Transverse Profile on
Section X=B of Strip	ΔY Error Surface at
	Section X=B of Strip

Figure 6-3. Example of Transverse Profile of an Error Surface

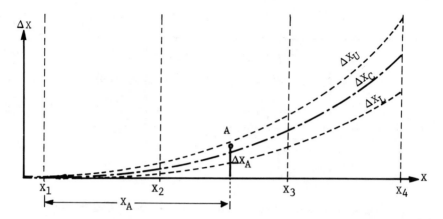

Figure 6-4. Set of Longitudinal Error Profiles for X-Coordinates

strip. The procedure will be clear by considering Figs. 6-1 and 6-4 with respect to point A.

The corrections (in ΔX, ΔY, and ΔZ) obtained graphically from the respective sets of longitudinal error profiles for the point in question are added to the observation data to obtain the adjusted values of the coordinates (separately for X, Y, and Z).

6.2 Analytical (Numerical) Strip Adjustment

This method has the advantage of being faster if a working computer program is available. However, if there are blunders, it becomes more difficult and time consuming to eliminate them by this method than with the graphical method.

The basic idea is to compute numerically the coefficients (the a's, b's, c's, etc.) of the error polynomials (see Eqs. (5.25) and (5.26)) by means of the known misclosures at the control points. Thereafter, the observed strip coordinates and the computed coefficients would yield the corrections $(-\Delta X, -\Delta Y, \text{ and } -\Delta Z)$ through computations by using the same polynomials.

If the number of given ground-control points is greater than the required minimum (for solving the polynomial expression), the coefficients can be obtained by a least-squares adjustment and it is possible to compute standard residual errors for the adjusted points. Such standard errors would give reliable indications on the accuracy of the strip triangulation if the number of superfluous given control points is adequately large.

Semianalytical Adjustment

Instead of carrying out the complete strip adjustment purely graphically (risk of not very high accuracy) or purely analytically (risk of delay and irrational corrections at times) a combination of graphical and analytical methods is undertaken very often. The extent to which such combination is made depends upon various factors such as precision of aerotriangulation aimed at the availability of ground control and computer facilities. A method sometimes used is as follows:

Step 1: A purely graphical method is followed to draw transverse error profiles.

Step 2: ΔX, ΔY, and ΔZ values at the points of intersection of the longitudinal and transverse sections are obtained from the graphical sections.

Step 3: Corrections for all points are obtained analytically after Step 2 is complete.

6.3 Mechanical Adjustment

There are several mechanical methods of adjustment; however, they are never complete (total). Generally they give only *partial* adjustment (e.g., for planimetry alone). Further, these are preferred for blocks rather than for single strips. Examples of such mechanical-adjustment procedures are:
1. Radial line method with
   a. Hand templets
   b. Slotted templets
2. Stereo-templet method
3. ITC-Jerie analog computer

These have been adequately discussed in the *Manual of Photogrammetry* [5] and will not be discussed here. These methods have, however, rather limited accuracy (about 0.5mm, m_p) in the scale of the assembly (or compilation).

6.4 Global (Total) Adjustment

The word ' "global" is used in the sense that the adjustment procedure is a "total" one, i.e., the phototriangulation procedure is not restricted to the provision of supplementary control points in each model (as needed), but provides all the orientation elements needed to reset the stereomodel at the instrument during map compilation. This procedure is more suitable to the aeropolygon method of triangulation.

In many mapping organizations a first-order stereoinstrument is teamed up with several second-order stereoplotters. The first-order instrument performs aerial triangulation to provide supplementary control in every model for subsequent map compilation at the second-order instrument. The first-order instruments have the capability of recording all the orientation elements in addition to the recording of the X, Y, and Z model coordinates of the control points.

This method will yield direct and comparatively better results if the same instruments are used in plotting as well. However, with careful arrangements, the idea can be extended for use on any other plotting instrument also.

Start with the assumption that there is available ground control adequate for the absolute orientation of each of the first and last models of the strip. The first model is oriented to ground control. The adjusted orientation elements of the first two exposures are recorded. All successive models are cooriented to the previous models, and the observed orientation elements of the new exposures are recorded. This process is continued to the last model in the strip. The last model is reoriented (absolute) to ground control; the adjusted orientation elements are recorded for the very last exposure. Then the adjusted orientation elements are computed using Eq. (6.1):

$$
\left.
\begin{aligned}
bx_{i_a} &= bx_{i_0} - \frac{\{bx_{(N+1)_0} - bx_{(N+1)_a}\}(i - 2)}{N - 1} \\[1.5em]
by_{i_a} &= by_{i_0} - \frac{\{by_{(N+1)_0} - by_{(N+1)_a}\}(i - 2)}{N - 1} \\[1.5em]
bz_{i_a} &= bz_{i_0} - \frac{\{bz_{(N+1)_0} - bz_{(N+1)_a}\}(i - 2)}{N - 1} \\[1.5em]
\kappa_{i_a} &= \kappa_{i_0} - \frac{\{\kappa_{(N+1)_0} - \kappa_{(N+1)_a}\}(i - 2)}{N - 1} \\[1.5em]
\omega_{i_a} &= \omega_{i_0} - \frac{\{\omega_{(N+1)_0} - \omega_{(N+1)_a}\}(i - 2)}{N - 1} \\[1.5em]
\phi_{ia} &= \phi_{io} - \frac{\{\phi_{(N+1)_0} - \phi_{(N+1)_a}\}(i - 2)}{N - 1}
\end{aligned}
\right\} \quad (6.1)
$$

where $i = 3, 4, 5 \ldots N-1, N, N+1$

N = The total number of models in the strip

N+1 = The total number of exposures in the strip.

Also, the camera (or projector) orientation elements (all) obtained during aerial strip triangulation are bx, by, bz, ω, ϕ, and κ. The first three are linear elements and the last three are rotation elements. The number of models (N) is one less than the number of exposures in the strip. The subscript i is the exposure number, the other subscripts, o and a, are for the observed and adjusted values, respectively.

The equations given in Eq. (6.1) are developed assuming that the first model is errorless (after absolute orientation) and no blunders occur during the strip triangulation. The equations help distribute the closing errors in the elements linearly through the strip, except for the first two exposures.

The next computation that may be necessary (in case an instrument other than the one for triangulation is used for map compilation) is the conversion of the adjusted orientation elements to the data necessary for reorienting the stereomodels at the plotter (see also Ghosh [33]).

This method has the advantage of minimizing the orientation time required during map compilation. The other direct advantage is a check on the error propagation. This method is easily adaptable to any first-order instrument (including the analytical plotters).

7 Aeroleveling

This is the type of aerial triangulation where the geometry of exposure is reproduced separately in each model. With the knowledge of the flying height of each exposure station (or height differences between exposure stations obtained from statoscope data or otherwise), the operator of the restitution instrument tries to make the model datum follow the instrument datum. This gives much less closing error in the coordinates (particularly Z) as compared with the situation in aeropolygon (also see Zeller [110], and Brandenberger [14]).

In this observation procedure, it is as if a level line is run along the projection centers (corresponding to the air stations). The individual projection centers are corrected during the observation procedure with respect to the instrument datum (a plain surface) which tends to approximate the level surface of the earth. Or, in other words, the operator tends to rectify the flight line into a straight line and correct only for elevation differences (Δbz).

This leveling is performed by means of a statoscope (liquid barometer), which measures air-pressure differences and is connected to the shutter of an automatic serial camera. The main part of the statoscope is a *manometer* (see Fig. 7-1). One end of the U-tube of the manometer is connected with the outside air. Normally amyl alcohol is used for the liquid. By an electric contact with an additional camera, the manometer is photographed along with the ground at the moment of the aerial exposure.

The statoscope in operation is locked until the first exposure station is reached. This working horizon ($\overline{H}$) is set so that at that altitude both limbs of the U-tube are at the same level—then it is put into action. Thereafter, from the readings, the altitude difference between the exposure stations can be computed when the scaled interval value in the altitude differences is known. An example is the Wild statoscope which has a range of ±40 m.

Figure 7-1 explains the principles of the statoscope, where a and b are the two arms of the U-tube (1) equipped with bulbs (3). (2) is the air container which is inserted into a thermos flask sunk into ice water. With changes of air pressure on the open arm, the liquid is pressed up in either of the bulbs (3). The air can bubble by and the liquid can sink back into the tube. This implies that no valves are required for working the statoscope which is a great advantage. Any change in altitude causes a pressure difference according to Eq. (7.1).

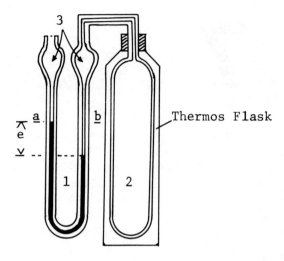

Figure 7-1. Principles of the Statoscope

$$\Delta H = e \cdot a \left(0.15 + \frac{1180}{B} \cdot C \right) \qquad (7.1)$$

where ΔH = altitude difference referred to the working horizon (isobaric surface)

e = difference of statoscope reading (on manometer, right minus left) for each air station

$a = 1 - \alpha t$ = temperature coefficient

   $= 1 - 0.0037 \cdot t$

α = temperature expansion coefficient for 1°C

t = temperature of air at flying height in °C

B = air pressure at flying height expressed in millimeters of mercury

C = specific gravity of the manometer liquid (e.g., amyl alcohol, $C = 0.82$)

1180 = an instrument constant

The elevation of the working horizon $(\overline{H})$ is set (obtained) at the instrument in the first model, corresponding to the position of the first exposure station (may be obtained by a space resection). Similarly, separately, the flying height H_{n+1} at the $(n+1)$th station in the nth (last) model of the strip may be also obtained by performing an absolute orientation (or space resection). Consider the value from the instrument (or space resection) data H_{n+1} and the value obtained from the statoscope: $H'_{n+1} = \overline{H} + \Delta H_{n+1}$. Their difference, that is, $H_{n+1} - H'_{n+1} = dH_{n+1}$ is the misclosure due to the isobaric surface not being parallel to sea level (see Fig. 7-2). This misclosure dH_{n+1} may be adjusted linearly (for short strips), e.g., for the ith exposure station:

$$dH_i = \frac{dH_{n+1}}{n}\,(i - 1) \tag{7.2}$$

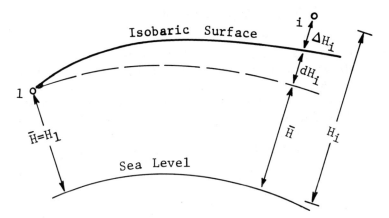

Figure 7-2 Schematic Diagram Involving Isobaric Surface

For a longer strip, or if circumstances demand, one can also have a central model absolutely oriented (or a space-resected photo) to perform a parabolic adjustment of the misclosure to obtain dH_i.

The corrected elevation of the ith station is, therefore,

$$H_i = \overline{H} + dH_i + \Delta H_i \tag{7.3}$$

and the corrected elevation difference of the ith air station from the first station is

$$\Delta H_{i_a} = dH_i + \Delta H_i \tag{7.4}$$

This corrected ΔH value may be used at the stereoinstrument during the aeroleveling procedure as the bz element (with respect to the first station):

$$bz_i = -\Delta H_{i_a} \cdot M_M \tag{7.5}$$

where M_M is the scale of the stereomodel.

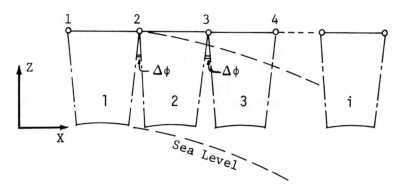

Figure 7-3. Principles of Aeroleveling

In this case bz is no longer an element of relative orientation (coorientation), but is introduced as the relative height between perspective centers. The relative orientation (i.e., coorientation) in each model is performed with ϕ_I and ϕ_{II}, that is, using the elements ϕ_I, ϕ_{II}, ω_{II}, κ_{II}, and by_{II} (not bz_{II}). These ϕ_I changes may create ϕ gaps ($\Delta\phi$). This $\Delta\phi$ involves earth's curvature, personal errors, refraction, statoscope error, etc. (see Fig. 7-3). Every other operation in aeroleveling is the same as in aeropolygoning. For $\Delta\phi$ the complete expression is:

$$\Delta\phi = Y + \alpha + \alpha' \qquad (7.6)$$

where $Y =$ the constant error due to the earth's curvature $\approx b/R$

   $\alpha =$ the accidental error due to aircraft height deviation

   $\alpha' =$ orientation and other errors (both accidental and systematic)

It may be noted that irregular errors are more significant in aeroleveling. The resulting misclosure in the coordinates may have contributions from systematic errors caused due to the tilt of the isobaric surface which do not get into the aeropolygon. It has been observed by Brandenberger [14] and others that in aeroleveling the propagation of the error in elevation (Z) is almost linear, but is parabolic in planimetry (X and Y). The use of Eqs. (5.25) or (5.26) or similar ones may be pertinent, however, for the adjustment of aerolevelled strips.

Some variations of the aeroleveling method are given below:

1. bz = 0 method. As a variation (approximate) of the aeroleveling method, the "bz = 0" method may be used for long strips when statoscope readings are not available. The flight is assumed to be at a constant altitude for the entire strip, thus $bz_I = bz_{II} = 0.00$ is maintained throughout the strip. The coorientation is performed with

$$\phi_I, \phi_{II}, \omega_{II}, \kappa_{II}, \text{ and } by_{II}$$

2. Systematic ϕ error. This may be performed in cases where flight at a constant level will be difficult to assume and yet statoscope data are not available. In this method, prior to the instrument work, the average $\Delta\phi$ gap (see Fig. 7-2) is computed by using

$$\Delta\phi = \frac{b}{R} \qquad (7.6a)$$

where   b = the average air base

R = the radius of the earth sphere

Before the coorientation of the ith model, the ith photo is given a $\Delta\phi$ movement in the positive (forward) direction and the coorientation is performed with elements of the (i + 1)th photo, i.e., with

$$\phi_{II}, \omega_{II}, \kappa_{II}, by_{II}, \text{ and } bz_{II}.$$

Both these variations yield workable results in small-scale (smaller than 1:25,000) mapping jobs.

8

Independent Models

The aeropolygon method involving the use of so-called "first-order instruments" is widely used. To avoid the need for a large number of cameras (projectors), the instrument has a base-in, base-out capability. This arrangement, although very convenient, requires complex engineering. Eventually, the cost of such instruments is very high; beyond the reach of small mapping agencies.

Several methods of analytical (computational) aerial triangulation (see Chap. 9) have recently been developed which make use of mathematical solutions of the geometric relationships of images on overlapping photographs. These require extremely large numbers of computations and can best be performed using high-speed electronic computers with large storage capabilities. This may become a problem for some mapping agencies with limited funds which restricts the purchase or use of such costly comparators and computers.

In recent years interest has been shown in combining aspects of analog and computational techniques. This advances the view that the numerical formation of strips (and, eventually, blocks) from independent stereomodels is a suitable combination of both the analog and analytical systems. The advantages are the possibilities of the use of less expensive and simpler (but not necessarily less accurate) plotters and more easily manageable numerical data which, in extreme cases, can be handled with desk calculators without deteriorating the quality of strip formation. The strips thus obtained can be adjusted graphically or numerically depending on the circumstances.

8.1 Basic Theory

The underlying principles are presented in the schematic diagram (Fig. 8-1). The essential idea is to perform a satisfactory relative orientation of each model by computation with comparator data or at the stereoplotting instrument directly to obtain three-dimensional coordinates of the necessary model points and the two projection centers. The absolute orientation of the first model and the scale transfer and coorientation of the second and successive models are performed numerically through computations. This then gives the complete strip coordinates (albeit inclusive of closing errors) in a numerically created aeropolygon. Finally, the strip (and block) may be adjusted numerically (using polynomials), empirically (e.g., using templets), or graphically (using error curves and graphs).

It is, however, imperative that interior orientation be satisfactory. The relative orientation may be performed using the same method of orientation and the same instrument base for each model. This means that by and bz elements may not be needed at all. An instrument with only five elements of relative orientation will be adequate for the purpose. However, instruments with the capability of reading parallaxes may be preferred so that numerical relative orientation can be used for greater accuracy and more systematic strip formation. The only requirement will be that the instrument is capable of reading (and possibly recording) all three coordinates (X, Y, Z).

Further, along with the coordinates of the model points, the coordinates of the two perspective (projection) centers need to be read in the same system. This is easily done directly in any first-order instrument. However, in a second-order instrument this has to be provided by precalibration (see also Sec. 8.2).

The method needs as the basic minimum requirements, all the coordinates to be read from the oriented model (relative orientation only) for the following points in model i, (see Figs. 8-1 and 8-2):

1. All available ground-control points
2. The two perspective centers: i_0 and $(i + 1)_0$
3. The four corner points: i_U, i_L, $(i + 1)_U$, and $(i + 1)_L$

Additional points i_C and $(i + 1)_C$ will provide stronger geometry in the strip assembly.

Mathematical Background

All the points of the first model are transformed to the ground system by considering (with the help of the given ground-control points):

1. Scale factor
2. Rotations through space
3. Translation through space

This may be expressed by the following (see also Ghosh [35]:

$$\begin{bmatrix} X^g \\ Y^g \\ Z^g \end{bmatrix} = k[M]' \begin{bmatrix} X \\ Y \\ Z \end{bmatrix} + \begin{bmatrix} X_0 \\ Y_0 \\ Z_0 \end{bmatrix} \tag{8.1}$$

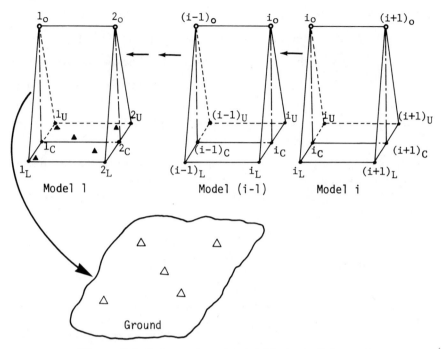

Figure 8-1. Independent Model Method (Schematic)

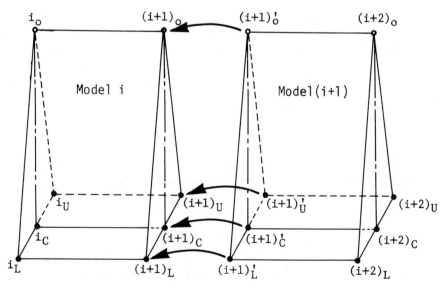

Figure 8-2. Connection of Models

where   X, Y, Z = the coordinates in the instrument

X^g, Y^g, Z^g = the coordinates in the ground system

k = the scale factor (considered linear in all directions)

M' = the transposed orientation matrix (defining rotations)

X_0, Y_0, Z_0 = the coordinates of the origin in the X^g, Y^g, Z^g system (elements of translation vector T)

The scale factor k being constant, in practice, is automatically applied along with the elements of the orientation matrix **M**.

The rotation angles, considered sequentially, in a right-handed system, are:

$$\Omega = \arctan (\Delta Z/\Delta Y)$$

$$\Phi = \arctan (\Delta Z/\Delta X)$$

$$K = \arctan (\Delta X/\Delta Y)$$

The rotation Ω around the X axis transforms Y and Z into the positions Y_Ω and Z_Ω, respectively. This is expressed by the rotation matrix

$$\mathbf{M}_\Omega = \begin{bmatrix} 1 & 0 & 0 \\ 0 & \cos \Omega & \sin \Omega \\ 0 & -\sin \Omega & \cos \Omega \end{bmatrix} \qquad (8.2a)$$

Next, the rotation Φ around the Y_Ω axis transforms the Z_Ω and X_Ω into $Z_{\Omega\Phi}$ and $X_{\Omega\Phi}$, respectively. This is expressed by the rotation matrix

$$\mathbf{M}_\Phi = \begin{bmatrix} \cos \Phi & 0 & \sin \Phi \\ 0 & 1 & 0 \\ -\sin \Phi & 0 & \cos \Phi \end{bmatrix} \qquad (8.2b)$$

Finally, the rotation K around the $Z_{\Omega\Phi}$ axis transforms $X_{\Omega\Phi}$ and $Y_{\Omega\Phi}$ into $X_{\Omega\Phi K}$ and $Y_{\Omega\Phi K}$, respectively. This is expressed by the matrix

$$\mathbf{M}_K = \begin{bmatrix} \cos K & -\sin K & 0 \\ \sin K & \cos K & 0 \\ 0 & 0 & 1 \end{bmatrix} \qquad (8.2c)$$

The total effect of all three rotations is then expressed in the orientation matrix **M** where

$$M = M_\Omega \cdot M_\Phi \cdot M_K \tag{8.3}$$

For the translation of the origin generally all available common known points between the two systems are used, the average being considered as the origin, i.e.,

$$
\left.
\begin{aligned}
X_0 &= \frac{\sum X^g}{n} \\[2mm]
Y_0 &= \frac{\sum Y^g}{n} \\[2mm]
Z_0 &= \frac{\sum Z^g}{n}
\end{aligned}
\right\} \tag{8.4}
$$

where n is the number of known points

The orientation matrix M is the sequential product of three orthogonal rotation matrices. Therefore, M itself is orthogonal, i.e., the inverse of M is equal to its transpose:

$M^{-1} = M'$ or $MM' = MM^{-1} = I$, the identity matrix.

Equation (8.1) assumes that the scale factor k is the same in all directions (common throughout the model).

It is interesting to note here that the M matrix has nine parameters giving a total of twelve unknowns. However, the number of real unknowns is only six (i.e., three rotations and three translations). To impose the condition $MM' = I$, six condition equations can be obtained, thereby increasing the degree of freedom by six. The six conditions between unknown parameters will now have the same effect as reducing the unknowns from twelve to six, restoring the correct degrees of freedom to such adjustments. Consider

$$
M' = \begin{bmatrix} a_{11} & a_{12} & a_{13} \\ a_{21} & a_{22} & a_{23} \\ a_{31} & a_{32} & a_{33} \end{bmatrix} \quad \text{and} \quad T = \begin{bmatrix} X_0 \\ Y_0 \\ Z_0 \end{bmatrix}
$$

Then

$$
kM' = \begin{bmatrix} ka_{11} & ka_{12} & ka_{13} \\ ka_{21} & ka_{22} & ka_{23} \\ ka_{31} & ka_{32} & ka_{33} \end{bmatrix} = \begin{bmatrix} R_{11} & R_{12} & R_{13} \\ R_{21} & R_{22} & R_{23} \\ R_{31} & R_{32} & R_{33} \end{bmatrix}
$$

Thus the scale factor can be absorbed in the rotation matrix. Then for any one point the transformation equations are given by

$$\left. \begin{array}{l} X^g = R_{11}X + R_{12}Y + R_{13}Z + X_0 \\ Y^g = R_{21}X + R_{22}Y + R_{23}Z + Y_0 \\ Z^g = R_{31}X + R_{32}Y + R_{33}Z + Z_0 \end{array} \right\} \quad (8.5)$$

With n points common between adjacent models, this gives a set of 3n equations.

It can be shown (see Dresden [27]) that the following six equations are necessary and sufficient to impose orthogonality of the rotation matrix:

$$\left. \begin{array}{l} a_{11}^2 + a_{12}^2 + a_{13}^2 = 1 \\ a_{21}^2 + a_{22}^2 + a_{23}^2 = 1 \\ a_{31}^2 + a_{32}^2 + a_{33}^2 = 1 \end{array} \right\} \quad \text{or} \quad \left. \begin{array}{l} R_{11}^2 + R_{12}^2 + R_{13}^2 = k^2 \\ R_{21}^2 + R_{22}^2 + R_{23}^2 = k^2 \\ R_{31}^2 + R_{32}^2 + R_{33}^2 = k^2 \end{array} \right\} \quad (8.6)$$

Further,

$$R_{11} R_{21} + R_{12} R_{22} + R_{13} R_{23} = 0$$

$$R_{11} R_{31} + R_{12} R_{32} + R_{13} R_{33} = 0$$

$$R_{21} R_{31} + R_{22} R_{32} + R_{23} R_{33} = 0$$

These equations are nonlinear and require iterations to obtain a precise solution.

It is seen that the mathematical model for the transformation, before imposing the orthogonality conditions is linear in the parameters. Therefore, no iteration is necessary for that part of the computation. However, the condition equations being nonlinear, require iterations to obtain a precise solution.

The transformations required in the independent-model method can be performed in one of two different ways:

Method I: Consider Eq. (8.1) which in linear form is:

$$\left. \begin{array}{l} X^g = k(a_{11}X + a_{12}Y + a_{13}Z) + X_0 \\ Y^g = k(a_{21}X + a_{22}Y + a_{23}Z) + Y_0 \\ Z^g = k(a_{31}X + a_{32}Y + a_{33}Z) + Z_0 \end{array} \right\} \quad (8.7)$$

where a_{ij} are the elements of the rotation matrix **M'**. The nine elements of the rotation matrix actually involve sines and cosines of the three rotations K, Φ, and Ω. Thus there are seven independent unknown parameters in this transformation, that is, k, K, Φ, Ω, X_0, Y_0 and Z_0.

In order to write observation equations in linear form the *Taylor expansion* is used. This requires that Eq. (8.7) be partially differentiated with respect to the unknown parameters. This gives the following observation equations:

$$\left.\begin{array}{l} v_X = p_{11} + p_{12}d\Omega + p_{13}d\Phi + p_{14}dK + p_{15}dk + p_{16}dX_0 \\[6pt] v_Y = p_{21} + p_{22}d\Omega + p_{23}d\Phi + p_{24}dK + p_{25}dk + p_{26}dY_0 \\[6pt] v_Z = p_{31} + p_{32}d\Omega + p_{33}d\Phi + p_{34}dK + p_{35}dk + p_{36}dZ_0 \end{array}\right\} \quad (8.8)$$

where p_{11}, p_{21}, and p_{31} are misclosures in X, Y, Z, respectively, based on the differences between the observed value and the value computed from approximate values for the unknown parameters

$p_{12} \cdots p_{16}$, $p_{22} \cdots p_{26}$, $p_{32} \cdots p_{36}$ are the partial derivatives of Eq. (8.5) evaluated with approximate values for the unknown parameters

$d\Omega$, $d\Phi$, dK, dk, dX_0, dY_0, and dZ_0 are the differential corrections to the approximate values of the unknown parameters

Using the partial derivatives, a matrix is formed with seven columns and $(2m + n)$ rows, where m is the number of plan control points and n is the number of elevation (or height) control points. Call this the $[\overline{O}]$ matrix. The normal equation matrix $[N]$ is formed by multiplying the $[\overline{O}]$ matrix by its transpose, assuming unit weight for all observations. The transpose of the $[\overline{O}]$ matrix is multiplied by a column vector composed of the misclosures. This forms a 7×1 column vector $[X]$, which contains the differential corrections to the unknown parameters:

$$[X] = \begin{bmatrix} d\Omega \\ d\Phi \\ dK \\ dk \\ dX_0 \\ dY_0 \\ dZ_0 \end{bmatrix} \quad (8.9)$$

The solution for $[X]$ is given by:

$$[\mathbf{X}] = -[\mathbf{N}]^{-1} [\mathbf{U}]$$

Thus, the [N] matrix must be inverted and multiplied by the [U] matrix, which is the constant vector of the normal equations (dimensions 7 × 1).

The approximate values used for the unknown parameters are corrected by the quantities from the [X] vector:

$$\left.\begin{array}{ll}
\Omega_\bullet + d\Omega = \Omega_a \\
\Phi_\bullet + d\Phi = \Phi_a & X_{0\bullet} + dX_0 = X_{0a} \\
K_\bullet + dK = K_a & Y_{0\bullet} + dY_0 = Y_{0a} \\
k_\bullet + dk = k_a & Z_{0\bullet} + dZ_0 = Z_{0a}
\end{array}\right\} \qquad (8.10)$$

where   the subscript • indicates approximate values

the subscript a indicates adjusted values

The adjusted values for the unknown parameters are used as new approximations and the adjustment procedure is repeated until the corrections to the rotation elements are all less than a predetermined value (e.g., 0.00001 rad considered by the U.S. National Oceanic Survey,[a] see [54]. Then final corrections are added to the unknown parameters. With these final adjusted values, points in one coordinate system can be transformed to the other using Eq. (8.5).

The first approximate values (also see Sec. 12.2) must be obtained from the seven unknown parameters: the rotations Ω and Φ are usually small angles in vertical aerial photography. These elements are given the value zero for a first approximation. K is computed by selecting two plan control points common between the two spaces (ground and model). The desired angle K is given by:

$$K = \arctan (\Delta Y/\Delta X) - \arctan (\Delta Y^g/\Delta X^g) \qquad (8.11)$$

The approximate scale factor is given by the ratio of the distance between the two plan control points:

$$1/k = \sqrt{(\Delta X^2 + \Delta Y^2)/(\Delta X^{g2} + \Delta Y^{g2})}, \qquad (8.12)$$

The approximate translations are obtained by taking the differences between the rotated and scaled instrument coordinates and the ground coordinates:

$$\left.\begin{array}{l}
X_0 = X^g - k(X \cos K + Y \sin K) \\
Y_0 = Y^g - k(X \sin K - Y \cos K) \\
Z_0 = Z^g - k \cdot Z
\end{array}\right\} \qquad (8.13)$$

[a]At the time of publication, the survey was known as the U.S. Coast and Geodetic Survey.

The first approximate values are then

$\Omega = 0$

$\Phi = 0$

K from Eq. (8.11)

k from Eq. (8.12)

$\left. \begin{array}{l} X_0 \\ Y_0 \\ Z_0 \end{array} \right\}$ from Eq. (8.13)

Method II: One may use it when the information on the rotation angles, etc., are not required directly.

Consider Eq. (8.6) by containing k in the elements a_{ij}. One obtains Eq. (8.14) in which there are 12 unknowns:

$$\left. \begin{array}{l} X^g = aX + bY + cZ + X_0 \\ Y^g = dX + eY + fZ + Y_0 \\ Z^g = gX + hY + iZ + Z_0 \end{array} \right\} \qquad (8.14)$$

Therefore, a direct solution is possible with four control points such that four equations for each of X^g, Y^g, and Z^g can be written, the solution of which give the a_{ij} elements and X_0, Y_0 and Z_0.

With a minimum of three control points, this can be simplified by using the centroid (in a way similar to the two-dimensional transformation discussed in Chap. 2).

First obtain the coordinates of the centroid in the ground and model spaces (note Eq. 8.4):

$$X^g_s = \frac{\Sigma X^g}{n}, \ Y^g_s = \frac{\Sigma Y^g}{n}, \ Z^g_s = \frac{\Sigma Z^g}{n}$$

$$X_s = \frac{\Sigma X}{n}, \ Y_s = \frac{\Sigma Y}{n}, \ Z_s = \frac{\Sigma Z}{n}.$$

Next obtain the coordinates with respect to the centroid:

$$X^{g\prime}_i = X^g_i - X^g_s, \qquad Y^{g\prime}_i = Y^g_i - Y^g_s, \qquad Z^{g\prime}_i = Z^g_i - Z^g_s;$$

$$X'_i = X_i - X_s, \qquad Y'_i = Y_i - Y_s, \qquad Z'_i = Z_i - Z_s.$$

These can be used now in Eq. (8.14), less translations:

$$\left. \begin{array}{l} X^{g\prime} = aX' + bY' + cZ' \\[4pt] Y^{g\prime} = dX' + eY' + fZ' \\[4pt] Z^{g\prime} = gX' + hY' + iZ' \end{array} \right\} \qquad (8.15)$$

By solving Eq. (8.15), (with more than three points, a least-squares fit, using normal equations, may be performed) one obtains a, b, c, d, e, f, g, h and i.

Now by using Eq. (8.14) one can obtain X_0, Y_0, and Z_0 to be used for all transformations for that particular unit.

By the aforementioned procedure, the first model is transformed first to the ground system. Next the same procedure is followed to transform the second model to the first model (already transformed to the ground system). This is followed by transforming the third model to the already transformed second model. This process is continued until the last model is reached.

In transforming the successive models, the points i_0, i_U, i_L, and i_C may be considered as the control points. Generally more information is available and a least-squares adjustment is desirable and easily performed with a (high-speed) computer. See Sec. 12.2 and App. C also.

8.2 Perspective Centers

The transformation as required between successive models could not work properly if the perspective centers were not involved. Therefore, their coordinates must be determined in the system of the model with reliability equal to the model points. This is more important with respect to the instruments of the so-called "second-order type" where slight changes over short periods in the course of operations may be expected. Also adjustment control of the instrument before or after the strip triangulation may be cumbersome or time-consuming in many cases.

A particular procedure developed by Philip [75] following an idea offered by Ligterink [61] is discussed below. Figure 8-3 shows the scheme suggested for such a procedure. Corresponding to the model point P, the photo points are p' and p" in the left and right cameras, respectively. The perspective centers are I and II, whose coordinates are to be determined.

After the relative orientation of the model is performed, the model coordinates of the points P_i (X_i, Y_i, Z_i) are obtained from stereoscopic observation. Next the carriage is brought to another level where the same points (now separated) are read monocularly (see points P' and P" in Fig. 8-3). Such monocular observations should be made for all the points at one Z = constant plane according to convenience and keeping in mind that

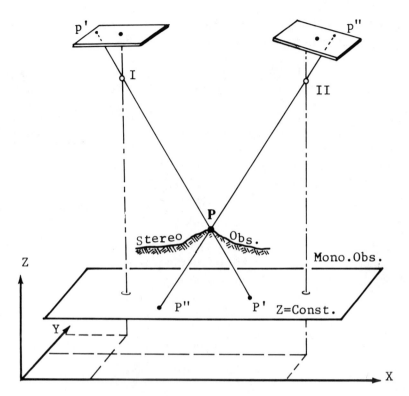

Figure 8-3. Determination of Perspective Centers

the accuracy of the coordinates determination (it is a kind of "space resection") would depend on the separation of P from P' and P". Since the line defined by P and P' passes through I, while the line defined by P and P" passes through II, the observed coordinates can be utilized into the equation of a straight line, in each case, in three-dimensional space. Since all such lines with respect to the left photo must pass through I and those for the right photo through II, their coordinates are directly obtained. With redundant observations a least-squares fit is applicable. Simultaneously, a minimum parallax condition at P_i can be implicitly enforced. Thus, a model in which the errors of relative orientation should be drastically curtailed is also numerically created.

Mathematical Model

Given the coordinates x_1, y_1, z_1 and x_2, y_2, z_2 of two fixed points on a straight line, the direction is determined by the ratios $x_2-x_1 : y_2-y_1 : z_2-z_1$, and the equation of the line can be expressed in the form

$$\frac{x - x_1}{x_2 - x_1} = \frac{y - y_1}{y_2 - y_1} = \frac{z - z_1}{z_2 - z_1} \qquad (8.16)$$

where (x, y, z) are the coordinates of a variable point on the line.

In the case under consideration, dealing with the left photograph only for the time being, the coordinates of point $P_i(X_i, Y_i, Z_i)$ and $P_i'(X_i', Y_i', Z_i')$ have been measured in model space, and, hence, the equation of the line defined by these points is

$$\frac{x - X_i}{X_i' - X_i} = \frac{y - Y_i}{Y_i' - Y_i} = \frac{z - Z_i}{Z_i' - Z_i}$$

Now, the perspective center I of the photograph to the left whose coordinates are (X_0', Y_0', Z_0') lies on this line, and so substituting in the above equation,

$$\frac{X_0' - X_i}{X_i' - X_i} = \frac{Y_0' - Yi}{Y_i' - Y_i} = \frac{Z_0' - Z_i}{Z_i' - Z_i} \qquad (8.16a)$$

This can be simplified into two equations

$$\left.\begin{array}{l} -X_0'(Z_i' - Z_i) + Z_0'(X_i' - X_i) = Z_iX_i' - Z_i'X_i \\ -Y_0'(Z_i' - Z_i) + Z_0'(Y_i' - Y_i) = Z_iY_i' - Z_i'Y_i \end{array}\right\} \qquad (8.17)$$

Or, expressed in matrix notation,

$$\begin{bmatrix} -(Z_i' - Z_i) & 0 & (X_i' - X_i) \\ 0 & -(Z_i' - Z_i) & (Y_i' - Y_i) \end{bmatrix} \begin{bmatrix} X_0' \\ Y_0' \\ Z_0' \end{bmatrix}$$

$$= \begin{bmatrix} X_i' & -X_i \\ Y_i' & -Y_i \end{bmatrix} \begin{bmatrix} Z_i \\ Z_i' \end{bmatrix} \qquad (8.18)$$

The same discrete point (P_i) referred to the right-hand photograph and its perspective center (X_0'', Y_0'', Z_0'') gives the equations:

$$\begin{bmatrix} -(Z_i'' - Z_i) & 0 & (X_i'' - X_i) \\ 0 & -(Z_i'' - Z_i) & (Y_i'' - Y_i) \end{bmatrix} \begin{bmatrix} X_0'' \\ Y_0'' \\ Z_0'' \end{bmatrix}$$

$$= \begin{bmatrix} X_i'' & -X_i \\ Y_i'' & -Y_i \end{bmatrix} \begin{bmatrix} Z_i \\ Z_i'' \end{bmatrix} \qquad (8.19)$$

Equations (8.18) and (8.19) can be considered as the condition equations. They constitute the mathematical model of the correction scheme. The observations are the coordinates of points P, P', and P'' and the unknowns are the coordinates of the perspective centers (I and II). That is,

1. If n discrete points are observed in the model, there are 4n equations in the system and this involves 4n monocular observations (X and Y, at P' and P'') plus 3n stereoscopic observations (X, Y, Z at P).

2. The X, Y, Z coordinates of each perspective center give six observations in each model. To this must be associated the constant Z at which the monocular observations are made. This gives seven observations.

A least-squares solution can be applied. The number of true observations (7n = 4n + 3n) are greater than the number of condition equations (4n). Also the number of condition equations (with two or more points in the model) is greater than the number of unknown parameters, the number of redundant equations being 4n−7. Interesting description of the development of the solution using the principles of least squares and its associated computer program has been presented by Philip [75].

8.3 Improvement with Affine Transformation

It has been noticed in many cases that the stereomodels reveal appreciable differences in the scales along different axes indicating affine deformations. Studies made in the Department of Geodetic Science at Ohio State University indicated situations in aerial triangulation where such affine deformation has been noticed to be very consistent. See also Ghosh [35], Das [24], and Nanayakkara [73] indicating consistent affine deformation in the models of stereometric camera systems. The above suggest a more general solution with affine transformation. Assuming different scales k_1, k_2, k_3 along X, Y, Z coordinate axes, respectively, one can replace Eq. (8.1) with:

$$\begin{bmatrix} X^g \\ Y^g \\ Z^g \end{bmatrix} = k[M]' \begin{bmatrix} k_1 X \\ k_2 Y \\ k_3 Z \end{bmatrix} + \begin{bmatrix} X_0 \\ Y_0 \\ Z_0 \end{bmatrix} \qquad (8.20)$$

The parameter k is highly correlated to k_1, k_2, k_3. In fact, k need not be solved if the other three are included in the solution. It has been observed, however, that if k_1, k_2, and k_3 are not significantly different from each other, then k may have to be solved. In the simplest case k is unity. Hence k is allowed to remain in the expression along with the other three scale factors in order to express the most general case, although it may not appear to be of the simplest form from a strict mathematical standpoint. The nine parameters of the **M** matrix are correlated and not independent. There are only three independent parameters (i.e., the three rotations). Further, subsequent imposition of the conditions for orthogonality is cumbersome and in one test (see Nanayakkara [73]) did not give sufficient precision. Therefore, the solution can be strengthened by using only three parameters (K, Φ, and Ω) in M and using the orthogonal form of the rotation matrix, also eliminating the need for the use of the condition for orthogonality.

Generally, reliable estimates of the rotations are easily obtained and the corrections to the assumed values are small. Therefore, in the least-squares solution where the corrections to the assumed values of the parameters are solved, it can be stated that after the approximate rotations are given, the order of the small rotations is not important. It does not affect the solution significantly.

The problem of avoiding the strong correlation due to the linear dependence of k with k_1, k_2 and k_3 has to be overcome. If this is not done, the high correlations between these parameters would give a very unstable normal matrix and an acceptable solution is not possible. This can be achieved by treating the parameters themselves as observations. Such an interpretation is compatible with conventional thinking if one realizes that an observation, associated with an infinitely large weight becomes a constant (i.e., a fixed variable) and its corresponding residual error is zero.

In order to assign weights in the system, first we have to assume that the real observations (coordinates of points) have a fixed variance [e.g., consider a standard error of reading a coordinate in the model of a Wild A8 being 0.03 mm, the variance of $(0.03)^2$ is logical].

To determine the affine scale factors k_1, k_2, and k_3, then, one has to keep k fixed. Further, by careful examination one can obtain as to what precision (standard deviation) in the determination of these parameters will be sufficient in the particular case. The weight can be assigned accordingly. For example, if the precision up to the tth decimal place is sufficient, in order to keep k fixed, one should give it the weight $1 \times 10^{t+2}$ when all other parameters have unit weight. Similarly, in order to keep k_1, k_2, k_3 fixed (i.e., for solving k) a similar procedure may be followed.

The advantage of this approach is that the parameters need not be recomputed with a new mathematical model each time it is decided to leave out (fix) a parameter from the solution. It permits the use of a most general model with all possible parameters, thus simplifying the programming and allowing a systematic analysis of the working system. This, on the other hand, assumes that a suitable number of observations are available to enable all the necessary parameters to be solved.

In two experimental researches involving several stereomodels using the Wild A8 to orient the independent models, this method of "weighting of parameters" and considerations of affine transformation yielded satisfactorily improved results.

The consideration of different scales along X, Y, and Z coordinates would be appropriate in the cases of individual models from the point of view of obtaining some correcting effects on model coordinates as may be required in high precision work, e.g., in cadastral photogrammetry. In many cases the deformations show the characteristic of conformity, at least to a first approximation. Assuming that the relative orientations of successive models in a strip (or block) triangulation are as correct as possible and the aerial triangulation consists of connecting successive models with each other, because the models, individually, are of finite dimensions while the analytical transformation is an infinitesimal one, one can consider that the angles are "locally correct" and, thus, the ideas contained in this section seem to be appropriate and more than adequate in the case of independent models.

Interesting ideas may be obtained from Schut's work [86] in this general area.

8.4 Instrument Settings

After the instrument is calibrated, X, Y, and Z counters (or scales) are set, and the entire procedure works better if the counters remain fixed to the origin. This would assure that the coordinates of the projection centers would not change.

The base (bx) of each model may be set at a constant value. A value may be predetermined so that points in each model stay reasonably well within the ranges of the instrument. The initial settings of each element of orientation may be zero. It is suggested that the *same* five orientation *elements* be used for the relative orientation and the *same method* of orientation (preferably numerical) be followed in each model. This would ensure further systematic error propagation in the bridged strip (see Ghosh [37]).

8.5 Final Adjustment

The final data contain the errors propagated through the strip due to various causes. However, these are revealed as closing errors (or misclosures) at the control points encountered in the strip. These misclosures are adjusted by any suitable and convenient method.

Research studies made by Philip [75] indicate no significant difference between the error surface of the analog aeropolygon and the computational aeropolygon of the independent-model method. Similar studies on the Nistri-Bendix analytic plotter (see Strahle [95]) also support this view.

The precision of such strip triangulation would increase if

1. Weights (and correlations) are used at the model connection stage

2. Simultaneous adjustments of models are applied to weighted (and correlated) strip coordinates and weighted ground control

In this respect, interesting concepts based on the collinearity principle, (see Sec. 9.2) have been recently presented by Maarek [63]. In this, the stereomodels are first relatively oriented; the model coordinates are then observed and transformed to the image plane. These transformed coordinates are used as observations together with exposure station unknowns and the pass-point coordinates as parameters in a simultaneous least-square solution. This mathematical model, according to Maarek, gives the best agreement between the observations and the parameters in the solution, uses a half-photograph as the basic unit in the solution, and assigns for each basic unit three rotation parameters. After the results were checked by statistical and geometric analyses using various test data and different stereoplotters and a stereocomparator, Maarek concludes that this approach seems to yield highly satisfactory results. He further concludes that in the adjustment procedure, mathematical correlation between the image coordinates may be neglected.

9 Computational Phototriangulation

During recent years a number of different good methods of computational (also known as analytical) phototriangulation have been developed. There are basic similarities in these approaches and yet there are considerable differences. The published methods are generally known either by the name of the author or by the name of the organization in which these were developed.

In all these the starting data are the photocoordinates (x_i, y_i) of points obtained with the help of comparators (mono or stereo). These data are refined (corrected for several known physical-error sources) and followed by a particular triangulation procedure.

In the computational approaches, the bundles of rays are defined by mathematical formulas. The formulas may represent certain approximations. The accuracy of the computation is limited by the number of decimal places used. The only instrumental errors that occur are those in the reading of coordinates at the comparator, whose effects can be kept under sufficient control with appropriate calibration.

Broadly speaking, there are two different approaches: *sequential* and *simultaneous*. In the first one, the triangulation is performed in steps. This approach may be visualized as analogous to the analog (instrumental) process of triangulation. It consists of the following computational steps:

1. Relative orientation and computation of individual basic unit in an arbitrary, independent coordinate system. (A basic unit can be a stereo pair, a triplet, a sub-block of m · n photographs, etc.)
2. Assembly of the basic units into a common coordinate system. Sometimes this step may be concurrent with Step 1.
3. Adjustment of the assembled block to known control.

Usually, the mathematical approaches to the sequential procedures are categorized according to the respective relative (or absolute) orientation methods (e.g., collinearity, coplanarity, scale-restraint conditions) and the method employed for strip or block adjustments (e.g., linear, second- or third-degree polynomial equations, iterative with number of equations, direct solutions, etc.). The basic sequential concept is used in two different procedures as follows:

1. *Aeropolygon*: The procedures of the first order stereoplotters are simulated insofaras the five elements of relative orientation (coorientation)

are first computed. These elements are computed generally by means of a (coplanarity) condition which states that corresponding rays must intersect in the epipolar plane. Next, without affecting the coorientation, the resulting model is scaled (using the scale-restraint condition) to that of the preceding model.

2. In the second procedure, all six orientation elements of the photograph are computed simultaneously and, in the presence of redundant observations, adjusted simultaneously. This means that for rays to points which are common with the preceding model, the condition of intersection with the corresponding ray from the first photograph in that model is used for the adjustment of all orientation elements.

In these procedures using more than one common point between models, model deformation of one model may cause the next model to deform also. This is because the position of the common points will be used in the determination of all orientation elements of the next photograph. Deformations of the new model will, in turn, cause deformations in the following models. Consequently, the results of a triangulation may depend on the initial model and the direction of the strip buildup. A logical improvement of this procedure is formed in the use of "triplets" which will be discussed in Sec. 9.1.

The *simultaneous* procedure offers another approach whereby the triangulation is performed in one step. The desired parameters are adjusted as a result of one simultaneous, least-squares adjustment of the n photos (strip or block) by a direct or iterative method. From a mathematical point of view, these methods are more rigorous and should provide (theoretically) the most accurate results. The fundamental and outstanding requirement in a simultaneous procedure is the need for estimates of exposure station positions and orientation elements. These are required prior to the adjustment of the n photo group. Furthermore, estimates for coordinates of all pass points may be needed depending on the approach taken. As a consequence, the simultaneous procedure should include a feasible method of obtaining the necessary estimated values.

The basic equation used in these is the "collinearity condition" (also see Sec. 9.2). There are, however, different approaches to the solution of the system of equations (e.g., matrix inversion, Gauss-Cholesky elimination, etc.).

9.1 Sequential Triangulation

Basically, the sequential procedure parallels the aeropolygon method as performed at the stereoplotting instrument (analogical procedure, see

Chap. 3). A typical example of the various stages (as practiced by the U.S. National Oceanic Survey, see [51]) is given below:

Stage I: Data procurement

1. Photo preparation
2. Stereo marking of various points
3. Coordinate measurements

At the end of this stage, one obtains the comparator coordinates x_i', y_i' and x_i'', y_i''.

Stage II. Data processing

1. Coordinate refinement (reduction). (Refined coordinates serve as inputs for triangulation.)
   a. Correction for comparator calibration
   b. Correction for film distortion
   c. Reduction to perspective center
   d. Correction for lens distortion (both symmetric and assymmetric)
   e. Correction for atmospheric refraction
   f. Correction for the earth's curvature
2. Provisional solution
   a. Iterative Coorientations (e.g., three-photo orientation or triplet solution)
   b. Cantilever assembly (also adjustment) of the strip
   c. Earth's curvature correction
   d. Strip transformation (adjustment) to the ground (control) system
3. Refined solution
   a. Secant plane (also geocentric) coordinate transformation
   b. Block adjustment
      (1) Simultaneous solution of the absolute orientation
      (2) Correction to the provisional coordinates

It may be noted here that most strip triangulations would terminate at Stage II 2(b), depending on the desired accuracy. Furthermore, the block adjustment may be performed without the three-photo orientation and strip-adjustment programs. But these are recommended to furnish improved and complete data for the block adjustment to reduce the number of iterations in the block program and, thus, to minimize cost.

Stage II 2(a), alternately, may be performed by (a) relative orientation (dependent) using the coplanarity condition (see Sec. 9.1) and (b) scale transfer, using the scale-restraint condition (see Sec. 9.1).

Brief elaborations of some of the above stages are given below.

Iterative coorientation. This is entirely independent of any ground-control data. The three-photo iterative solution (see Sec. 9.1) is simply coorientational and determines the positions of all pertinent points in a three-dimensional coordinate system at the approximate photo scale. Here the collinearily condition (see Sec. 9.2) is imposed and the discrepancies in the observed photo coordinates are minimized through the application of the principle of least squares. The residual errors are analyzed by the computer, blunders are discarded (removed), and "clean" data obtained for subsequent operations.

Strip transformation to ground system. This means the transformation of the three-photo model coordinates into the prevailing ground-control system by fitting to control data through the application of polynomial formulas (empirical, see Chap. 5) and the principle of least squares. This results in providing provisional coordinates (X, Y, Z) of all points in the strip. The same program can be used to adjust a strip which contains insufficient control points (say, by fitting to common points of an adjacent strip). Large residual discrepancies may be detected by human inspection and may be either discarded or corrected. This provides another step of freeing the data of blunders prior to entering the block-adjustment program.

Secant plane coordinate transformation. The work may be performed through a geocentric and three-dimensional cartesian coordinate system that takes earth curvature into account automatically. Subsequent block adjustment can be completed using secant plane coordinates for various points. The adjusted secant plane coordinates are then transformed back into the original ground coordinate system by applying the transformation in its reverse mode.

Block adjustment (also see Sec. 9.2 and Chap. 12). This involves (1) simultaneous solution of the absolute orientation (i.e., three linear elements: dX_0, dY_0, dZ_0 and three angular elements $d\omega$, $d\phi$, $d\kappa$ of all the photographs and (2) corrections to the provisional coordinates (X, Y, and Z) of each point. It consists of three phases:

1. *Space resection.* It begins with reading into storage the (given) ground coordinates of weighted control stations, and also the provisional ground coordinates of points whose ground coordinates may be finalized in the second (block-orientation) phase. The space-resection routine fits the image data from each photograph to the corresponding provisional ground coordinates in order to determine the initial values for the camera parameters. This would involve the formation of a set of equations having the six incremental corrections to the camera parameters (as unknowns), and solving repeatedly until further corrections are insignificant.

2. *Block orientation*. The simultaneous solution of the absolute orientation of all the photographs and the computation of the final ground coordinates for each point (pass points as well as weighted control stations) is performed. The output of this phase are (in the NOS program):

   a. The maximum angular correction required by each program pass
   b. The ground coordinates of all the relative orientation pass points
   c. The misfits of the solution to the weighted control points
   d. The residual discrepancies of all images on each photograph and the RMS values for the entire block
   e. The sines and cosines of the final three orientation angles of each photograph
   f. The final three coordinates of each camera station

3. *Object intersection*. This phase gives the points other than pass points and the control stations for which accurate ground coordinates are to be computed (e.g., points for low-flown models from a high-flown block). Because these points are not uniformly distributed, it is not desirable to include them in the orientation (phase), because their very presence could weight the solution according to their locations. The ground coordinates of an unlimited number of points may be determined in this phase.

For interesting ideas on sequential methods, see Anderson [7] and Stewart and Hull [94].

Coplanarity Condition

The coplanarity condition equation (see also Ghosh [35] and the *Manual of Photogrammetry* [5]) illustrated in Fig. 9-1 is fundamental to relative orientation. When relative orientation is achieved, the vector $\vec{R}_{1i}$ from 0_1 to P_i will intersect the vector $\vec{R}_{2i}$ from 0_2 to P_i, and these two vectors together with air base vector, $\vec{b}$, will be coplanar. Hence, their scalar triple product is zero. That is

$$F_i = \vec{b} \cdot \vec{R}_{1i} \times \vec{R}_{2i} = 0 \tag{9.1}$$

where F_i is the mathematical model. Furthermore,

$$\vec{b} = \begin{bmatrix} b_X \\ b_Y \\ b_Z \end{bmatrix} = \begin{bmatrix} X_{02} - X_{01} \\ Y_{02} - Y_{01} \\ Z_{02} - Z_{01} \end{bmatrix}$$

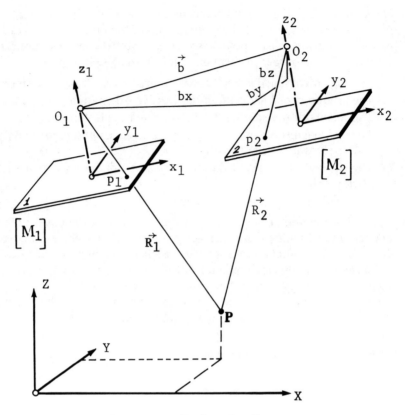

Figure 9-1. Coplanarity Concept

$$\vec{R}_{1i} = \begin{bmatrix} X_{1i} \\ Y_{1i} \\ Z_{1i} \end{bmatrix} = k_1 \mathbf{M}_1^T \begin{bmatrix} x_{1i} - x_{c1} \\ y_{1i} - y_{c1} \\ -f \end{bmatrix} = k_1 \mathbf{M}_1^T \cdot \vec{r}_1$$

$$\vec{R}_{21} = \begin{bmatrix} X_{2i} \\ Y_{2i} \\ Z_{2i} \end{bmatrix} = k_2 \mathbf{M}_2^T \begin{bmatrix} x_{2i} - x_{c2} \\ y_{2i} - y_{c2} \\ -f \end{bmatrix} = k_2 \mathbf{M}_2^T \cdot \vec{r}_2$$

k_1 and k_2 are scale factors, $\vec{r}_1$ and $\vec{r}_2$ are the corresponding location vectors in camera space.

$$\mathbf{M}^{\mathrm{T}} = \begin{bmatrix} m_{11} & m_{21} & m_{31} \\ m_{12} & m_{22} & m_{32} \\ m_{13} & m_{23} & m_{33} \end{bmatrix}$$

$$= \begin{bmatrix} \cos\phi\cos\kappa & -\cos\phi\sin\kappa & \sin\phi \\ \cos\omega\sin\kappa & \cos\omega\cos\kappa & -\sin\omega\cos\phi \\ +\sin\omega\sin\phi\cos\kappa & -\sin\omega\sin\phi\sin\kappa & \\ \sin\omega\sin\kappa & \sin\omega\cos\kappa & \cos\omega\cos\phi \\ -\cos\omega\sin\phi\cos\kappa & +\cos\omega\sin\phi\sin\kappa & \end{bmatrix}$$

The assumptions made about the rotation matrix M are:

1. The rotations are in a right-handed system
2. The rotations, proceeding from the ground (or model) system to the photo system of coordinates are ω primary, ϕ secondary, and κ tertiary.

Equation (9.1) may be written in determinant form as,

$$\mathbf{F_i} = \begin{bmatrix} b_X & b_Y & b_Z \\ X_{1i} & Y_{1i} & Z_{1i} \\ X_{2i} & Y_{2i} & Z_{2i} \end{bmatrix} = 0 \tag{9.2}$$

Now, let $k_1 = k_2 = 1$ and $x_c = y_c = 0$. Then, using photo 2 for the dependent method of relative orientation,

$$\omega_1 = \phi_1 = \kappa_1 = by_1 = bz_1 = 0$$

Here

$$b_Y = by_2 - by_1 \text{ and } b_Z = bz_2 - bz_1.$$

The vectors $\vec{R}_{1i}$ and $\vec{R}_{2i}$ are then reduced to

$$\vec{R}_{1i} = \begin{bmatrix} X_{1i} \\ Y_{1i} \\ Z_{1i} \end{bmatrix} = \begin{bmatrix} 1 & 0 & 0 \\ 0 & 1 & 0 \\ 0 & 0 & 1 \end{bmatrix} \begin{bmatrix} x_{1i} \\ y_{1i} \\ -f \end{bmatrix} = \begin{bmatrix} x_{1i} \\ y_{1i} \\ -f \end{bmatrix} \tag{9.3}$$

$$\vec{R}_{2i} = \begin{bmatrix} X_{2i} \\ Y_{2i} \\ Z_{2i} \end{bmatrix} = \begin{bmatrix} x_{2i}\cos\phi\cos\kappa - y_{2i}\cos\phi\sin\kappa - f \cdot \sin\phi \\ x_{2i}(\cos\omega\sin\kappa + \sin\omega\sin\phi\cos\kappa) \\ + y_{2i}(\cos\omega\cos\kappa - \sin\omega\sin\phi\sin\kappa) \\ + f \cdot \sin\omega\cos\phi \\ x_{2i}(\sin\omega\sin\kappa - \cos\omega\sin\phi\cos\kappa) \\ + y_{2i}(\sin\omega\cos\kappa + \cos\omega\sin\phi\sin\kappa) \\ - f \cdot \cos\omega\cos\phi \end{bmatrix} \quad (9.4)$$

Note here that ω, ϕ, and κ are for camera 2 (i.e., the right-hand-side camera).

Substituting Eqs. (9.3) and (9.4) in Eq. (9.2) and then expanding and rearranging, the mathematical model, F_i, is given by:

$$\begin{aligned} F_i &= \{b_X y_{1i} - by_2 x_{1i}\} \{x_{2i}(\sin\omega\sin\kappa - \cos\omega\sin\phi\cos\kappa) \\ &\quad + y_{2i}(\sin\omega\cos\kappa + \cos\omega\sin\phi\sin\kappa) - f \cdot \cos\omega\cos\phi\} \\ &\quad + \{b_X f + bz_2 x_{1i}\} \{x_{2i}(\cos\omega\sin\kappa + \sin\omega\sin\phi\cos\kappa) \\ &\quad + y_{2i}(\cos\omega\cos\kappa - \sin\omega\sin\phi\sin\kappa) + f \cdot \sin\omega\cos\phi\} \\ &\quad + \{by_2 f + bz_2 y_{1i}\} \{y_{2i}\cos\phi\sin\kappa - x_{2i}\cos\phi\cos\kappa + f \cdot \sin\phi\} \\ &= 0 \end{aligned} \quad (9.5)$$

Linearization of the Coplanarity Condition Equation. The coplanarity condition equation, (Eq. (9.5)), is linearized into the general form (after the *Manual of Photogrammetry* [5]):

$$[A_i](V_i) + [B_i](\Delta) + (F_{oi}) = 0 \quad (9.6)$$

where $[A_i] = \partial(F_i)/\partial(\text{observed quantities})$

$[B_i] = \partial(F_i)/\partial(\text{parameters})$

$(F_{oi}) = F_i(\text{evaluated with observations and approximate parameters})$

$(V_i) = $ a vector of residuals

$(\Delta) = $ a vector of corrections to approximate parameters

The matrices $[A_i]$ and $[B_i]$ are derived in App. A. Here A_i and B_i are row matrices and V_i and Δ are column vectors.

Solution of the Coplanarity Condition Equation. The observed quantities are the image coordinates, x_{1i}, y_{1i} and x_{2i}, y_{2i}, each corrected for systematic errors (see also Chap. 4).

The unknown parameters are by_2, bz_2, ω_2, ϕ_2, and κ_2.

Thus,

$$[A_i] = \left[\begin{array}{cccc} \dfrac{\partial F_i}{\partial x_{1i}} & \dfrac{\partial F_i}{\partial y_{1i}} & \dfrac{\partial F_i}{\partial x_{2i}} & \dfrac{\partial F_i}{\partial y_{2i}} \end{array} \right] \qquad (9.7)$$

$$[B_i] = \left[\begin{array}{ccccc} \dfrac{\partial F_i}{\partial by_2} & \dfrac{\partial F_i}{\partial bz_2} & \dfrac{\partial F_i}{\partial \omega_2} & \dfrac{\partial F_i}{\partial \phi_2} & \dfrac{\partial F_i}{\partial \kappa_2} \end{array} \right] \qquad (9.8)$$

$$(V_i) = \left[\begin{array}{c} v_{x1} \\ v_{y1} \\ v_{x2} \\ v_{y2} \end{array} \right]_i \qquad (9.9)$$

$$(\Delta) = \left[\begin{array}{c} \delta by_2 \\ \delta bz_2 \\ \delta \omega_2 \\ \delta \phi_2 \\ \delta \kappa_2 \end{array} \right] \qquad (9.10)$$

The sizes and forms of these matrices and vectors are shown in App. A.

Coordinate observations at five selected points give a unique solution of the parameters. However, when redundant observations are made, an adjustment situation arises, and the principles of least squares is applied to minimize the sum of the squares of the residuals. The derivation of the relevant equations can be found in the *Manual of Photogrammetry* [5] and Uotila [102]:

The solution vector Δ is given by

$$\Delta = -(B^T M^{-1} B)^{-1} B^T M^{-1} F_0 \qquad (9.11)$$

where $\qquad M = A W^{-1} A^T$

$\qquad W = $ weight matrix associated with the observations

$$V^T W V = -K_L^T F_0 \qquad (9.12)$$

where $\qquad K_L = -M^{-1}(B \Delta + F_0)$

The unit variance m_0^2 is given by

$$m_0^2 = \frac{V^T W V}{r - u} \qquad (9.13)$$

where r = number of condition equations

         u = number of unknown quantities

     $(r-u)$ = the degrees of freedom

The weight coefficient matrix of Δ can be written as

$$Q_\Delta = (B^T M^{-1} B)^{-1} \qquad (9.14)$$

The variance-covariance matrix of unknown parameters is

$$\Sigma_\Delta = m_0^2 Q_\Delta \qquad (9.15)$$

The corrections Δ are added to the approximate values of the parameters which were used in computing the coefficients of F_i, $[A_i]$, and $[B_i]$. It is sometimes necessary to iterate the solution until the corrections are negligible. Quantities related to both the parameters and the observations (i.e., $[A_i]$, $[B_i]$, and F_i) should be updated for each iteration (also see Pope [76] in this respect). The number of required iterations depends on the initial approximations, the total number of parameters, and the geometric strength of the model. There are several criteria, one of which may be used to terminate the iteration in a particular case, e.g., minimum variances of 0.00001 rad for the angular orientation elements (as used by NOAA).

The intersection of five pairs of rays $\vec{R}_1$ and $\vec{R}_2$ is the condition for relative orientation. After the relative orientation one may find, however, that the rays fail to intersect, i.e., there may be residual parallaxes. Therefore, one must define a point which will represent the location of intersection (acceptable for model point coordinates). A suitable point is one midway along the vector $\vec{D}$ between vectors $\vec{R}_1$ and $\vec{R}_2$ (see Fig. 9.2) in the region where the rays come closest together. The direction (but not the length) of vector $\vec{D}$ which is perpendicular to both $\vec{R}_1$ and $\vec{R}_2$ is given by:

$$\vec{D} = \vec{R}_1 \times \vec{R}_2 \qquad (9.16)$$

From this it is apparent that

$$k_1 \cdot \vec{R}_1 + d \cdot \vec{D} + k_2 \cdot \vec{R}_2 = \vec{b} \qquad (9.17)$$

where k_1, k_2 and d are three unknown scalar multipliers (scale factors). Equation (9.17) has three components and, therefore, it may be solved for the three scalars.

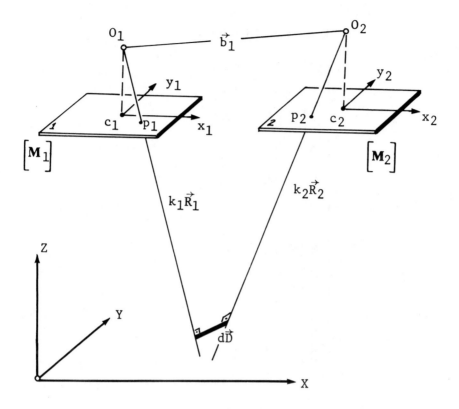

Figure 9-2. Non-intersection in Coplanarity Condition

The vectors $\vec{R}_1$ and $\vec{R}_2$ are determined using Eqs. (9.3) and (9.4) after evaluating the final matrices $[M_1]$ and $[M_2]$. The base components (bx, by, bz) are also determined after the relative orientation procedure. The coordinates of exposure station 0_1, in the case of the dependnet method, are assumed to be (0,0,0). In the case of strip formation, they are equal to the right exposure station of the preceding model.

Equation (9.16) can be written in the form:

$$\vec{D} = \begin{bmatrix} D_X \\ D_Y \\ D_Z \end{bmatrix} = \begin{bmatrix} Y_1Z_2 - Z_1Y_2 \\ Z_1X_2 - X_1Z_2 \\ X_1Y_2 - Y_1X_2 \end{bmatrix} \tag{9.18}$$

The scalars k_1 and k_2 are then determined:

$$k_1 = \frac{\begin{bmatrix} bx & D_X & R_{2X} \\ by & D_Y & R_{2Y} \\ bz & D_Z & R_{2Z} \end{bmatrix}}{\begin{bmatrix} R_{1X} & D_X & R_{2X} \\ R_{1Y} & D_Y & R_{2Y} \\ R_{1Z} & D_Z & R_{2Z} \end{bmatrix}} = \frac{\vec{b} \cdot \vec{D} \times \vec{R}_2}{\vec{R}_1 \cdot \vec{D} \times \vec{R}_2} \qquad (9.19)$$

$$k_2 = \frac{\begin{bmatrix} R_{1X} & D_X & bx \\ R_{1Y} & D_Y & by \\ R_{1Z} & D_Z & bz \end{bmatrix}}{\begin{bmatrix} R_{1X} & D_X & R_{2X} \\ R_{1Y} & D_Y & R_{2Y} \\ R_{1Z} & D_Z & R_{2Z} \end{bmatrix}} = \frac{\vec{R}_1 \cdot \vec{D} \times \vec{b}}{\vec{R}_1 \cdot \vec{D} \times \vec{R}_2} \qquad (9.20)$$

The coordinates of each model point are determined next.

$$\begin{bmatrix} X \\ Y \\ Z \end{bmatrix} = \begin{bmatrix} X_{o1} \\ Y_{o1} \\ Z_{o1} \end{bmatrix} + k_1 \begin{bmatrix} R_{1X} \\ R_{1Y} \\ R_{1Z} \end{bmatrix} + \tfrac{1}{2}k_2 \begin{bmatrix} D_X \\ D_Y \\ D_Z \end{bmatrix} \qquad (9.21)$$

The coordinates of the right-hand side-projection center (0_2) are obtained from:

$$\begin{bmatrix} X_{o2} \\ Y_{o2} \\ Z_{o2} \end{bmatrix} = \begin{bmatrix} X_{o1} \\ Y_{o1} \\ Z_{o1} \end{bmatrix} + \begin{bmatrix} bx \\ by \\ bz \end{bmatrix} \qquad (9.22)$$

The residual parallax at each model point is computed as follows:

$$\text{Parallax} = k_2(D_X^2 + D_Y^2 + D_Z^2)^{1/2} \qquad (9.23)$$

This condition involves the interior and exterior orientation of the two photographs, but it does not include the coordinates of the object points. It may be written any time a point appears on two or more photographs (in the strip or otherwise).

Since the triangulation is performed in the X direction (of strip), it is possible, as a harmless approximation (variation) of this condition, to choose for $\vec{D}$ the unit vector along the Y direction (i.e., Y parallax in the model space). In this case the scalars k_1 and k_2 are given by (see simplified explanation later in this chapter):

$$k_1 = \frac{R_{2Z} \cdot bx - R_{2X} \cdot bz}{R_{2Z} \cdot R_{1X} - R_{2X} \cdot R_{1Z}} \tag{9.24}$$

and

$$k_2 = \frac{R_{1X} \cdot bz - R_{1Z} \cdot bx}{R_{2Z} \cdot R_{1X} - R_{2X} \cdot R_{1Z}} \tag{9.25}$$

Here, the coordinates of the required point P are

$$\left. \begin{array}{l} X_P = X_{o1} + k_1 \cdot R_{1X} \\ Y_P = \tfrac{1}{2}[(\, Y_{o2} + k_2 \cdot R_{2Y}\,) + (\, Y_{o1} + k_1 \cdot R_{1Y}\,)] \\ Z_P = Z_{o1} + k_1 \cdot R_{1Z} \end{array} \right\} \tag{9.26}$$

The residual Y parallax which is the scalar d_1 is given by

$$d_1 = (Y_{o2} + k_2 \cdot R_{2Y}) - (Y_{o1} + k_1 \cdot R_{1Y}) \tag{9.27}$$

In the system developed as NRC, Canada, (see Schut [86] also) before these computations are performed for all measured points, Eqs. (9.24) to (9.26) are used to compute the Z coordinates of points common to the preceding model.

These coordinates are compared with those in the preceding model and are used for the computation of a scale factor. The three base components of the new model (bx, by, bz) are multiplied by this scale factor and then added to the coordinates of the projection center 0_i to obtain those of projection center 0_{i+1}.

A simplified geometric explanation of Eq. (9.24) is given in Fig. 9-3.

Assume correct scale for R_2 (i.e., X_2, Z_2),

Then

$$Z_2 X_2 = X_2 Z_2$$

$$Z_2(k_1 X_1 - bx) = X_2(k_1 Z_1 - bz)$$

or

$$k_1(Z_2 X_1 - X_2 Z_1) = Z_2 \cdot bx - X_2 \cdot bz$$

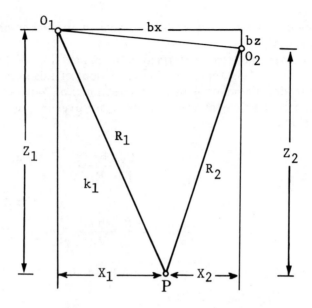

Figure 9-3. Explanation of Scale Factor

that is,

$$k_1 = \frac{Z_2 \cdot bx - X_2 \cdot bz}{Z_2 X_1 - X_2 Z_1} \tag{9.28}$$

Scale-restraint Condition

This condition corresponds to "scale transfer" as performed in the aeropolygon method (see Secs. 3.2 and 5.1). In the analog procedure this is performed by making the coordinates of points in the triple overlap area have the same values in model i as were in model i−1. In the independent-model method (Chap. 8) this is achieved through computations via the transformation equations. The condition is illustrated in Fig. 9-4.

The three object (or model) space vectors $\vec{R}_1$, $\vec{R}_2$, and $\vec{R}_3$ to a point P may fail to intersect at a common point for various reasons. The object space vectors $\vec{R}_1$ and $\vec{R}_2$ are obtained in stereomodel 1-2 and similarly, $\vec{R}_2$ and $\vec{R}_3$ are obtained in model 2-3. The vector $\vec{D}$ in model 1-2 which is perpendicular to both $\vec{R}_1$ and $\vec{R}_2$, is given by (see Eq. (9.16)):

$$\vec{D}_1 = \vec{R}_1 \times \vec{R}_2 \tag{9.29}$$

From this it is apparent that (see Eq. (9.17))

$$k_1 \cdot \vec{R}_1 + d_1 \cdot \vec{D}_1 + k_2 \cdot \vec{R}_2 = \vec{b}_1 \tag{9.30}$$

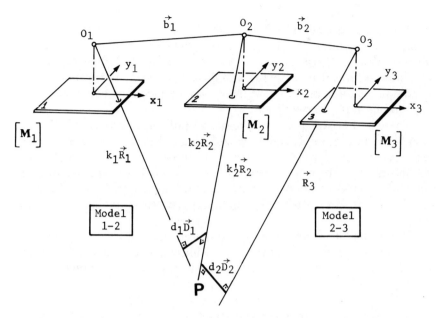

Figure 9-4. Scale Restraint Condition

where k_1, d_1, and k_2 are three unknown scalar multipliers (scale factors) in model 1-2, and

$$\vec{b}_1 = \begin{bmatrix} bx_1 \\ by_1 \\ bz_1 \end{bmatrix} = \begin{bmatrix} X_{o2} - X_{o1} \\ Y_{o2} - Y_{o1} \\ Z_{o2} - Z_{o1} \end{bmatrix}$$

Equation (9.30) has three components and this may be solved for three scalars. The solution for k_2 is obtained by using Eq. (9.20) for model 1-2:

$$k_2 = \frac{\vec{R}_1 \cdot \vec{D}_1 \times \vec{b}_1}{\vec{R}_1 \cdot \vec{D}_1 \times \vec{R}_2} \tag{9.31}$$

Similarly, for stereomodel 2-3, for the same vector $\vec{R}_2$ one gets k_2' (this corresponds to k_1 in Eq. (9.19)):

$$k_2' = \frac{\vec{b}_2 \cdot \vec{D}_2 \times \vec{R}_3}{\vec{R}_2 \cdot \vec{D}_2 \times \vec{R}_3} \tag{9.32}$$

The scale-restraint condition states that the two scalar multipliers of vector $\vec{R}_2$ are equal in magnitude but opposite in sign, i.e.,

$$k_2 + k_2' = 0 \tag{9.33}$$

This scale-restraint equation is always used in conjunction with the coplanarity equations. In model 1-2 its coplanarity condition assures that vectors $\vec{R}_1$ and $\vec{R}_2$ will intersect. Similarly in model 2-3, its coplanarity condition assures that vectors $\vec{R}_2$ and $\vec{R}_3$ will intersect. The scale-restraint-condition equation assures that these two intersections take place at the same point in the model space.

There may arise a question whether a third coplanarity condition equation between vectors $\vec{R}_1$ and $\vec{R}_3$ would accomplish the same result. However, in the normal straight line flights, the three vectors $\vec{R}_1$, $\vec{R}_2$, and $\vec{R}_3$ may lie on the same (or nearly same) plane. Consequently, the vectors may mutually intersect without intersecting at the same point. Even if they do not fall on the same plane, the situation will be close, giving a very weak geometry.

During the strip formation it is required that the relative orientation (coorientation) and scale transfer (i.e., using coplanarity and scale restraint conditions, respectively) are performed successively. The practical steps are as follows:

Step 1: At the $(n-1)$th model (i.e., photos $n-1$, n), k_1 and k_2 are known (actually $k_1 = k_2$). Compute X_{Pn-1}, Y_{Pn-1}, Z_{Pn-1} in this model, of all points including those common with the next (nth) model. Also known in this model are:

$$X_{o1} = X_{on-1}; \; Y_{o1} = Y_{on-1}; \; Z_{o1} = Z_{on-1}$$

$$X_{o2} = X_{on}; \; Y_{o2} = Y_{on} \text{ and } Z_{o2} = Z_{on}$$

Step 2: At the nth model (i.e., photos n, $n+1$), perform coorientation and consider $k_{1n} = k_{2n-1}$ of the previous model.

With this k, compute Z_{Pn} of the same point as in the previous model.

Also compute bx, by, and bz of this model.

If $Z_{Pn-1} = Z_{Pn}$ it is alright. If not, obtain corrections to k_{1n} of this model. Then, in proportion, correct bx, by, and bz.

Next add these such that

$$X_{on} + bx_n = X_{on+1}$$

$$Y_{on} + by_n = Y_{on+1}$$

$$Z_{on} + bz_n = Z_{on+1}$$

Next, using Eqs. (9.24) and (9.25) check if $k_{1n} = k_{2n-1}$. If not, repeat Step 2. If so, compute X_{Pn}, Y_{Pn}, and Z_{Pn}.

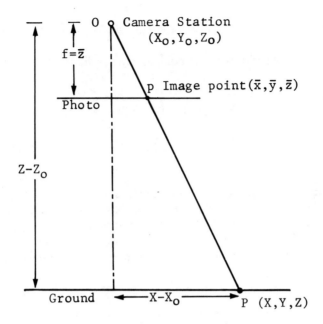

Figure 9-5. Rectified Photo

Step 3: At the (n+1)th model (i.e., photos n+1, n+2), repeat the operations of Step 2.

Triplets

The concept of analytical relative orientation uses two photos. The use of three photographs as an improvement (combining relative orientation and scale transfer) in phototriangulation has been developed by McNair, Anderson, and Mikhail (see [8] and [69]).

Consider the following relationship between the rectified (rotated through space into a perfectly vertical position) photo coordinates $(\bar{x}, \bar{y}, \bar{z})$ and the measured photo coordinates (x, y, z) (see Fig. 9.5):

$$
\begin{bmatrix} \bar{x} \\ \bar{y} \\ \bar{z} \end{bmatrix} = \begin{bmatrix} a_{11} & a_{21} & a_{31} \\ a_{12} & a_{22} & a_{32} \\ a_{13} & a_{23} & a_{33} \end{bmatrix} \begin{bmatrix} x \\ y \\ z \end{bmatrix} \tag{9.34}
$$

Here "a" matrix is the orientation matrix **M** familiar to us (see Chap. 8 and Sec. 9.2).

We also obtained from the collinearity condition (see Eq. (9.51)):

$$
\left.
\begin{aligned}
\frac{\overline{x}}{\overline{z}} &= \frac{(X-X_0)a_{11} + (Y-Y_0)a_{12} + (Z-Z_0)a_{13}}{(X-X_0)a_{31} + (Y-Y_0)a_{32} + (Z-Z_0)a_{33}} \\[2ex]
\frac{\overline{y}}{\overline{z}} &= \frac{(X-X_0)a_{21} + (Y-Y_0)a_{22} + (Z-Z_0)a_{23}}{(X-X_0)a_{31} + (Y-Y_0)a_{32} + (Z-Z_0)a_{33}}
\end{aligned}
\right\} \quad (9.35)
$$

This pair of equations give the conditions on which the analytical aerial triangulation procedure followed by the National Oceanic Survey was based. The scheme was initiated during the early 1960s. This method consisted of a scheme analogous to the conventional empirical methods with a first-order stereoplotter by the principles of aeropolygon in seven steps as follows:

1. *Measure* image coordinates $(x, y, z = -f)$
2. *Transformation* of observed image coordinates, incorporating *corrections* due to film distortion, objective (lens) distortion, atmospheric refraction, and earth's curvature
3. *Relative* orientation of each pair independently, seeking and eliminating grossly erroneous observations
4. *Cantilever transformation* based on Step 3 but without using any ground control with assumed nominal scale and datum in the first model (pair)
5. *Cantilever adjustment* transforming coordinates of ground points in Step 4 to fit ground control
6. *Resection* of *each picture* to fit data of Step 5. This way Steps 5 and 6 yield refined values for $\omega, \phi, \kappa, X_0, Y_0, Z_0$ for each photograph and X, Y, Z for each point in ground object (still unadjusted)
7. *Final adjustment* (generally needs iterations)

Step 7 requires the longest computing time and, thus, is the most expensive. The scheme is set forth in a way such that Step 7 is needed only once, i.e., iteration is avoided.

Some researchers claim that with the idea and condition of triplets, this final step may be omitted except for rare cases where very precise results are required.

In general practice, in relative orientation, only residuals in the Y direction (Y parallax) can be interpreted as errors and minimized. The residuals in the X direction (X parallax) are interpreted as differences in elevation, i.e., depending on the sign the elevation will be higher or lower. In relative orientation only two rays determine the position (two rays originating from two pictures) and without the absolute value of the elevation of the point in question, x residual cannot be utilized.

By using three photographs for points in the triple overlap area one obtains a *check on* x *parallax* and a *double check on* y *parallax*. This helps tie the first pair (1 and 2) with the second pair (2 and 3) which were oriented separately by the old method. The scheme may be set for groups of three photographs (triplets), each triplet oriented separately (1-2-3, 2-3-4, 3-4-5, etc.).

The method previously being used by the U.S. Coast and Geodetic Survey (presently NOS, NOAA) involved single models (somewhat similar to the procedures discussed in Sec. 9.1 and utilized the collinearity condition equation. In that method one had to consider:

First model

$$\omega_1 = \phi_1 = \kappa_1 = X_{01} = Y_{01} = Z_{01} = 0$$

(that is, the first picture is fixed.) Select a value for the base, i.e., $X_{02} = 1$. Then work with the five unknowns left, i.e., ω_2, ϕ_2, κ_2, Y_{02}, Z_{02}. Number of images = 12, i.e., number of equations = 24.

Second model (also subsequent models)

$$\omega_2 = \phi_2 = \kappa_2 = X_{02} = Y_{02} = Z_{02} = 0$$

(that is, the second picture is fixed.)

In a Triplet. Consider picture 2 fixed, and picture 1 and 3 tied to it simultaneously on both sides. Also a value for either X_{01} or X_{03} is assigned. This way, seven of the $6 \times 3 = 18$ elements are fixed initially. For practical reasons, to avoid negative values for X, $X_{01} = 0$ and $X_{02} = 1$ are considered. This gives:

Picture 1: $X_{01} = 0$ and ω_1, ϕ_1, κ_1, Y_{01}, Z_{01} initially are assumed to be zero.
Picture 2: $X_{02} = 1$ and $\omega_2 = \phi_2 = \kappa_2 = Y_{02} = Z_{02} = 0$ kept fixed.
Picture 3: X_{03}, ω_3, ϕ_3, κ_3, Y_{03}, and Z_{03} initially are assumed to be zero.

That is,

Photo Number	Number of Unknowns	Number of Images	Number of Observation Equations
1	5	6	12 (= 6 × 2)
2	0	9	18 (= 9 × 2)
3	6	6	12 (= 6 × 2)
Total	11	21	42

This means in the triplet we have 42 observation equations and 11 unknowns. The 42 observation equations are reduced through the principles of least squares to 11 normal equations to solve for the 11 unknowns.

Again also (see Fig. 9-6) points a, b, c and g, h, i are common to two pictures and are, therefore, capable of being used to check X and Y coordinates only. Points d, e, f are common to all three pictures and, hence, may be used to check X, Y, and Z.

When the second triplet is tied with the first, Z values are taken from the triplet I in points d, e, f and from triplet II in points g, h, i. X and Y values are checked together from both triplets.

This procedure is then followed to the end of the strip.

The basic condition equations (collinearity condition) in this case are:

$$\left.\begin{aligned}
\frac{x_{i1}}{z_{i1}} &= \frac{(X_{i1}-X_{01})a_{11} + (Y_{i1}-Y_{01})a_{12} + (Z_{i1}-Z_{0i})a_{13}}{(X_{i1}-X_{01})a_{31} + (Y_{i1}-Y_{01})a_{32} + (Z_{i1}-Z_{01})a_{33}} \\[2ex]
\frac{y_{i1}}{z_{i1}} &= \frac{(X_{i1}-X_{01})a_{21} + (Y_{i1}-Y_{01})a_{22} + (Z_{i1}-Z_{01})a_{23}}{(X_{i1}-X_{01})a_{31} + (Y_{i1}-Y_{01})a_{32} + (Z_{i1}-Z_{01})a_{33}}
\end{aligned}\right\} \quad (9.36)$$

These two are for photo pair 1-2 (i.e., the first stereogram of triplet I). Similarly,

$$\left.\begin{aligned}
\frac{x_{i3}}{z_{i3}} &= \frac{(X_{i3}-X_{03})d_{11} + (Y_{i3}-Y_{03})d_{12} + (Z_{i3}-Z_{03})d_{13}}{(X_{i3}-X_{03})d_{31} + (Y_{i3}-Y_{03})d_{32} + (Z_{i3}-Z_{03})d_{33}} \\[2ex]
\frac{y_{i3}}{z_{i3}} &= \frac{(X_{i3}-X_{03})d_{21} + (Y_{i3}-Y_{03})d_{22} + (Z_{i3}-Z_{03})d_{23}}{(X_{i3}-X_{03})d_{31} + (Y_{i3}-Y_{03})d_{32} + (Z_{i3}-Z_{03})d_{33}}
\end{aligned}\right\} \quad (9.37)$$

These two are for photo pair 2-3 (i.e., the second stereogram of triplet I).

These equations are rather complicated and a *direct solution* for all nine unknowns (ω, ϕ, κ, X_o, Y_o, Z_o and X_p, Y_p, Z_p) is *not attempted*.

Instead, a logical approximation is made for each unknown. Then corrections are computed which enforce the collinearity condition, using equations formed from the above condition equations by means of partial differential calculus. These are then the observation equations of the following form (for detailed derivations see Harris, Tewinkel, and Whitten [43]):

$$\left.\begin{aligned}
V_{xi1} &= P_{11} + P_{12}d\omega_1 + P_{13}d\phi_1 + P_{14}d\kappa_1 - P_{15}dX_{01} - P_{16}dY_{01} \\
&\quad - P_{17}dZ_{01} + P_{15}dX_{i1} + P_{16}dY_{i1} + P_{17}dZ_{i1} \\
V_{yi1} &= P_{21} + P_{22}d\omega_1 + P_{23}d\phi_1 + P_{24}d\kappa_1 - P_{25}dX_{01} - P_{26}dY_{01} \\
&\quad - P_{27}dZ_{01} + P_{25}dX_{i1} + P_{26}dY_{i1} + P_{27}dZ_{i1}
\end{aligned}\right\} \quad (9.38)$$

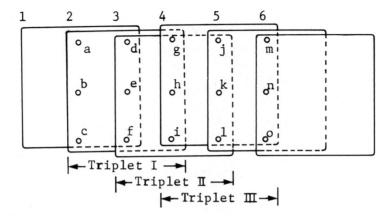

Figure 9-6. Arrangement of Triplets

These are for the first stereogram. Next, for the second stereogram:

$$
\left.
\begin{aligned}
V_{xi3} ={}& Q_{11} + Q_{12}d\omega_3 + Q_{13}d\phi_3 \\
& + Q_{14}d\kappa_3 - Q_{15}dX_{03} - Q_{16}dY_{03} \\
& - Q_{17}dZ_{03} + Q_{15}dX_{i3} + Q_{16}dY_{i3} + Q_{17}dZ_{i3} \\
V_{yi3} ={}& Q_{21} + Q_{22}d\omega_3 + Q_{23}d\phi_3 \\
& + Q_{24}d\kappa_3 - Q_{25}dX_{03} - Q_{26}dY_{03} \\
& - Q_{27}dZ_{03} + Q_{25}dX_{i3} + Q_{26}dY_{i3} + Q_{27}dZ_{i3}
\end{aligned}
\right\} \quad (9.39)
$$

The coefficients $P_{11} \ldots P_{27}$ and $Q_{11} \ldots Q_{27}$ in Eqs. (9.38) and (9.39) are derived by partial differentiation of the basic pairs in Eqs. (9.36) and (9.37). The coefficients thus obtained have initially only preliminary values that are changed according to the (Newton) method of successive approximation through the iterative procedure of computing and adding corrections to the variables.

The unknowns involved in these equations are of *two different* groups:

1. $d\omega$, $d\phi$, $d\kappa$, dX_0, dY_0, and dZ_0 remain *constant for one picture*, i.e., remain constant for all points in the same picture
2. dX_i, dY_i, dZ_i differ for each image point (model coordinates)

Model Coordinates. Consider Fig. 9-5. The relation

$$
\frac{\bar{x}}{\bar{z}} = \frac{X_i - X_0}{Z_i - Z_0}
$$

gives

$$\frac{\overline{x}'}{\overline{z}'} = \frac{X_i - X_{01}}{Z_i - Z_{01}}$$

with respect to a point in photo 1

also,

$$\frac{\overline{x}''}{\overline{z}''} = \frac{X_i - X_{02} + X_{01}}{Z_i - Z_{02}}$$

with respect to the same point in photo 2

or,

$$\overline{x}'(Z_i - Z_{01}) = \overline{z}'(X_i - X_{01})$$

$$\overline{x}''(Z_i - Z_{02}) = \overline{z}''(X_i - X_{02} + X_{01})$$

that is,

$$\overline{x}'\overline{z}''(Z_i - Z_{01}) = \overline{z}'\overline{z}''(X_i - X_{01})$$

$$\overline{x}''\overline{z}'(Z_i - Z_{02}) = \overline{z}'\overline{z}''(X_i - X_{02} + X_{01})$$

Now, subtracting one from the other and rearranging,

$$Z_i(\overline{x}'\overline{z}'' - \overline{x}''\overline{z}') - Z_{01}\overline{x}'\overline{z}'' + Z_{02}\overline{x}''\overline{z}' = \overline{z}'\overline{z}''(X_{02} - 2X_{01})$$

From the above,

$$Z_i = \frac{(X_{02}-2X_{01})\overline{z}'\overline{z}'' + Z_{01}\overline{x}'\overline{z}'' - Z_{02}\overline{x}''\overline{z}'}{\overline{x}'\overline{z}'' - \overline{x}''\overline{z}'} \qquad (9.40)$$

Here the single and double primes refer to the first and second pictures, respectively, and the bars above x and z refer to the *rectified* picture coordinates.

Equation (9.40) may be applied to both stereograms in the triplet. After substituting the values assigned to the respective terms, that is, $X_{02} = 1$ and $X_{01} = Z_{02} = 0$ we get:

$$Z_{i1} = \frac{\overline{z}'\overline{z}'' + Z_{01}\overline{x}'\overline{z}''}{\overline{x}'\overline{z}'' - \overline{x}''\overline{z}'} = \frac{\overline{z}' + Z_{01}\overline{x}'}{\overline{x}' - (\overline{x}''/\overline{z}'')\overline{z}'} \qquad (9.41)$$

In our familiar terms:

$$Z_{i1} = \frac{\overline{z}_{i1} + Z_{01}\overline{x}_{i1}}{\overline{x}_{i1} - (x_{i2}/z_{i2})\overline{z}_{i1}} \qquad (9.41a)$$

And in the second stereogram, from Eq. (9.40):

$$Z_{i3} = \frac{(X_{03} - 2)z_{i2}\overline{z}_{i3} + Z_{02}x_{i2}\overline{z}_{i3} - Z_{03}\overline{x}_{i3}z_{i2}}{x_{i2}\overline{z}_{i3} - \overline{x}_{i3}z_{i2}}$$

$Z_{02} = 0$ being assumed:

$$Z_{i3} = \frac{(X_{03}-2)\bar{z}_{i3} - Z_{03}\bar{X}_{i3}}{(x_{i2}/z_{i2})\bar{z}_{i3} - \bar{X}_{i3}} \qquad (9.42)$$

Here x_{i2} and z_{i2} do not have bars above them, being unrectified coordinates of the corresponding image on the middle (second) picture of the triplet.

Equations (9.41) and (9.42) allow:

1. An approximate Z to be computed for each model point in the triplet in terms of the other approximate parameters (Z_0, ω, ϕ, and κ), and also the observed image coordinates in both stereograms
2. The other two coordinates (X, Y) of the object point to be evaluated. X and Y become valid model coordinates only upon subsequent iterative modifications of the approximate Z

Once Z is determined, X and Y model coordinates can be determined from similar triangles (see Fig. 9-5) and based on the image coordinates of picture 2.

$$\left. \begin{array}{llll} X_{i1} = \dfrac{x_{i2}}{z_{i2}}\, Z_{i1} & & Y_{i1} = \dfrac{y_{i2}}{z_{i2}}\, Z_{i1} \\[3mm] X_{i3} = \dfrac{x_{i2}}{z_{i2}}\, Z_{I3} & & Y_{i3} = \dfrac{y_{i2}}{z_{i2}}\, Z_{i3} \end{array} \right\} \qquad (9.43)$$

Elimination of the Model Coordinate Terms. For every image we have two condition (observation) equations and they contain terms dX, dY, and dZ (corrections to the approximate model coordinates). These cannot be handled very easily because of the increase in the number of unknowns with each added image (because X, Y, Z are variables that differ with each image point). Therefore, an elimination of these variables is necessary. This is done by substituting their values as given earlier (X_p, Y_p, Z_p) in terms of other variables that are fixed in value for every picture (that is, ω, ϕ, κ, X_o, Y_o, Z_o). Then the final form of the observation equations are (for the derivations see [43]):

$$\left. \begin{array}{l} V_{xi1} = \quad P_{11} + (P_{12}+K_1)d\omega_1 + (P_{13}+K_2)\,d\phi_1 + (P_{14}+K_3)d\kappa_1 \\[2mm] \qquad\quad - P_{16}dY_{01} - (P_{17}-K_4)dZ_{01} \\[4mm] V_{yi1} = \quad P_{21} + (P_{22}+L_1)d\omega_1 + (P_{23}+L_2)\,d\phi_1 + (P_{24}+L_3)d\kappa_1 \\[2mm] \qquad\quad - P_{26}dY_{01} - (P_{27}-L_4)dZ_{01} \end{array} \right\} \qquad (9.44)$$

and

$$
\left.
\begin{aligned}
V_{xi3} = \ & Q_{11} + (Q_{12}+K_1')d\omega_3 + (Q_{13}+K_2')d\phi_3 + (Q_{14}+K_3')d\kappa_3 \\
& -(Q_{15}-K_4')dX_{03} - Q_{16}dY_{03} - (Q_{17}-K_5')dZ_{03} \\
V_{yi3} = \ & Q_{21} + (Q_{22}+L_1')d\omega_3 + (Q_{23}+L_2')d\phi_3 + (Q_{24}+L_3')\,d\kappa_3 \\
& -(Q_{25}-L_4')dX_{03} - Q_{26}dY_{03} - (Q_{27}-L_5')dZ_{03}
\end{aligned}
\right\} \quad (9.45)
$$

Here $K_1 \ldots K_4$, $L_1 \ldots L_4$ are factors obtained through partial differentiation of the model coordinate equations involving the variables ω_1, ϕ_1, κ_1, and Z_{01}.

Similarly $K_1' \ldots K_5'$, $L_1' \ldots L_5'$ are factors involving the variables ω_3, ϕ_3, κ_3, and Z_{03}.

In these, Y_{01} and Y_{03} are not considered because one supposes that they do not contribute to any error in Z_i which is directly used in obtaining X and Y in this case. Further to this is the idea of two directional triplets for a block adjustment (see Mikhail [69]).

9.2 Simultaneous Triangulation

As stated earlier, the key to the simultaneous procedure lies in the appropriate use of the collinearity condition. A thorough understanding of this is essential for many other computational procedures in the field of photogrammetry.

Collinearity Condition

The basic projective (transformation) equation describing the relationship between two mutually associated three-dimensional (rectangular) coordinate systems can be expressed by (see also Fig. 9-7):

$$
\begin{bmatrix} X' \\ Y' \\ Z' \end{bmatrix} = k[M] \begin{bmatrix} X - X_0 \\ Y - Y_0 \\ Z - Z_0 \end{bmatrix} \quad (9.46)
$$

where
X', Y', Z' = the coordinates in the transformed system

k = a scale factor

M = the rotation matrix

X_0, Y_0, Z_0 = the coordinates of the origin (o) in the X, Y, Z system

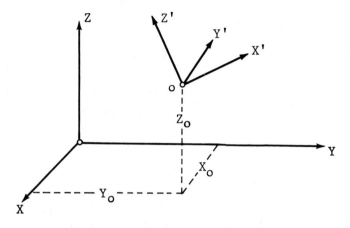

Figure 9-7. Transformation Concept

See Chap. 8 for an explanation of the rotation matrix.

Now, considering a diapositive (see Fig. 9-8), any image point p may be located in the photo (system) by its coordinates x, y, 0.

The optical axis is normal to the plane of the diapositive and the z axis (of the photo system) is parallel to the optical (camera) axis. The camera axis intersects the diapositive plane at O', whose coordinates are: x_0, y_0, 0. The perspective center O has its coordinates: x_0, y_0, f.

In this system, a line from O to point p defines a vector $\vec{r}$ which has three components:

$$\vec{r} = \begin{bmatrix} x_p - x_0 \\ y_p - y_0 \\ z_p - z_0 \end{bmatrix} = \begin{bmatrix} x_p - x_0 \\ y_p - y_0 \\ 0 - f \end{bmatrix} \qquad (9.47)$$

If the camera is well-adjusted, $x_0 = y_0 = 0$; then

$$\vec{r} = \begin{bmatrix} x_p \\ y_p \\ -f \end{bmatrix} \qquad (9.47a)$$

In a continuous, systematic work like phototriangulation, where the same adjusted camera is used, x_0, y_0, and f are constants.

The corresponding vector locating the ground point P with respect to the perspective center O is $\vec{R}$, which is given by (in terms of the ground system of coordinates):

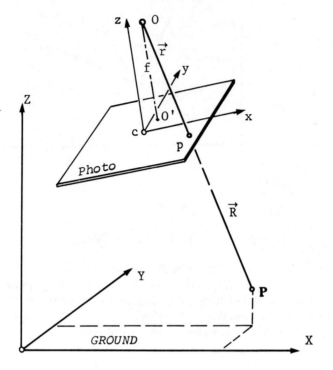

Figure 9-8. Photo-Ground Relationship (Collinearity)

$$\vec{R} = \begin{bmatrix} X_P - X_o \\ Y_P - Y_o \\ Z_P - Z_o \end{bmatrix} \qquad (9.48)$$

In accordance with the fundamental relationship shown in Eq. (9.46), the photo point p can be related to its corresponding ground point P by:

$$\vec{r} = \begin{bmatrix} x_p - x_o \\ y_p - y_o \\ -f \end{bmatrix} = k\,[\mathbf{M}] \begin{bmatrix} X_P - X_o \\ Y_P - Y_o \\ Z_P - Z_o \end{bmatrix} = k[\mathbf{M}]\,\vec{R} \qquad (9.49)$$

The scale factor

$$k = \frac{|\,r\,|}{|\,R\,|} \qquad (9.50a)$$

Further, the orientation matrix **M** (3×3 orthogonal) is:

$$[\mathbf{M}] = \begin{bmatrix} a_{11} & a_{12} & a_{13} \\ a_{21} & a_{22} & a_{23} \\ a_{31} & a_{32} & a_{33} \end{bmatrix}. \qquad (9.50b)$$

In Eq. (9.49), if the first and second rows are divided by the third row and the resulting expressions multiplied by $-f$, one obtains the collinearity condition equations:

$$\left. \begin{aligned} x' = (x_p - x_0) &= -f \; \frac{(X-X_0)a_{11} + (Y-Y_0)a_{12} + (Z-Z_0)a_{13}}{(X-X_0)a_{31} + (Y-Y_0)a_{32} + (Z-Z_0)a_{33}} \\[2mm] y' = (y_p - y_0) &= -f \; \frac{(X-X_0)a_{21} + (Y-Y_0)a_{22} + (Z-Z_0)a_{23}}{(X-X_0)a_{31} + (Y-Y_0)a_{32} + (Z-Z_0)a_{33}} \end{aligned} \right\} (9.51)$$

These two equations simply express the fact that the object point P, the photoimage point p, and the perspective center or exposure station O, all lie on the same straight line.

Each measured photo point leads to two condition equations, one for the image x coordinate and the other for the image y coordinate. The collinearity equations are applicable to a single photo. These equations contain all elements of the problem (interior orientation, exterior orientation, image coordinates, and object-space coordinates). They are sufficient in themselves for the solution of any problem in conventional photogrammetry. This is particularly of advantage in organizing triangulation computations involving simultaneous solution of all photographs in a single strip or block.

The problem is to determine the nine "a" elements and the coordinates of the exposure stations. In the case of phototriangulation, the unknown parameters are: κ, ϕ, ω, X_0, Y_0, Z_0, and X, Y, Z. Unfortunately, these elements are nonlinear. Consequently, a Taylor expansion, neglecting the second and higher order terms is performed on Eq. (9.51) to obtain the linearized observation equations.

The Equation (9.51) can be written as nonlinear functions (i referring to the photo and j referring to the point):

$$\begin{aligned} f(x_{ij}) &= F\{(\kappa, \phi, \omega, X_0, Y_0, Z_0)_i, (X,Y,Z)_j\} \\ f(y_{ij}) &= F\{(\kappa, \phi, \omega, X_0, Y_0, Z_0)_i, (X,Y,Z)_j\} \end{aligned} \qquad (9.52)$$

or, simply,

$$f(L) = F\{O, \overline{X}\} \qquad (9.52a)$$

where   L = the observed x, y coordinates (corrected for systematic distortions) of the photo point p

O = the orientation parameters

$\overline{X}$ = the object space coordinates

This gives:

$$L + V = F(O^\circ + \Delta O, \overline{X}^\circ + \Delta\overline{X}) \tag{9.53}$$

where   V = the discrepancies (errors) or residuals

$O^\circ, \overline{X}^\circ$ = the approximations

$\Delta O, \Delta\overline{X}$ = the successive corrections

Linearization by a Taylor series expansion (in which initial estimates
are assumed for the nine unknown parameters) give:

$$f(L^\circ) + \frac{\partial f}{\partial L} \Delta L = F(O^\circ, \overline{X}^\circ) + \frac{\partial F}{\partial O} \Delta O + \frac{\partial F}{\partial \overline{X}} \Delta\overline{X} \tag{9.54}$$

Then, compactly stated, the matrix general forms of the observation
equations are:

$$\begin{array}{cccccc} \mathbf{V}_{ij} & + & \mathbf{A}_{ij} & \Delta\mathbf{O}_i & + & \mathbf{B}_{ij} & \Delta\overline{\mathbf{X}}_j & = & \mathbf{F}^0_{ij} \\ 2\times1 & & 2\times6 & 6\times1 & & 2\times3 & 3\times1 & & 2\times1 \end{array} \tag{9.55}$$

where (boldface symbols denote matrices):

$\mathbf{V}^T_{ij} = [v_x \ v_y]_{ij} =$ residuals of measured plate coordinates $(\mathbf{v})$

$$\mathbf{A}_{ij} = \begin{bmatrix} a_1 & a_2 \ldots a_6 \\ b_1 & b_2 \ldots b_6 \end{bmatrix}_{ij} =$$ coefficient matrix in which elements are partial differentials of Eq.
9.51 with respect to the unknown
parameters (elements) of photo $(\dot{\mathbf{B}})$

$\Delta\mathbf{O}^T_i = [\delta_\kappa, \delta_\phi, \ldots, \delta Z_o]_i =$ corrections to estimates for unknown elements of photo $i(\dot{\delta})$

$$\mathbf{B}_{ij} = \begin{bmatrix} a_7 & a_8 & a_9 \\ b_7 & b_8 & b_9 \end{bmatrix}_{ij} =$$ coefficient matrix in which elements are partial differentials of Eq.
9.51 with respect to object point
coordinates $(\ddot{\mathbf{B}})$

$\mathbf{\Delta \bar{X}_j^T} = [\Delta X, \Delta Y, \Delta Z]_j =$ corrections to estimates for unknown coordinates of point $\mathbf{j}(\dot{\boldsymbol{\delta}})$

$\mathbf{F_{ij}^{OT}} = [f(x), f(y)]_{ij} =$ the value of Eq. (9.52) with estimated values being substituted for unknown parameters $(\boldsymbol{\epsilon})$

Equation (9.55) may be expressed by simplified notations:

$$\mathbf{v} + \dot{\mathbf{B}}\,\dot{\boldsymbol{\delta}} + \ddot{\mathbf{B}}\,\ddot{\boldsymbol{\delta}} = \boldsymbol{\epsilon} \tag{9.55a}$$

or, equivalently,

$$\mathbf{v} + \mathbf{B}\,\boldsymbol{\delta} = \boldsymbol{\epsilon} \tag{9.55b}$$

This finally yields the following observation equations (see Harris *et al* [43] for derivations), by way of clearing fractions and transposing from Eq. (9.51):

$$
\left.
\begin{aligned}
& x[(X-X_o)\sin\phi + (Y-Y_o)(-\sin\omega\cos\phi) + (Z-Z_o)\cos\omega\cos\phi] \\
& \quad + f[(X-X_o)\cos\phi\cos\kappa + (Y-Y_o)(\cos\omega\sin\kappa + \sin\omega\sin\phi\cos\kappa) \\
& \quad + (Z-Z_o)(\sin\omega\sin\kappa - \cos\omega\sin\phi\cos\kappa)] = 0 \\[6pt]
& y[(X-X_o)\sin\phi + (Y-Y_o)(-\sin\omega\cos\phi) + (Z-Z_o)\cos\omega\cos\phi] \\
& \quad + f[(X-X_o)(-\cos\phi\sin\kappa) + (Y-Y_o)(\cos\omega\cos k - \sin\omega\sin\phi\sin\kappa) \\
& \quad + (Z-Z_o)(\sin\omega\cos\kappa + \cos\omega\sin\phi\sin\kappa)] = 0
\end{aligned}
\right\} \tag{9.56}
$$

Equations (9.56) are "transcendental" and in most general cases all 12 terms are considered as unknowns. A form of Newton's method (see Eshbach [30]) is used to solve them. This is an iterative method based on initial approximations, which are easily obtained for all unknowns. After applying partial differentiation of Eq. (9.56), rearranging the terms and using $dx = v_x$, $dy = v_y$, one obtains the following linearized observation equations:

$$
\left.
\begin{aligned}
v_{x_{ij}} &= \{p_{11_{ij}} + p_{12_{ij}}d\omega_i + p_{13_{ij}}d\phi_i + p_{14_{ij}}d\kappa_i - p_{15_{ij}}dX_{oi} \\
& \quad - p_{16_{ij}}dY_{oi} - p_{17_{ij}}dZ_{oi} + p_{15_{ij}}dX_j + p_{16_{ij}}dY_j \\
& \quad + p_{17_{ij}}dZ_j\} / A_{ij} \\[6pt]
v_{y_{ij}} &= \{p_{21_{ij}} + p_{22_{ij}}d\omega_i + p_{23_{ij}}d\phi_i + p_{24_{ij}}d\kappa_i - p_{25_{ij}}dX_{oi} \\
& \quad - p_{26_{ij}}dY_{oi} - p_{27_{ij}}dZ_{oi} + p_{25_{ij}}dX_j + p_{26_{ij}}dY_j \\
& \quad + p_{27_{ij}}dZ_j\} / A_{ij}
\end{aligned}
\right\} \tag{9.57}
$$

where p_{11} and p_{12} = misclosures in x and y, respectively; observed value less the value computed using the approximate values of the unknowns

P_{12} ... P_{17} and P_{22} ... P_{27} = partial derivatives of Eq. (9.51) evaluated using the approximate values of the unknowns

$d\omega$, $d\phi$, and $d\kappa$ = small corrections to be applied to the approximate (initial) values of the unknowns ω, ϕ, and κ

dX_0, dY_0, and dZ_0 = small corrections to be applied to the approximate (initial) values of X_0, Y_0 and Z_0

dX, dY, and dZ = small corrections to be applied to the approximate (initial) values of X, Y, and Z

A = a constant for the point observed and the photo considered

See Harris *et al* [43] for convenient equations of computing the p coefficients using determinant notations. Equation (9.56) is, in a way, "universal." It is used to solve various problems in photogrammetry, viz., relative orientation, resection, triangulation, etc. They have to be adapted to the requirements of specific problems, however. In case of strip or block triangulation, the presence of all nine terms ($d\omega$ ... dZ) is required. Space resection computations (where X, Y, Z ground coordinates of points are known) uses first six terms ($d\omega$ ... dZ_0) because dX, dY, dZ terms would be zero in this case. In the problem of relative orientation, these equations can be further simplified because one photo (say the left one) may be considered as fixed, that camera station can be selected as the origin and the abscissa of the second station can be selected as unity (i.e., dX_0 then has no significance); the dX, dY, dZ terms can be eliminated by substitution and expressed in terms of the other unknowns, giving (in a general form):

$$v_x = a_1 d\omega + a_2 d\phi + a_3 d\kappa + a_4 dY_0 + a_5 dZ_0$$

$$v_y = d_1 d\omega + d_2 d\phi + d_3 d\kappa + d_4 dY_0 + d_5 dZ_0$$

$$\left.\begin{array}{c}\\ \\ \end{array}\right\} \quad (9.58)$$

The pair of observation equations, Eqs. (9.57) or (9.58), occurs for each image point on each photo. In problems like resection or phototriangulation, both equations are applicable, whereas in dependent relative orientation only the y equation is significant (corresponding to the use of Y parallaxes).

Note: Such iterative methods should be used with a clear indication as to when to terminate the iterations. They should terminate when the incremental corrections to the angular or linear parameters are smaller than the observational precision. The NOS, e.g., considers specifically, when each of three, $d\omega$, $d\phi$, $d\kappa$ is less than 10^{-5} rad.

Normal Equations

From Eq. (9.57) one can see that for every point observed on a photograph, two observation equations can be written. With an adequate number of points (which is usually the case) one will always have more observation equations than unknown parameters and should, therefore, reduce this set of observation equations to a system of normal equations having n equations with n unknowns. If one divides all p coefficients in Eq. (9.57) by their respective A_{ij} values and puts the results in an augmented observation equation matrix $\overline{O}_a$ such that the misclosure terms appear in the last column, the augmented normal equation matrix N_a is obtained by matrix multiplication:

$$\overline{O}^T \quad \cdot \quad \overline{O}_a \quad = \quad N_a \qquad (9.59)$$
$$n \times n \qquad n \times (n+1) \qquad n \times (n+1)$$

where $\overline{O}$ is the coefficient observation equation matrix. This normalization process satisfies the basic condition of "Least Squares," viz., the sum of the weighted (generally unit weight is assigned in practice) squares of the residuals after the adjustment reduces to a minimum.

The augmented normal equation matrix obtained from Eq. (9.59) has dimensions $n \times (n+1)$. The first n columns form the coefficient matrix N and the $(n+1)$th column is the constant vector U. The standard expression for a system of n equations with n unknowns is therefore:

$$N \cdot X + U = 0 \qquad (9.60)$$

where   N = the coefficient matrix of the normal equations (dimensions, $n \times n$)

X = the solution vector of the normal equations (dimensions, $n \times 1$)

U = the constant vector of the normal equations (dimensions, $n \times 1$).

Equation (9.60) is usually solved by one of the standard matrix inversion routines. The solution vector X resulting from the inversion contains the corrections to be applied to the approximate values of the unknown parameters. The results of these additions are the adjusted values of the parameters:

$$\left.\begin{array}{lll} \omega_i^a = \omega_i + d\omega_i & X_{oi}^a = X_{oi} + dX_{oi} & X_j^a = X_j + dX_j \\[2mm] \phi_i^a = \phi_i + d\phi_i & Y_{oi}^a = Y_{oi} + dY_{oi} & Y_j^a = X_j + dX_j \\[2mm] \kappa_i^a = \kappa_i + d\kappa_i & Z_{oi}^a = Z_{oi} + dZ_{oi} & Z_j^a = Z_j + dZ_j \end{array}\right\} \quad (9.61)$$

where   the superscript a refers to the adjusted values of the parameters; subscript i refers to the photo; subscript j refers to the point and $d\omega$, $d\phi$, $d\kappa$, dX_o, dY_o, dZ_o, dX, dY, dZ are the corrections derived from the solution of Eq. (9.60) to be added to the approximate values of the respective parameters.

Consideration of Weights

The normal equations, as formed from the condition equations (see Eq. (9.55)) are:

$$N\delta = c \qquad (9.62)$$

where, in view of precision,

$$\left.\begin{array}{l} N = B^T W B \\[2mm] c = B^T W \epsilon \end{array}\right\} \qquad (9.63)$$

and W is the weight matrix of the photocoordinates.

The solution of the normal equation, Eq. (9.62) is

$$\delta = N^{-1}c \qquad (9.64)$$

Equation (9.64) gives, directly, the solutions. With partitioning employed in Eq. (9.55), the normal equations, Eq. (9.62) become:

$$\begin{bmatrix} \dot{N} & \bar{N} \\ \bar{N}^T & \ddot{N} \end{bmatrix} \begin{bmatrix} \dot{\delta} \\ \ddot{\delta} \end{bmatrix} = \begin{bmatrix} \dot{c} \\ \ddot{c} \end{bmatrix} \qquad (9.65)$$

where

$$\dot{N} = \dot{B}^T W \dot{B} \quad \text{and} \quad \dot{c} = \dot{B}^T W \epsilon$$

$$\bar{N} = \dot{B}^T W \ddot{B}$$

$$\ddot{N} = \ddot{B}^T W \ddot{B} \qquad \ddot{c} = \ddot{B}^T W \epsilon$$

Further consideration of weights may be made by enforcing "weight constraints" (see Case [21]) by utilizing the standard deviations of various parameters in the condition equations. For example, if the standard deviations of the camera station coordinates (X_{oi}, Y_{oi}, Z_{oi}) are known or can be approximated, say, from auxiliary data as:

$$\sigma_{Xi}, \sigma_{Yi}, \sigma_{Zi},$$

etc., the variance-covariance matrix Σ_i of the camera station coordinates is:

$$\Sigma_i = \begin{bmatrix} \sigma_{X_i}^2 & \sigma_{X_i Y_i} & \sigma_{X_i Z_i} \\ \sigma_{X_i Y_i} & \sigma_{Y_i}^2 & \sigma_{Y_i Z_i} \\ \sigma_{X_i Z_i} & \sigma_{Y_i Z_i} & \sigma_{Z_i}^2 \end{bmatrix} \tag{9.66}$$

in which the off-diagonal elements, for the sake of simplification, may be considered as zeros. Finally, the weight matrix W_i of the camera position coordinates is the inverse of the variance-covariance matrix, i.e.,

$$W_i = \Sigma_i^{-1} \tag{9.67}$$

Similarly, the weight matrices of the camera inner orientation parameters, the camera exterior-orientation parameters and the object-space point coordinates can be determined. In order to utilize the weight matrices in the solution of block triangulation problems the partitioned normal equation, Eq. (9.65), becomes (also see Brown [18]):

$$\left[\begin{array}{c|c} \dot{N} + \dot{W} & \bar{N} \\ \hline \bar{N}^T & \ddot{N} + \ddot{W} \end{array}\right] \left[\begin{array}{c} \dot{\delta} \\ \hline \ddot{\delta} \end{array}\right] = \left[\begin{array}{c} \dot{c} - \dot{W}\dot{e} \\ \hline \ddot{c} - \ddot{W}\ddot{e} \end{array}\right] \tag{9.68}$$

The augmented weight matrices $\dot{W}$ and $\ddot{W}$ are diagonal[a] matrices consisting of the individual weight matrices $\dot{W}_i$ and $\ddot{W}_j$ as given by the inverses of the variance-covariance matrices Σ_i and Σ_j. For those parameters which are treated as completely unknown, the appropriate positions of the augmented weight matrix are filled with zero elements. The augmented supplementary discrepancy vectors $\dot{e}$ and $\ddot{e}$ also would contain zero elements in the appropriate locations for unknown quantities. The elements of the vectors $\dot{e}$ and $\ddot{e}$ are the difference between the observed values and the approximate values of the camera-station and object-space parameters. For the first iteration of the solution of such normal equations, Eq. (9.68),

---

[a]Some recent studies indicate (e.g., Maarek [63]) that mathematical correlation between coordinates may be neglected at all times in practice without causing any appreciable change in such results.

the supplementary discrepancy vectors would be normally zero. This is because the observed values are taken as the first approximations. For further ideas in this line see Case [21]. Also see Sec. 11.2 (Eqs. (11.7) and (11.8)) for interesting ideas. See App. B for the relevant computer program developed in the Department of Geodetic Science at Ohio State University.

Some Specific Examples

Several successful "silmultaneous" methods have been documented during the recent years. These are nothing but modified or extended and expanded methods of the basic principles described in this section earlier. Some of the more popular ones are briefly described below:

Aerotriangulation by SAPGO. Aerotriangulation by SAPGO, developed by Wong and Elphingstone (see [107]), gives a mathematical solution developed to include geodetic measurements in a simultaneous solution for aerotriangulation. In addition to the conventional photogrammetric measurements such as photocoordinates and auxiliary data, the solution is capable of incorporating into the adjustment such geodetic measurements as distances, horizontal angles, Laplace azimuths, elevation differences, longitudes, latitudes and elevations. This solution, code-named SAPGO (the acronym for *S*imultaneous *A*djustment of *P*hotogrammetric and Geodetic *O*bservations), has been coded in Fortran IV and has been tested for both strips and blocks.

The SAPGO computer package consists of the following separate programs:

1. *Image refinement program*: Used to correct the comparator data (image coordinates) for lens distortion, atmospheric refraction and film shrinkage;
2. *SAPGO program*: The principal program for performing phototriangulation;
3. *Error propagation program*: Used to compute the standard deviations of the computed ground coordinates. The inverse of N-matrix in SAPGO is stored on disk for use in this program.

Aerotriangulation by MUSAT. Developed by the U.S. Army Engineer Topographic Laboratories (see Doyle [26] and Matos [66]), this provides a highly sophisticated technique for the automatic triangulation and adjustment of a model, strip or block of aerial photos in a single computer run. The technique was given the name MUSAT (an acronym for *MU*ltiple

*S*tation *A*nalytical *T*riangulation). Two variations of the MUSAT program have been completed by the Raytheon Corporation (Autometric Operation) under contract with the U.S. Army Engineer Topographic Laboratories. The first (called: MUSAT), completed in 1968, employs the coplanarity condition for the intersection of two rays (in a stereo pair) and the second (called: Expanded MUSAT), completed in 1969, uses the collinearity condition. The latter version also includes blunder elimination, data editing and a technique (called: AutoRay) for rapid solution and inversion of large systems of normal equations.

The MUSAT programs are coded in Fortran IV for the IBM 7094. They are also coded to run on the UNIVAC 1108. The expanded MUSAT is claimed to be capable of triangulation and adjustment of up to 2000 photographs at a time. It is also capable of statistical analysis of results and error propagation.

The observations and parameters that may be used as input in this program are:

1. Photograph data
   a. Réseau coordinates
   b. Standard deviations
   c. Fiducial coordinates
   d. Image-point coordinates
2. Comparator calibration data
   a. Weave of the ways
   b. X and Y scale factors
   c. Nonorthogonality of axes
3. Ground-control data
   a. Geodetic stations
   b. Standard deviations
   c. Equal elevation points
4. Exposure station data
   a. Air base
   b. Position
   c. Orientation
   d. Standard deviation
5. Camera calibration data
   a. Focal length
   b. Réseau master
   c. Lens characteristics
   d. Frame characteristics
6. Atmospheric refraction data

The output of the programs are, basically, the camera station and ground point position data, the orientation matrix for each camera station and plate residuals for each measured image point. Position data output may be in geographic, UTM, geocentric, or local coordinate systems. Expanded MUSAT is believed to have been modified lately to include the functional restraints of air and ground distance measurements to supplement standard control requirements.

Brown Method. The Brown method of multiple station analytical stereotriangulation (see Brown [18] and [20]) has the approach based upon "rigorous simultaneous adjustment of all photos" covering a block. In Brown's words,

The problem is basically one of obtaining the best possible reconstruction of both object space and image space by utilizing to the maximum all of the metric information contained in a general photogrammetric model—one in which no restrictions are placed upon the number of exposure stations obtaining interrelated data; upon the type and distribution of the control; or upon the elements of orientation to be considered as unknown. To provide for the desirable possibility of redundancy, the assumption is made that the observations are distributed by the multivariate normal distribution with known relative covariance matrix. The criterion for the adjustment is the principle of maximum likelihood (to preserve continuity with classical concepts of error theory, the expression 'rigorous least squares adjustment' has been employed to denote the maximum likelihood adjustment of observations having the multivariate normal distribution). Accordingly it may be asserted that, within the framework of the assumptions, the solution leads to results of highest possible precision in the senses of having the optimal properties of minimum variance and maximum probability.

The solution, despite its generality, is based directly upon a pair of (collinearity) condition equations (see Sec. 9.2) for each point.

In the solution, a duality exists between all quantities associated with the unknown elements of orientation and the corresponding quantities associated with the unknown coordinates of the control points. Hence there exists two forms of the solution, depending upon the interpretation assigned to the primary matrices and their associated indices. The most convenient form is determined mainly by the number of unknowns for orientation relative to the number of unknowns for control.

The solution, being iterative, requires a set of initial approximations to the unknown elements of orientation and to the unknown coordinates of the control. It has been shown that the approximations for the $\dfrac{\text{Coordinates of the control}}{\text{Elements of orientation}}$ can be chosen in a manner leading to a convenient solution for the $\dfrac{\text{Elements of orientation}}{\text{Coordinates of the control}}$ $\dfrac{\text{The unknown coordinates of the control}}{\text{The unknown elements of orientation}}$ can then be expressed directly in terms of the resulting $\dfrac{\text{Elements of orientation}}{\text{Coordinates of the control}}$. The fact that the solution is iterative makes it possible to avoid the use of trigonometrical routines.

The complete error propagation associated with the adjustment emerges as a by-product of the solution. The mean errors and correlations of $\dfrac{\text{The unknown}}{\text{The unknown}}$ $\dfrac{\text{elements of orientation}}{\text{coordinates of the control}}$ are obtained directly from the inverse of the coefficient matrix of the reduced normal equations. The mean errors and correlations of $\dfrac{\text{The}}{\text{The}}$ $\dfrac{\text{unknown coordinates of the control}}{\text{unknown elements of orientation}}$ are obtained from those of the $\dfrac{\text{Elements of}}{\text{Coordinates of}}$ $\dfrac{\text{orientation}}{\text{the control}}$.

The facility with which the error propagation can be accomplished makes the purely analytical approach to error studies especially attractive.

Since the solution considers the possibility of correlation between the errors in the plate coordinates of each image, it is valid also for measurements made with polar coordinate comparators or with goniometers.

Brown has shown that the solution to many of the major problems of analytical photogrammetry may be regarded either as special cases or immediate extension of the general solution. A partial listing of such problems would include, Brown claims:

1. The silmultaneous adjustment of an entire photogrammetric strip or block.
2. The least squares determination of the orientation of an individual camera from absolute and/or directional control points.
3. An n-station, least squares solution for photogrammetric triangulation with cameras of known orientation.
4. Various methods of cantilever extension.
5. Moving strip extension.
6. Various methods of block extension.
7. Utilization of externally obtained, relative values for elements of orientation.
8. The combined determination of the relative and absolute orientations of several cameras occupying a common exposure station.
9. The combined use of circles and target boards to obtain the precise orientation of a phototheodolite.
10. Photogrammetric triangulation of missile trajectories when the precise times of the exposures for the star calibrations are unknown.
11. Photogrammetric triangulation of trajectory points obtained by unsynchronized, flame chopping performed at constant rates at different stations.
12. Photogrammetric flare triangulation.

The general solution may also be extended to permit the inclusion of externally obtained information different in nature from that already considered. Examples of such data are the distances between partially absolute or relative control points and the fact that certain points lie on space curves of known functional form (e.g., points on a straight railroad or canal; points on a ballistic trajectory). It is the author's feeling, however, that the incorporation of such data into the general solution, though theoretically straightforward, would compromise the essential simplicity and symmetry of the mathematical model and would therefore unduly complicate the computations.

Schmid Method. The Schmid method is based on the work of Hellmut Schmid [84]. This method resembles the system developed in the NOS (see Keller and Tewinkel [54]) and uses so-called "bundles". A program written in Fortran IV for the CDC 6400/6500 has been documented by Schenk [83] for a block of 500 photographs including a maximum of 49 points per photo and a maximum of 2048 points for the block.

Aerotriangulation by RABATS. Aerotriangulation by RABATS (*R*apid *A*nalytical *B*lock *A*erial *T*riangulation *S*ystem) is a comprehensive strip and/or block aerial triangulation software package developed by the firm of John F. Kenefick, Photogrammetric Consultant, Inc., for both semi and fully computational triangulation. The author (see Kenefick [56]) claims that in comparison with other aerial triangulation systems in present day use, RABATS is unique in several respects:

1. The main body of RABATS is programmed in modules to permit implementation on small computers without placing a practical limit on the size of block which can be processed.
2. The modular design allows the user to process a project in a series of logical steps, each of which provides intermediate results to assist in detection of measurement and/or ground control errors.
3. Although unnecessary from a computational point of view, a rigorous least squares three dimensional rigid body transformation is initially performed for individual strips prior to the actual adjustment. This computation is incorporated to help isolate erroneous ground control points.
4. Adjustment of the strip or block is based upon polynomial smoothing functions; one horizontal and one vertical function for each strip. A simultaneous least squares solution is determined for all planimetric smoothing functions and a separate simultaneous solution is computed for all vertical smoothing functions. The simultaneous solutions avoid instabilities and ambiguities which often times occur with iterative solutions when ground control is sparse.
5. Control points are weighted individually in all computations as a function of their estimated standard deviations as expressed in ground units; another feature which assists in detection of ground control errors and which provides a statistically rigorous least squares solution as well.
6. A control point edit program permits the user to eliminate and/or change ground control point coordinates and/or estimated standard deviations during the

course of computations, eliminating the necessity of starting over when such changes are desired.

7. A passpoint edit program allows the user to change erroneous ground point identification numbers and/or "untie" bad strip tie points without starting over.

8. Provision is also made for readjustment of a strip and/or block solution to independently measured distances and azimuths. (Absolute control points are also admitted.)

9. A group of "support" programs are provided for computations peripheral to the aerial triangulation solution itself. For instance, calibration of mono-comparators, computation of lens distortion coefficients, computation of "true" fiducial coordinates from measurements of flash plates, computation of coordinates of projection centers for analogue plotters not equipped with devices for direct measurement of the locations of the perspective centers, and a preprocessor program to scan input to the aerial triangulation solution for common blunders in the data.

10 Independent Geodetic Control

The method of strip triangulation with independent geodetic control may be of extreme help in areas having geodetic (or ground) control which is inadequate for regular aeropolygon or aeroleveling. Some field work is required but this is considerably less. This is also known as the "cross-base" method because of the use of cross-bases to provide such localized control as is necessary. The principles, extendable to blocks from strips, are applicable with success in remote areas like extensive desert land, ice-covered areas, etc. In this respect, see also Brandenberger [16], Colcord [23], Morgan [72], Ghosh [32], and Zeller [110].

Error propagations (see examples from an actual case given in Fig. 10-1) along a strip during aeropolygon or aeroleveling may be expressed by polynomials (Eqs. (5.25) or (5.26)). Each of such expressions represents a "space curve," expressed functionally as

$$R = F(X, Y, Z) \tag{10.1}$$

Such space (error) curves may be differentiated with respect to the independent variables X, Y, or Z. However, in a strip of aerial photographs it is expected that the extension is the maximum in X, followed by Y and Z (Z being practically zero in almost flat terrain). This would indicate their primary, secondary and tertiary effects on X, Y, and Z strip coordinates, respectively. The resulting differentials represent the rate of change of the space curve in the particular direction. One can express the differentials by the following:

$$\begin{bmatrix} \dfrac{d\Delta X}{dX} & \dfrac{d\Delta X}{dY} & \dfrac{d\Delta X}{dZ} \\[2em] \dfrac{d\Delta Y}{dX} & \dfrac{d\Delta Y}{dY} & \dfrac{d\Delta Y}{dZ} \\[2em] \dfrac{d\Delta Z}{dX} & \dfrac{d\Delta Z}{dY} & \dfrac{d\Delta Z}{dZ} \end{bmatrix} \tag{10.2}$$

Revelant Information: (refer to Fig. 10-1)

Strip: Laufen-Bauma, Switzerland

143

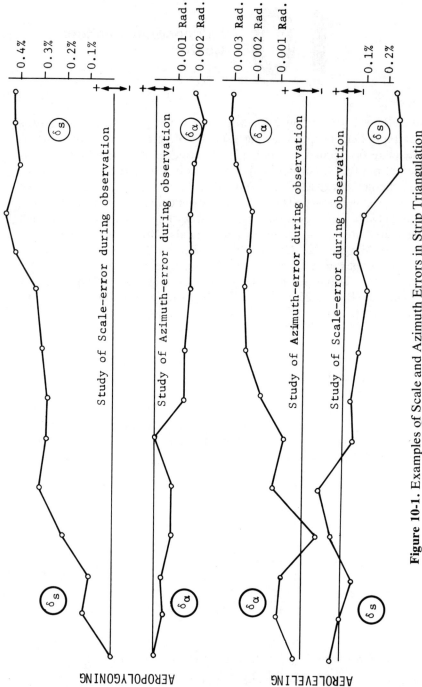

Figure 10-1. Examples of Scale and Azimuth Errors in Strip Triangulation (Ref: Fig. 5.15) [see pp. 143-145 for relevant data]

Camera: Wild RC7a; f=100.26 mm; 14 cm² format

Strip length: 110 km (36 models)

Flying height: 6000 m

Instrument: Wild Autograph A7

Photo scale: 1:60,000

Model scale: 1:15,000

Control point locations—see Fig. 5-15.

Expressed in photogrammetric terminology, this is:

$$\begin{bmatrix} \delta_s & \delta_\alpha & \delta_\phi \\ \delta_\alpha & \delta_s & \delta_\tau \\ \delta_\phi & \delta_\tau & \delta_s \end{bmatrix} \qquad (10.2a)$$

i.e., the diagonal terms are scale distortion (error) terms and the off-diagonal terms are rotation distortion terms. These may be computed as follows:

$$\left. \begin{aligned} \delta_s &= \frac{\text{observed length} - \text{given length}}{\text{given length}} \\ \delta_\alpha, \delta_\phi \text{ or } \delta_\tau &= \text{observed angle} - \text{given angle} \end{aligned} \right\} \qquad (10.3)$$

It can, therefore, be noted that lengths, azimuths, longitudinal (to strip) and lateral (to strip) tilts of carefully designed or/and selected lines placed in the strip possess sufficient information for the determination of the adjustment polynomials.

Consider a strip with cross-bases (two bases) in each of the first, one middle and the last stereomodels (see Fig. 10-2, models A, M and E, respectively). Now consider that each cross-base (see Fig. 10-2b) comprises four ground stations, clearly identifiable on the photographs, such that the following information are obtained from field work:

1. The base lengths: 1-3 and 2-4, i.e., bases B_E and B_N
2. Their azimuths: α_{B_E} and α_{B_N}
3. Their slopes: β_{B_E} and β_{B_N}

This information can be obtained by using suitable geodetic methods. There may be no geodetic connections between the data obtained for the different models (cross-bases). Nevertheless, these data are sufficient to establish a strip's adjustment. The data may be obtained from field work in a local rectangular (X-Y-Z) system of coordinates.

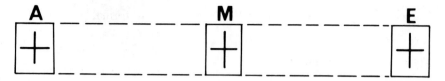

Figure 10-2a. Strip with Cross-Bases

10.1 Strip Triangulation

For individual strips, assuming a local (strip) system of coordinates, the error propagations (see section 5.3), for the Y=constant sections in the strip, are given by the following general expressions (considering flat terrain, i.e., Z=constant):

$$\left.\begin{aligned}
\Delta X &= a_0 + a_1 X + a_2 X^2 + a_3 X^3 \\
\Delta Y &= c_0 + c_1 X + c_2 X^2 + c_3 X^3 \\
\Delta Z &= d_0 + d_1 X + d_2 X^2 + d_3 X^3
\end{aligned}\right\} \quad (10.4)$$

where a, c, and d are constants.

Furthermore, contributory to the above, one may consider the following equations:

$$\left.\begin{aligned}
\text{Rotation deformation} &= \Delta X_r = e_0 Y + e_1 XY + e_2 X^2 Y \\
\text{Scale deformation} &= \Delta Y_s = i_0 Y + i_1 XY + i_2 X^2 Y \\
\text{Torsion deformation} &= \Delta Z_\tau = g_0 Y + g_1 XY + g_2 X^2 Y
\end{aligned}\right\} \quad (10.5)$$

where e, i, and g are constants.

By differentiating Eq. (10.4) with respect to X, one obtains:

$$\left.\begin{aligned}
\text{Scale distortion} \quad &= \delta_s = \frac{d\Delta X}{dX} = a_1 + 2a_2 X + 3a_3 X^2 \\[2mm]
\text{Azimuth distortion} &= \delta_\alpha = \frac{d\Delta Y}{dX} = c_1 + 2c_2 X + 3c_3 X^2 \\[2mm]
\begin{aligned}\text{Longitudinal tilt}\\ \text{distortion}\end{aligned} &= \delta_\phi = \frac{d\Delta Z}{dX} = d_1 + 2d_2 X + 3d_3 X^2
\end{aligned}\right\} \quad (10.6)$$

Similarly, by differentiating Eq. (10.5) with respect to Y, one obtains:

$$\left.\begin{aligned}
\text{Rotation distortion} &= \delta_\alpha = \frac{d\Delta X}{dY} = e_0 + e_1 X + e_2 X^2 \\[2mm]
\text{Scale distortion} \quad &= \delta_s = \frac{d\Delta Y}{dY} = i_0 + i_1 X + i_2 X^2 \\[2mm]
\text{Torsion distortion} &= \delta_\tau = \frac{d\Delta Z}{dY} = g_0 + g_1 X + g_2 X^2
\end{aligned}\right\} \quad (10.7)$$

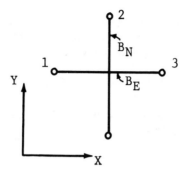

Figure 10-2b. Situation at One Cross-Base

These establish the obvious similarities amongst Eqs. (10.6) and (10.7) and also explain the terms in Eq. (10.2).

Apart from the error propagation expressed in Eq. (10.4) the X coordinates suffer from the secondary effects of azimuth or rotation distortion and the tertiary effects of longitudinal tilt distortion. Similar considerations for Y and Z can be made, which give:

$$\left.\begin{aligned}
\Delta X' &= a_0 + a_1 X + a_2 X^2 + a_3 X^3 + Y \cdot \delta_\alpha + Z \cdot \delta_\phi \\
\Delta Y' &= c_0 + c_1 X + c_2 X^2 + c_3 X^3 + Y \cdot \delta_s + Z \cdot \delta_\tau \\
\Delta Z' &= d_0 + d_1 X + d_2 X^2 + d_3 X^3 + Y \cdot \delta_\tau + Z \cdot \delta_s
\end{aligned}\right\} \quad (10.8)$$

If in a strip one has three cross-bases (A, M, E in Fig. 10-2) during the strip formation (aeropolygon or aeroleveling) at a stereoplotter, or (numerically) at the computer, the following may be obtained:

In the first model (A): $\delta_{sA} \; \delta_{\alpha A} \; \delta_{\phi A} \; \delta_{\tau A}$

In the middle model (M): $\delta_{sM} \; \delta_{\alpha M} \; \delta_{\phi M} \; \delta_{\tau M}$

In the last model (E): $\delta_{sE} \; \delta_{\alpha E} \; \delta_{\phi E} \; \delta_{\tau E}$

Thereafter one can solve for the constants, e.g., considering Eq. (10.6):

$$\left.\begin{aligned}
\delta_{sA} &= a_1 + 2a_2 X_A + 3a_3 X_A^2 \\
\delta_{sM} &= a_1 + 2a_2 X_M + 3a_3 X_M^2 \\
\delta_{sE} &= a_1 + 2a_2 X_E + 3a_3 X_E^2
\end{aligned}\right\} \quad (10.9)$$

Note that the X_A, X_M and X_E are the strip coordinates of the centers of the cross-bases in models A, M and E, respectively. By solving the set of equations in Eq. (10.9), one obtains a_1, a_2, and a_3. Similarly, by solving a set of three equations corresponding to $\delta_{\alpha A}$, $\delta_{\alpha M}$ and $\delta_{\alpha E}$, one can obtain c_1, c_2

and c_3. The d's and g's are obtainable from the $\delta\phi$ and δ_τ equations. These can then be used in Eq. (10.8) to compute the final misclosures $\Delta X'$, $\Delta Y'$ and $\Delta Z'$ for any arbitrary point whose X, Y, Z strip coordinates obtained from the observation data are used in this computation.

In practice, Eq. (10.9) can be simplified, e.g.,

Simplification 1: Consider the strip coordinates originating at the cross-base A, i.e., $X_A = 0$. This gives

$$\left. \begin{aligned} \delta_{sA} &= a_1 \\ \delta_{sM} &= a_1 + 2a_2X_M + 3a_3X_M^2 \\ \delta_{sE} &= a_1 + 2a_2X_E + 3a_3X_E^2 \end{aligned} \right\} \tag{10.10}$$

Simplification 2: Consider the first model being absolutely oriented to fit the cross-base A in the beginning, i.e., $\delta_{sA} = a_1 = 0$. This gives

$$\left. \begin{aligned} \delta_{sM} &= 2a_2X_M + 3a_3X_M^2 \\ \delta_{sE} &= 2a_2X_E + 3a_3X_E^2 \end{aligned} \right\} \tag{10.11}$$

Simplification 3: Consider the strip to comprise of two strips with two cross-bases each (i.e., A & M and M & E), i.e., the middle base M is considered as the last base for the first half-strip and the first base for the second half-strip. In such a case, the distortion propagations δ_s, δ_α, δ_ϕ and δ_τ may be considered to be linear (corresponding up to the second order terms in Eq. (10.4) for the first half:

$$\left. \begin{aligned} \delta_{sA} &= a_1 = 0 \\ \delta_{sM} &= 2a_2X_M \end{aligned} \right\} \tag{10.12a}$$

and, similarly, separately,

$$\left. \begin{aligned} \delta_{sM} &= 2a_2X_M \\ \delta_{sE} &= 2a_2X_E + 3a_3X_E^2 \end{aligned} \right\} \tag{10.12b}$$

Such simplifications would offer simpler solutions to the constants, a's, c's, d's, and g's. Further simplification will be to consider, from the very beginning, instead of one strip with three cross-bases, two strips with two cross-bases each. Furthermore, in such a case, the distortions may be considered as being propagated linearly. This gives, for the first half-strip:

$$\left. \begin{aligned} \delta_{sA} &= a_1 + 2a_2X_A \\ \delta_{sM} &= a_1 + 2a_2X_M \end{aligned} \right\} \tag{10.13a}$$

From these one can obtain a_1 and a_2.
Next, for the second half-strip:

$$\left. \begin{array}{l} \delta'_{s_M} = a'_1 + 2a'_2 X_M \\[2mm] \delta'_{s_E} = a'_1 + 2a'_2 X_E \end{array} \right\} \tag{10.13b}$$

From these one can obtain a'_1 and a'_2.
Similar considerations can be made for the c's, d's, and g's.

Tolerances for the ground (field) work at the cross-bases must depend on the equipment to be used, e.g., for work at a first order stereoplotter (Wild A7, A10; Zeiss C8, Nistri-Bendix AP/C, etc. are examples):

Standard error in length (in meters)

$$m_B \leq \pm \frac{0.00001 \cdot \sqrt{2}}{M_M} \tag{10.14a}$$

Standard error in azimuth (in centesimal minutes)

$$m_\alpha^c \leq \pm \frac{0.00001 \cdot \sqrt{2}}{B \cdot M_M} \cdot \rho^c \tag{10.14b}$$

Standard error in slope (in centesimal minutes)

$$m_\beta^c \leq \pm \frac{0.00005 \cdot h \cdot \sqrt{2}}{B} \cdot \rho^c \tag{10.14c}$$

where M_M is the Model-Scale

$\quad\quad\quad$ B is the Base-length in m.

$\quad\quad\quad$ h is the Flying-height in m.

Note: The above expressions consider standard pointing errors in X or Y coordinates being 0.00001 m. and in elevation being 0.05 per thousand of h (at the stereo instrument).

10.2 Block Triangulation

Experience indicates that (also see Brandenberger [16]) the principles of strip triangulation by the method of independent geodetic control can be extended to block triangulation. In such cases it will be advisable to obtain a framework of 'principal' and 'tie' strips as shown in Fig. 10-3. The strips that constitute the framework would provide the control necessary for triangulating other (filling) strips. The framework strips can be adjusted in 'loops'. For instance, in Fig. 10-3, the figure ABCD forms a loop consisting

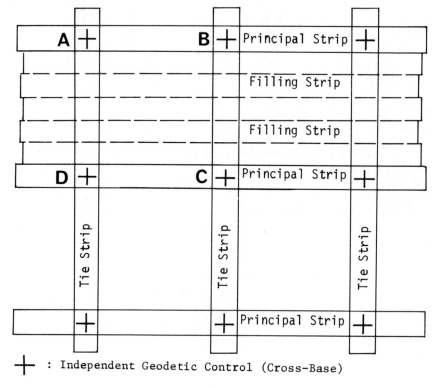

$\boldsymbol{+}$: Independent Geodetic Control (Cross-Base)

Figure 10-3. Framework of Strips for Block Triangulation

of four strips adjusted according to the method of independent geodetic control.

If strips AB, BC, CD, and DA are put together, there may be final misclosures at B, C, D, and A. Such a loop can be adjusted according to the principles used in "closed traverses" in land surveying.

For the determination of the standard errors, one may consider the following true errors (deviations) before a loop adjustment:

δ_1 = X, Y or Z misclosure at end of Strip 1 (AB)

$\delta_1 + \delta_2$ = X, Y or Z misclosure at end of Strip 2 (BC)

$\delta_1 + \delta_2 + \delta_3$ = X, Y or Z misclosure at end of Strip 3 (CD)

$\delta_1 + \delta_2 + \delta_3 + \delta_4$ = X, Y or Z misclosure at end of Strip 4 (DA)

The true residual errors after a loop adjustment are:

$$\text{At B: } \delta_1 - \frac{\delta_1+\delta_2+\delta_3+\delta_4}{4} = \frac{3\delta_1-\delta_2-\delta_3-\delta_4}{4}$$

$$\text{At C: } \delta_1 + \delta_2 - \frac{2(\delta_1+\delta_2+\delta_3+\delta_4)}{4} = \frac{\delta_1+\delta_2-\delta_3-\delta_4}{2}$$

$$\text{At D: } \delta_1 + \delta_2 + \delta_3 - \frac{3(\delta_1+\delta_2+\delta_3+\delta_4)}{4} = \frac{\delta_1+\delta_2+\delta_3-3\delta_4}{4}$$

$$\text{At A: } \delta_1 + \delta_2 + \delta_3 + \delta_4 - \frac{4(\delta_1+\delta_2+\delta_3+\delta_4)}{4} = 0$$

$$(10.15)$$

If one assumes that all four strips of the loop have the same accuracy, one obtains, for the standard residual errors in B, C, D and A:

$$\text{At B: } m_X = \frac{\sqrt{3}}{2} m_{Xo}; \quad m_Y = \frac{\sqrt{3}}{2} m_{Yo}; \quad m_Z = \frac{\sqrt{3}}{2} m_{Zo}$$

$$\text{At C: } m_X = m_{Xo}; \quad m_Y = m_{Yo}; \quad m_Z = m_{Zo}$$

$$\text{At D: } m_X = \frac{\sqrt{3}}{2} m_{Xo}; \quad m_Y = \frac{\sqrt{3}}{2} m_{Yo}; \quad m_Z = \frac{\sqrt{3}}{2} m_{Zo}$$

$$\text{At A: } m_X = 0; \quad m_Y = 0; \quad m_Z = 0$$

$$(10.16)$$

where m_{Xo}, m_{Yo} and m_{Zo} are the standard closing errors of one strip.

It is of further interest to note the results of research by Morgan [72] on the use of this method in strip triangulation. Although the results are not very conclusive, they indicate that different adjustment polynomials can sometimes be considered for use in this method. They are sometimes able to yield acceptable results. Morgan's results do not seem to be statistically equivalent to the optimum results obtained by the ANOVA (Analysis of Variance) technique. However, the final results thus obtained do rival those obtained from using normal geodetic control and any standard aerial triangulation method. For the ANOVA technique, the reader is suggested to consult any standard text book on statistics.

11 Use of Auxiliary Data

Integration of auxiliary data into an aerial-triangulation process is a relatively new approach to the problem of extending control by photogrammetric means. It involves the determination of one or more of the elements of exterior orientation of the aerial camera at the moment of exposure. As an alternative to establishing additional ground control, the auxiliary data provide an excellent means of controlling the propagation of errors because they are independently obtained for each exposure (or strip) and provide checks.

The actual application of auxiliary data can take place either in the process of strip and block formation or in the adjustment phase. In the analog approaches, the application is in the former area, while in the computational approaches, the latter application may be more convenient.

The significance of phototriangulation with auxiliary data has considerably increased during the last decade. Auxiliary data are used at the present time in practically all known methods of triangulation. Their uses are not affected by the specific measuring and data processing means and systems (analogical, analytical, or computational). The following systems producing auxiliary data (usable in phototriangulation) may be considered (also see Brandenberger [17]):

1. Electronic distance measuring systems, e.g., HIRAN, SHIRAN, AERODIST, etc., with which the planimetric coordinates of the camera (exposure) station are determined. Best standard error attained so far:
   a. In AERODIST: $m_p = \pm 0.85$ m (see Stewart [93])
   b. In others: $m_p = \pm 1.20$ m (see Brandenberger [17])

2. Radar-Doppler navigation system (see Zarzycki [109]) with which the length of the air base may be determined. This information would help determine the scale of the stereomodel. Best standard error (relative) attained so far:

$$m_s = \pm 0.27 \text{ percent}$$

   where, scale

$$s = \Delta b / b$$

3. Statoscope, with which the difference between the heights of the exposure stations may be determined. This corresponds to the bz element of

the exterior orientation (see Chap. 7). Best standard error obtained so far:

$$m_{bz} = \pm 1 \text{ m}$$

4. Airborne Profile Recorder (APR) with which the clearance between the exposure stations and the ground may be determined. This corresponds to the flying height above the ground and can be used as a scale condition in each model. Best standard error attained (see Stewart [93]):

$$m_H = \pm 2 \text{ m}$$

5. Solar periscope of Santoni (see Santoni [81]), horizon cameras (see Weissman [105]), gyroscope recordings, etc., with which information on X and Y tilts (ω and ϕ tilts) may be obtained. Best standard error obtained:

$$m_\omega = m_\phi = \pm 1^c$$

6. AN/USQ 28 system (see Livingston [62]) developed by the U. S. Air Force with which the camera position and camera altitude at the time of exposure may be determined. Best standard errors attained:

$$m_\omega = m_\phi = m_\kappa = \pm 0^c.3$$

$$m_X = m_Y = m_Z = \pm 3 \text{ m}$$

Apart from the problem of the availability and adaptability of such systems, in order to evaluate the potentials of phototriangulation with auxiliary data, one should compare the accuracy of such data with the accuracy resulting in the corresponding elements from triangulation performed without using any of such systems. The examples from a series of tests performed during 1967-1972 in the Department of Geodetic Science at Ohio State University are given below:

Job specifications:

Strip: Laufen-Bauma, Switzerland
Camera: Wild RC7a; f= 100.26 mm; Format: 14 cm²
Strip length: ~110 km
Number of models: 36
Flying height: ~6000 m
Photo scale: ~1:60,000
The field control in this test area (with signalized and thoroughly identified points) was with a standard error in each coordinate of less than ±5 cm in the ground.

Instruments used: Wild A7 (model scale: 1:15,000)
Nistri-Bendix AP/C
Zeiss PSK stereocomparator

At the Autograph A7 both empirical and numerical relative orientation procedures (with comparable results) were used, with six orientation points in each model. Both aeropolygon and independent model methods of strip triangulation were studied at the A7 and the AP/C. The PSK stereocomparator data were utilized in a sequential method of strip triangulation. After the strip adjustment (using standard 5-3-3 control points) the standard errors obtained were:

	From A7	From AP/C	From PSK	Remarks
m_{bx}	$\pm 0.01\%$	$\pm 0.01\%$	$\pm 0.01\%$	Relative error
m_{by}	± 0.032mm	± 0.030mm	± 0.030mm	At photo scale
m_{bz}	± 0.026mm	± 0.025mm	± 0.025mm	At photo scale
m_{ω}	$\pm 0^c.76$	$\pm 0^c.75$	$\pm 0^c.75$	
m_{ϕ}	$\pm 1^c.10$	$\pm 1^c.11$	$\pm 1^c.09$	
m_{κ}	$\pm 0^c.53$	$\pm 0^c.53$	$\pm 0^c.52$	

It must be kept in mind that the use of auxiliary data permits essential savings in the required ground control as long as the standard error of the auxiliary data are smaller than the standard residual error of a triangulation performed without using such data.

Whereas the applicability of the linear data (corresponding to bx, by, and bz elements) would depend on the photo/mapping scale, the angular data are independent of such considerations. In some cases of high precision mapping jobs, such data may not be adequately reliable for direct use in each photo/model but may be used in controlling error propagations through strip/block. Therefore, judgment in their use in specific jobs is imperative.

Excepting the AN/USQ 28 system quoted earlier (this, incidentally is currently inoperative), all other available systems give partial control. Therefore, sometimes a combination of two or more such auxiliary systems may provide meaningful control. One example is the use of Aerodist in combination with the APR. It has been proven (see Stewart [93]) that such a combination will be adequate for controlling medium scale mapping aerial photography without performing rigorous triangulation and without using ground control provided from classical geodetic field work.

In view of the potentials of the systems providing angular elements' data, it will be pertinent to discuss some of them.

11.1 Solar Periscope

This system developed by Santoni [81] is capable of determining the attitude of the aerial camera by photographing the sun concurrently with the ground. This requires an additional special camera and a special mount. The two cameras, a terrain camera and a sun camera, are locked in diametrically opposite directions and work with synchronized shutters.

The solar photograph provides information on the sun's direction at the time of exposure. This, in turn, provides information on the κ, ϕ, and ω rotations of the terrain (mapping) camera.

The use of this system, apart from the complications in adapting to the aircraft, involves complicated data acquisition and data processing (computations) before the data could be handled directly in aerial photogrammetry.

In order to obtain the zenithal and azimuthal position of the sun, one would require (a) the geographical coordinates of the camera locations, and (b) the exact time of exposure. A chronometer is used for recording the time (precisely) on the film of the Solar camera. The geographical coordinates of the exposure stations are determined from an approximate strip triangulation performed prior to the precision work. For this, however, control in the first and the last models are necessary. The κ values (required for azimuth determination) are then adjusted from the strip data. The ω and ϕ values are either computed or determined from a solar calculator (a mechanical analog computer, designed specifically for this purpose).

Finally, the angular data, (a) adjusted κ and (b) computed ω and ϕ are introduced into the instrument camera during the stereotriangulation of each strip or used directly in the orientation matrix for computational solutions.

11.2 Horizon Photography

Perhaps the most valuable tool to provide auxiliary data in aerial triangulation is the horizon camera because it provides ϕ and ω tilt information (and under certain conditions also κ) with a fairly high degree of accuracy.

From its development in 1928 by General V.P. Nenonen (of Finland), the horizon camera has, in turn, almost fallen into oblivion and also became a valuable tool in photogrammetry. Its original use was in finding the inclination of the optical axis of the principal (mapping) camera only to use the information in the rectification procedure for single image jobs. Prior to World War II, men such as Löfström, von Gruber, and Brucklacher improved and investigated techniques of extracting the exterior orientation elements ϕ and ω from photographs obtained from the original horizon

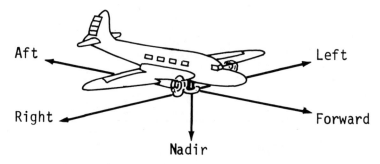

Figure 11-1. Principles of the Horizon Camera

camera built by Zeiss (HS 20/18.24). In the late 1950s the investigations were renewed and with the advent of the HC-1 camera built by Wild Co. in 1962, the interest in this area has increased considerably. The Wild HC-1 camera, by means of four separate photographs taken of the horizon in four directions (forward, aft, left and right) can establish the attitude of the main, nadiral camera (see Fig. 11-1).

The Wild HC-1 camera is designed for use directly with any survey camera of Wild manufacture. Synchronized with each exposure of the survey camera, the horizon camera takes four horizon photos in directions separated by 90°. The four horizon sectors are recorded on 35-mm cinefilm (see Fig. 11-2) with the images of an adjustable counter, "note tablet," and a seconds clock. For measurements of the horizon photographs a micro-stereocomparator (e.g., Wild MSTK) can be used also.

The ω and ϕ angle determinations can be accomplished by either or both of the two methods (the declination or the inclination) when determined monocularly. Alternately, it can be accomplished stereoscopically through the use of parallax measurements. Theoretically, it is possible to determine κ also. However, from a practical approach, the swing (κ) cannot be determined to any great degree of accuracy.

Inclination Angle Method

The inclination angle method involves the determination of angle α between the horizon line and the horizontal fiducial axis in one of the following ways:

1. The inclination angle of the horizon line is measured with a protractor.
2. Lines b and c (see Fig. 11-3) are measured with a scale, a mono-comparator, or some other instrument, and substituted into the relationship:

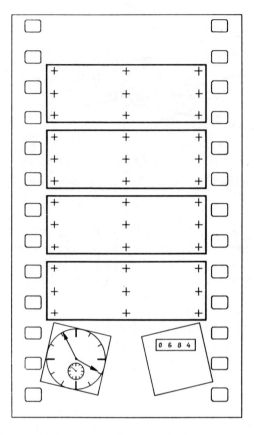

Figure 11-2. Schematic Representation of Horizon Camera (Wild HC-1) Recordings

$$\tan \alpha = (b-c)/D \qquad (11.1)$$

where D is the distance between fiducial marks 1 and 3.

Declination Angle Method

The declination angle method involves the determination of the angle β between the optical axis and the line connecting the perspective center to the intersection of the horizon line and the vertical fiducial axis, in one of the following ways:

1. Line a in Fig. 11-3 is measured with some measuring device and substituted into the relationship:

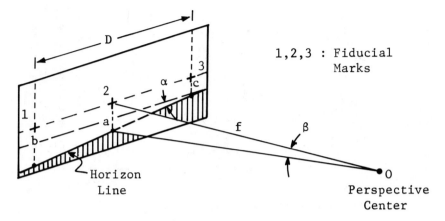

Figure 11-3. Configuration of the Horizon Photo

$$\tan \beta = a/f \qquad (11.2)$$

where f is the principal distance (focal length) of the horizon camera.

2. Lines a, b, and c in Fig. 11-3 are measured and substituted into the relationship:

$$\tan \beta = (a+b+c)/3f \qquad (11.3)$$

Stereoscopically

Stereoscopically, any stereoscopic instrument and measuring device, such as a mirror stereoscope and parallax bar, stereocomparator, or stereoplotter, can be used in the relative orientation of photographs i and i + 1 (both turned 90°) and measurement of the horizontal (X) parallaxes of the central fiducial marks (R_1, R_2, R_3) and the horizontal parallaxes of the corresponding points on the horizon line (h_1, h_2, h_3). The differences of these parallax readings $(R_1-h_1, R_2-h_2, \text{ and } R_3-h_3)$ express the displacement of the horizon line in photo i+1 relative to the horizon line in photo i. These parallax differences can then be substituted into the relationships:

$$\Delta\alpha^c = \frac{(R_1 - h_1) - (R_3 - h_3)}{D} \cdot \rho^c \qquad (11.4)$$

$$\Delta\beta^c = \frac{(R_1 - h_1) + (R_2 - h_2) + (R_3 - h_3)}{3f} \cdot \rho^c \qquad (11.5)$$

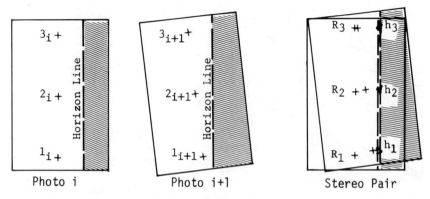

Figure 11-4. Stereoscopic Model of Horizon Photos

These equations correspond to Eqs. (11.1) and (11.3) with the exception that these are differential values (differences between tilts on adjacent photos) whereas the monocular determinations resulted in absolute values (actual tilts of each photo). The concept is illustrated in Fig. 11-4.

Essentially, the horizon equations utilized in the monocular determinations do not differ from those used in the stereoscopic determinations except for the fact that the former give absolute values and the latter give differential values. But application of the law of error propagation to the equations utilizing the inclination angle method and to those utilizing the declination angle method indicates that the accuracy of Eqs. (11.3) and (11.5) is superior to that of Eqs. (11.1) and (11.4).

Several studies of the accuracies obtained for ϕ and ω (with respect to the photo coordinate system) have been made by different individuals and the results seem to be mutually supporting.

With the Wild HC-1 system, generally,

$$m_\phi : m_\omega = 1 : 0.8 \tag{11.6}$$

m_ϕ and m_ω being the standard errors in ϕ and ω angles derived from the horizon photos. This relationship can be considered in assigning weights to the appropriate diagonal elements of the normal equation matrix (see Sec. 9.2), as follows:

$$w_{\phi i} = m_0^2/m_\phi^2 \text{ and } w_{\omega i} = m_0^2 /m_\omega^2 \tag{11.7}$$

where $(w_\phi, w_\omega)_i$ are the weights for exposure station i and m_0^2 is the variance of unit weight. The value of m_0^2 must be obtained empirically with respect to the particular working system:

$$m_0^2 = [ee]/n \tag{11.8}$$

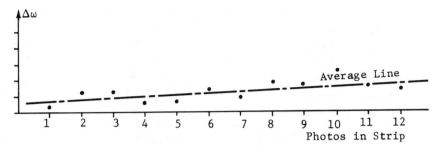

Figure 11-5. Example of Adjusting Horizon Data in Aeropolygon

where [ee] is the sum of the squares of "true errors" of an observation and n is the number of observations.

In the use of horizon data, it may be noted that weights to the other elements of exterior orientation will have to be obtained separately. In addition, no covariance for ϕ and ω is involved. This, however, is a valid assumption for the absolute determination of ϕ and ω but not for the differential case unless the differential values are converted to absolute values and used as such.

In a simultaneous (computational) triangulation, the horizon data may be applied directly in the orientation matrix or the collinearity equations (with or without the consideration of weights). The sequential (computational) or the independent model (analog or computational) triangulation will also be strengthened if the horizon data are used directly.

In the pure aeropolygon (with a first order stereoplotting instrument or an analytical plotter) work, such data may be used in the following way: (note: subscript i refers to photos)

Step 1: Obtain ω_{hi}, ϕ_{hi} from horizon photography.

Step 2: Obtain ω_{Ii}, ϕ_{Ii} from the instrument during the strip triangulation without considering horizon data.

Step 3: Adjust the differences: $\Delta\omega_i = (\omega_h - \omega_I)_i$ and $\Delta\phi_i = (\phi_h - \phi_I)_i$ linearly through the strip (see Figure 11-5).

Step 4: In a second (iterative) run of the strip triangulation, at the rth model (photos r, r+1): First, introduce the corrections to elements ϕ_r, ω_r, ϕ_{r+1} and ω_{r+1} as obtained in Step 3 to the instrument data (Step 2). Next, carry out dependent relative orientation (co-orientation) using κ_{r+1}, by_{r+1} and bz_{r+1} elements. Now, the model should be oriented. In case residual parallaxes so indicate, elements ω_r and ϕ_r may be used in the end.

Other procedures of the strip triangulation will be exactly the same as discussed in Chap. 3.

The linear adjustments of $\Delta\omega_i$ and $\Delta\phi_i$ (Step 3 above) are explained in Fig. 11-5. The idea is that one can trust the orientation elements at the first order instrument and the differences in the $\Delta\omega$ and $\Delta\phi$ are due to systematic (instrumental) plus some random errors. Such systematic errors are linear through the strip.

The difference of the individual $\Delta\omega$ (or, similarly, $\Delta\phi$) value from the average line is the random part. The corrections to be applied in Step 4 above are taken off the values along the average line.

12

Block Triangulation and Adjustment

In order to provide the necessary control for stereophotogrammetric mapping of a large area, one may perform a block triangulation. A block would consist of several parallel strips with adequate side-lap (lateral overlap) between adjacent ones. In some cases (see Chap. 10) it is advantageous to obtain also several transverse (tie) strips. These can be at both ends of the parallel strips and one or more in the middle, all flown across the parallel, filling or principal, strips (see Fig. 12-1).

Block formation and adjustment may be performed in one of the following ways:

1. *Sequential–Strips*

   a. *Independent,* where each strip is formed and adjusted separately and the discrepancies between adjacent strips (as revealed at the common points) are used for the block adjustment. After each strip has been adjusted for systematic and quasi-systematic error propagations, such discrepancies may be considered as purely random in nature and are adjusted as such, numerically (see Sec. 12.1).

   b. *Connected,* where the coordinates of all strips are reduced to the system of one strip (by means of linear or affine transformation of coordinates, based on points common to the adjacent strips). Thereafter, the entire block is adjusted to fit to the given ground coordinates of all control points (graphically, using correction graphs or numerically, using adequate and appropriate polynomials).

2. *Sequential–Models*

   Here the coordinates of all models in the block are reduced to one model (by coordinate transformation—independent-model method). The entire block is next adjusted to fit to the given ground control coordinates, graphically or numerically (see Sec. 12.2).

3. *Simultaneous*

   Here both triangulation and adjustment are performed for all photographs in the block simultaneously by using high-speed computers (see Sec. 9.2).

There are various mechanical-graphical methods of block triangulation and adjustment. These are, however, partial (e.g., for planimetry or elevation) and have been well documented elsewhere. Therefore, they will not

163

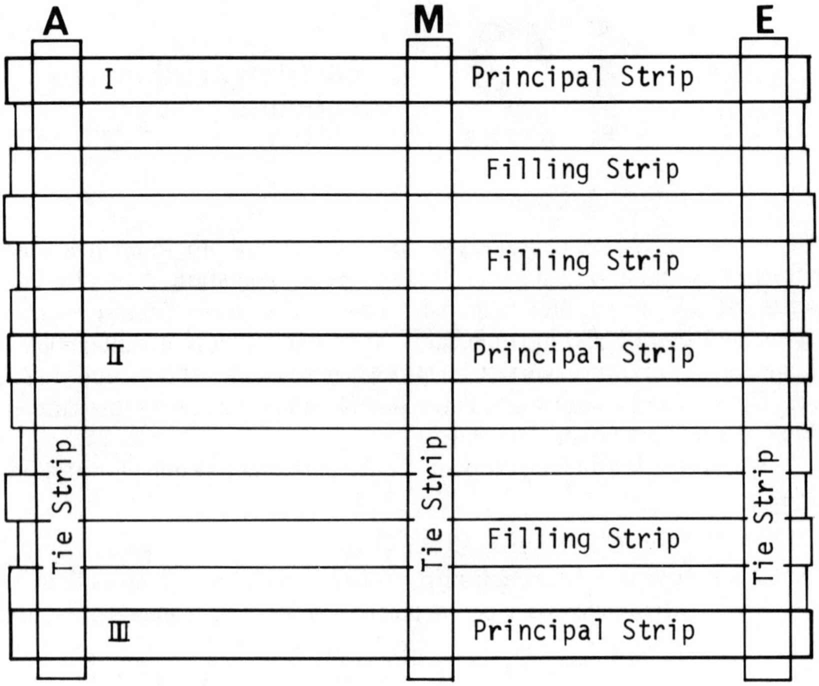

Figure 12-1. Strips in a Block

be discussed here. Reference can be made of the extensive discussions on these in the *Manual of Photogrammetry* [5]. The following fall in this category:

1. Radial (principal point) triangulation
2. Radial triangulation with slotted templets
3. Stereotemplet triangulation
4. Triangulation with ITC-Jerie analog computer, etc.

12.1 Sequential—Strips

Independent

Assuming adequate ground control being available, all of the principal and filling strips are first triangulated by using any suitable method and are adjusted by means of given ground control points as described in the previous sections. Alternately, first a framework of the principal and tie strips (see strips A, M, E, I, II, and III in Fig. 12-1) is triangulated and adjusted. This framework (of strips) provides control for adjusting all the filling strips. A certain number of pass points (transfer, tie, or wing points) in the sidelap between adjacent filling strips are determined in both strips. This yields two sets of values X, Y, and Z for each common point (apparently, these are values obtained after adjustment for systematic and quasi-systematic errors within each strip).

The differences $\Delta X_{r,r+1}$, $\Delta Y_{r,r+1}$ and $\Delta Z_{r,r+1}$ between the corresponding values obtained in strips r and r+1 at any point should not exceed certain tolerance values. The following tolerances have been suggested in the Manual of Photogrammetry [5]:

$$\left. \begin{aligned} T_X &= 3\sqrt{2} \cdot m_X \\ T_Y &= 3\sqrt{2} \cdot m_Y \\ T_Z &= 3\sqrt{2} \cdot m_Z \end{aligned} \right\} \tag{12.1}$$

where m_X, m_Y, and m_Z are the acceptable (from block triangulation) standard errors in X, Y and Z, respectively. If all of the differences are less than m_X, m_Y and m_Z the averages may be considered without further adjustment. If, however, the differences ΔX, ΔY and ΔZ exceed those tolerance values, the filling strips in question should be retriangulated or readjusted (individually). Such large discrepancies could be due to blunders or some inadequacies. In all other cases it is important that these differences are eliminated by an appropriate procedure.

It is important to note that the internal accuracy of a single model is considerably higher than the positional accuracy of the model within the block. The block adjustment therefore, should not disturb the shape of the model (thus causing model-deformation which is not desirable for eventual map compilation). This means that such a block adjustment should yield small corrections (in scale, translations and rotations) for each model, which would minimize differences ΔX, ΔY and ΔZ. This could be done by means of a least-squares adjustment. However, such adjustments would require complicated and tremendously large computations, especially in large blocks where such adjustments would be needed most. This consideration was behind the development of simpler procedures, e.g., one described by Brandenberger [14] in 1951 and Zeller [110] in 1952. Below is given a simple explanation of this procedure.

This method presupposes that all points (see Fig. 12-2) common to the adjacent strips will fall in a neat pattern of rows where X = constant (Note: In practice, small deviations from such an ideal situation is no cause of concern. Furthermore, such a pattern can be easily obtained by having 80 percent forward overlap during photography, so that overlaps can be selected to obtain this pattern. This is strongly recommended in view of other considerations also, viz., fewer required control points, fewer points handled, systematic location of points giving more systematic error propagations, convenience in the use of the stereomodels for map compilation, etc.)

The adjustment is performed for all points falling in one section ($X =$ constant, in block), and with respect to one coordinate at a time. Table 12-1 gives a numerical example of such an adjustment with respect to the X coordinates of points along an $X =$ constant section through the block.

Consider $v_1, v_2, v_3 \ldots v_n$ are the absolute errors in each strip (these are the residual random parts after systematic and quasi-systematic errors have been adjusted within each strip). Then the differences (i.e., discrepancies of the coordinate values between adjacent strips as revealed at the common points), d_i are (see column 3, Table 12-1):

$$\left.\begin{aligned} d_1 &= v_2 - v_1 \\ d_2 &= v_3 - v_2 \\ d_3 &= v_4 - v_3 \\ &\vdots \qquad \vdots \\ d_{n-1} &= v_n - v_{n-1} \end{aligned}\right\} \tag{12.2}$$

Their progressive totals are (see column 4, Table 12-1):

$$\left.\begin{aligned} v_2 &- v_1 \\ v_3 &- v_1 \\ v_4 &- v_1 \\ &\vdots \\ v_n &- v_1 \end{aligned}\right\} \tag{12.3}$$

Sum (T) of these progressive totals is:

$$T = \sum_{i=2}^{n} v_i - (n-1)v_1 \;=\; \sum_{i=1}^{n} v_i - nv_1 \tag{12.4}$$

Because the v's are the random errors,

$$\sum_{i=1}^{n} v_i = 0 \tag{12.5}$$

Therefore, considering Eq. (12.4),

$$T/n = -v_1 \tag{12.6}$$

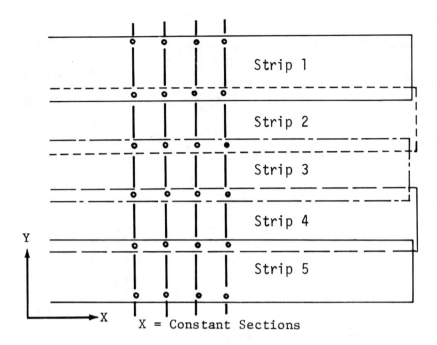

Figure 12-2. Scheme of Common Points in Block

Now, consideration of Eqs. (12.3) and (12.6) gives (see column 5, Table 12-1):

$$
\left.
\begin{aligned}
-v_2 &= -v_1 - (v_2 - v_1) \\
-v_3 &= -v_1 - (v_3 - v_1) \\
-v_4 &= -v_1 - (v_4 - v_1) \\
&\quad \vdots \qquad\qquad \vdots \\
-v_n &= -v_1 - (v_n - v_1)
\end{aligned}
\right\}
\tag{12.7}
$$

The errors (v's) with changed signs are the corrections to be applied for the final adjustment (see column 6, Table 12-1). Figure 12-3 explains the basic principles involved in this adjustment technique.

This adjustment needs to be performed separately for X, Y and Z coordinates for each X = constant section. This method offers a simple procedure based on sound principles and gives good relative accuracy.

The absolute precision of the block can be improved if sufficient ground control points are available such that use of polynomial adjustment (computational) or correction-graphs (graphical) can be made after such adjustments for X = constant sections are completed.

Table 12-1
Example of Block Compensation for One X = Constant Section

Section No.					Coordinates Adjustment
Strips	X, Y, Z Coordinates after each Strip is Adjusted	Differences d_i	Progressive total $\sum_1^i d_i$	$v's =$ $-v_i - \sum_1^i d_i$	Compensated Value in Block (columns 2 + 5)
(1)	(2)	(3)	(4)	(5)	(6)
1	95.32		0.00		95.39
	xx xx			+0.07	yy yy
	94.87				94.94
2	94.94	+0.07	+0.07		94.94
	xx xx			0.00	yy yy
	95.06				95.06
3	95.24	+0.18	+0.25		95.06
	xx xx			−0.18	yy yy
	94.71				94.53
4	94.64	−0.07	+0.18		94.53
	xx xx			−0.11	yy yy
	95.02				94.91
5	95.04	+0.02	+0.28		94.91
	96.00			−0.13	95.87
	95.46				95.33
6	95.30	−0.16	+0.04		95.33
	xx xx			+0.03	yy yy
	95.15				95.18
7	95.08	−0.07	−0.03		95.18
	xx xx			+0.10	yy yy
	94.98				95.08
8	95.01	+0.03	0.00		95.08
	xx xx			+0.07	yy yy
	95.14				95.21
9	95.06	−0.08	−0.08		95.21
				+0.15	
	95.12				95.27

$$\frac{Sum}{n} = \frac{T}{n} = -v_1$$

$$\frac{0.63}{9} = +0.07$$

For determining the differences (d_i) in case the series of points do not fall on sections X = constant, a method has been suggested by Branden-berger [14], which assumes that the differences ΔX, ΔY, ΔZ are known for the regular transfer pass points common to two adjacent strips. Because of

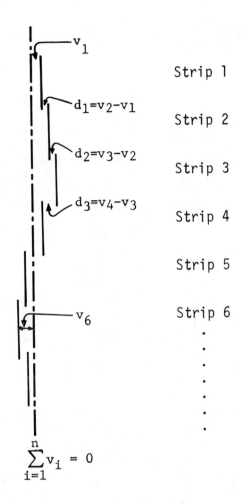

Strip 1

Strip 2

Strip 3

Strip 4

Strip 5

Strip 6

$$\sum_{i=1}^{n} v_i = 0$$

Figure 12-3. Representation of Discrepancies

the different X values of these transfer points, the differences ΔX, ΔY and ΔZ are, therefore, not related to a X = constant section. The procedure is that these differences are plotted graphically as a function of X and the points connected by a curve. From these profiles one can then obtain for the X values of the individual points the corresponding new differences ΔX, ΔY, and ΔZ which are now related to a X = constant straight line. The block compensation is then accomplished with these latter differences.

When these corrections (v's) have been determined for the series of points, the individual v's (for X, Y or Z coordinate) are plotted graphically as a function of X for each longitudinal strip (see Fig. 12-4). The points thus obtained are connected by a continuous curve. The final correction to any point in a certain longitudinal strip can then be derived directly for the particular X from the corresponding curves.

Connected

This approach to block triangulation and adjustment consists of tying together the unadjusted strips by means of sidelap pass-points (instead of operating with the discrepancies between the adjacent, adjusted, filling strips as has been discussed in the previous section). This gives a distorted error surface, which can then be corrected by means of a conformal or nonconformal block adjustment. Thereby, the discrepancies at the given ground control points are minimized. Mahoney [64] developed a system which allows for insertion of scale and azimuth conditions.

An operational procedure was discussed by McKenzie and Eller [67], in which the individual "models are joined analytically to form strips of pass-points and then cross-strips are constructed by successive joining of two-model sections from adjoining strips. The cross-strips may, if desired, be skewed across the regular strips so as to include the maximum number of ground control points." Such pseudo-strips (cross-strips) are fitted to the ground control (see Fig. 12-5) in a linear transformation in which the internal shape of the model terrain is held rigid but translated, rotated and scaled (i.e., corrections in terms of dX_0, dY_0, dZ_0, $d\Omega$, $d\Phi$, dK and dS are considered). This preliminary fit to the ground control serves two purposes: (a) it effects a transformation from the instrumental strip coordinates to the ground coordinate system with a minimum loss of accuracy and (b) it provides a check on blunders at control points that must be rejected.

Next, these pseudo-strips are again fitted to the ground control with a second degree transformation. This provides bending and nonlinear scale corrections in order to fit the control. A block is then formed by a second-degree transformation of the regular strips to the pass-points of the pseudo-strips and then the block is translated and rotated and the scale corrected with a linear transformation so as to fit the ground control in a least-squares solution. Discrepancies between tie points of adjoining strips are averaged.

12.2 Sequential—Models

This method is simply an extension of the principles given in Chap. 8 (see also Ghosh [32]). The essential idea is to perform, first, a satisfactory relative orientation of each of the stereomodels. This may be performed either by computational (analytical) means or by instrumental (analogical)

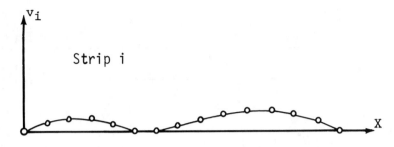

Figure 12-4. Sample Graph of Corrections For a Longitudinal Strip

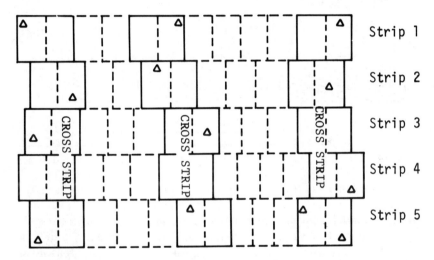

Figure 12-5. Pseudo-strips (solid line) Formed From Sections of Regular
Strips

means such that the model yields three-dimensional coordinates of all the required model points and the two perspective centers (lens points). The absolute orientation of the first model and the successive connections (i.e., scale transfer and coorientation) of other models are then performed numerically. This gives the complete block coordinates in a numerically created block of connected stereo-models (see Fig. 12-6). Finally, the block is adjusted numerically (using polynomials), empirically (using templets), or graphically (using error graphs).

The significant feature of this technique is the computational connection of the stereomodels, which are the essential units in a kind of three-dimensional mosaicking. The connecting of the models is performed by analytical (numerical) transformations by using the common points, inclusive of the projection centers (camera stations) or otherwise.

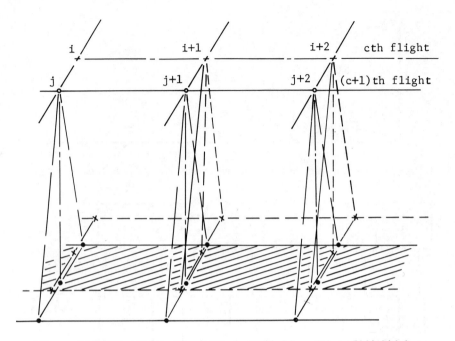

Figure 12-6. The Basic Block Mode With More Than 50% Sidelap

The coordinates of the camera station common to the adjacent models (in a strip) are required to give sufficient geometric strength to the connection of the models. On the other hand, the connections of adjacent strips can be stronger if these points (camera stations) are mutually available. This, however, is not the normal case. Because of economical reasons, in view of minimizing the number of models (and thus time and cost) about 20 to 25 percent side-lap between adjacent strips is resorted in practice generally.

The computer program (see App. C) developed in the Department of Geodetic Science at Ohio State University is meant to work in any situation. The rigidity and the strength of the connection will depend on the number, locations and quality of the points used for such connections. The absolute minimum number required is three noncollinear points. With more points, a least squares fit is possible and generally desirable.

The mathematical basis is Eq. (8.1) (see Chap. 8), which represents a conformal transformation of an arbitrarily defined system of model coordinates (X, Y, Z) into a system of ground coordinates (X^g, Y^g, Z^g), by means of the general three-dimensional rotation matrix (M), a scale factor (k) and a translation of the centroid of the control points in the model system to that of the ground system.

Normally the seven parameters pertaining to the transformation are not given and must be computed by solving Eq. (8.1). This solution is not usually unique, but rather of the minimum variance type as more than seven linear observation equations are usually available for the solution of the unknown parameters. In this work, the solution of the seven parameters, is done with Eq. (8.1) forming the mathematical model.

Method of Solution

It is assumed that the given set of data contains at least three noncollinear points whose X^g, Y^g, Z^g and X, Y, Z coordinates are known. It should be recognized that the special case of $X_i^g = X_i$, $Y_i^g = Y_i$ and $Z_i^g = Z_i$ is admissible, as are other cases where not all Z_i's are known for every X_i and Y_i. Equation (8.1) can be symbolically written in the following manner:

$$L_a = F(X_a) \qquad (12.8)$$

where L_a are the adjusted values of the observations

and X_a are the adjusted values of the parameters.

The above relationship is based on the fact that the observed quantities (X, Y, Z) are only functions of the unknown parameters under the assumption that the ground coordinates (X^g, Y^g, Z^g) are known without error. Solutions of systems of equations of the above type are easily accomplished by the well known method of parameters.

A brief summary of this method, following the notation of Uotila [102] follows:

Consider the following symbols

X_0: approximate values of unknown parameters

X_a: adjusted values of unknown parameters

$\Delta = X_a - X_0$: the corrections to the approximate values

L_b: observed quantities (X, Y, Z)

L_a: adjusted values of observed quantities

L_o: numerical values of observed quantities computed through mathematical model by use of approximate parameter values

$V = L_a - L_b$: the residuals on observed quantities; and

$L = L_o - L_b$: the discrepancies on observed quantities.

Then Eq. (12.8) can be expressed as

$$L_b + V = F(X_a) \qquad (12.9)$$

$$= F(X_0 + \Delta) \qquad (12.9a)$$

Because Eq. (12.9) and (12.9a) are nonlinear in the unknown parameters it is necessary to apply the Taylor series expansion:

$$[F(X) = \sum_0^\infty \frac{f^n(a)}{n!} (X - a)^n$$

for a function $f(X)$ analytic in the region $\{-R < (X - a) < R\}$ and where

$$\lim_{n \to \infty} R_{n+1}(X) \to 0].$$

This application yields, for a first order expansion:

$$\mathbf{L_b} + \mathbf{V} = F(X_o) + \mathbf{A\Delta} \tag{12.10}$$

where $\mathbf{A}$ is a partial derivative matrix defined as

$$A = \frac{\partial L}{\partial X}$$

Equation (12.10), by virtue of the relationships,

$$\mathbf{L_o} = F(X_o) \quad \text{and} \quad \mathbf{L} = \mathbf{L_o} - \mathbf{L_b}$$

can now be rewritten as

$$\mathbf{V} = \mathbf{A\Delta} + \mathbf{L} \tag{12.11}$$

Equation (12.11) represents the usual observation equation set which is subjected to the principle of minimim variance. This principle is expressed by the following mathematical definition

$$\mathbf{V'PV} = \text{minimum} \tag{12.12}$$

where $\mathbf{P}$ is a weight matrix assumed to be a unit matrix in this application.

Hence,

$$\mathbf{V'PV} = (\mathbf{A\Delta} + \mathbf{L})' \mathbf{I} (\mathbf{A\Delta} + \mathbf{L})$$

$$= \mathbf{\Delta'A'IA\Delta} + 2\mathbf{\Delta'A'IL} + \mathbf{L'IL}$$

that is

$$\mathbf{V'PV} = \mathbf{\Delta'A'A\Delta} + 2\mathbf{\Delta'A'L} + \mathbf{L'L} \tag{12.13}$$

From this it can be seen that $\mathbf{V'PV}$ is a positive definite mathematical quantity. The minimum of such quantities are obtained by differentiation with respect to the variables ($\mathbf{\Delta}$), equating the result to zero and the subsequent solution for those values of the variables which satisfy this condition.

That is

$$\frac{\partial \mathbf{V}'\mathbf{PV}}{\partial \mathbf{\Delta}'} = 2\mathbf{\Delta}'\mathbf{A}'\mathbf{A} + 2\mathbf{L}'\mathbf{A}$$

equating to zero yields

$$\mathbf{\Delta}'\mathbf{A}'\mathbf{A} + \mathbf{L}'\mathbf{A} = 0$$

which can be, alternatively, written as

$$\mathbf{A}'\mathbf{A}\mathbf{\Delta} = -\mathbf{A}'\mathbf{L}$$

and thus

$$\mathbf{\Delta} = -(\mathbf{A}'\mathbf{A})^{-1}\mathbf{A}'\mathbf{L} \qquad (12.14)$$

The correction vector $\mathbf{\Delta}$ given by Eq. (12.14) will only be the final answer in those cases where the given mathematical model is linear (not so in this case) or when the accepted approximations are very close to their minimum variance values. This latter case is normally reached after three iterations of the procedure.

In this program, the above mathematical steps are applied to Eq. (8.1). These steps will be discussed at length with particular reference as to how the presented program accomplishes each step.

The Approximate Values (also see Chap. 8). The approximate scale is simply estimated by comparing the planimetric distance between two points in the model space with their corresponding terrain distance:

$$k = \{[(X_1-X_2)^2 + (Y_1-Y_2)^2] / [(X_1^g-X_2^g)^2 + (Y_1^g-Y_2^g)^2]\}^{1/2}. \qquad (12.15)$$

The common kappa, could be readily assumed to be $0°$. However, it is easily estimated as follows. The angle between a coordinate system X axis and a line joining two arbitrary points is given by:

$$\alpha = \arctan \frac{Y_1 - Y_2}{X_1 - X_2} \qquad (12.16)$$

Equation (12.16) holds both for the model and the terrain spaces. Hence the difference in these two angles represents the amount of common kappa, (K).

Thus

$$K = \arctan \frac{Y_1 - Y_2}{X_1 - X_2} - \arctan \frac{Y_1^g - Y_2^g}{X_1^g - X_2^g} \qquad (12.17)$$

Finally, the approximate values of the translations are obtained by taking the difference between the rotated and subsequently scaled terrain coordinates and the corresponding model coordinates:

$$X_0 = X - \lambda(X^g \cos K + Y^g \sin K)$$
$$Y_0 = Y - \lambda(X^g \sin K + Y^g \cos K) \left.\right\} \quad (12.18)$$
$$Z_0 = Z - \lambda(Z^g)$$

The Partial Derivative Matrix (A) and the L Matrix. The partial derivatives of Eq. (8.1) evaluated at the approximate values are formed in the appropriately named section of the program. A careful examination of the general rotation matrix (**M**) shows that it is only necessary to form the partials of the nine elements with respect to Φ, as the remaining 18 terms can be formed from the original rotation matrix **M**.

This can be further explained as follows (also see Chap. 8):

$$\mathbf{M} = \begin{bmatrix} a_{11} & a_{12} & a_{13} \\ a_{21} & a_{22} & a_{13} \\ a_{31} & a_{32} & a_{33} \end{bmatrix} =$$

$$\begin{bmatrix} \cos\Phi\cos K & \cos\Omega\sin K + \sin\Omega\sin\Phi\cos K & \sin\Omega\sin K - \cos\Omega\sin\Phi\cos K \\ -\cos\Phi\sin K & \cos\Omega\cos K - \sin\Omega\sin\Phi\sin K & \sin\Omega\cos K + \cos\Omega\sin\Phi\sin K \\ \sin\Phi & -\sin\Omega\cos\Phi & \cos\Omega\cos\Phi \end{bmatrix}$$

$$(12.19)$$

then

$$\frac{\delta a_{11}}{\delta K} = -\cos\Phi\sin K = a_{21}$$
$$\frac{\delta a_{12}}{\delta \Omega} = -\sin\Omega\sin K + \cos\Omega\sin\Phi\cos K = -a_{13} \left.\right\} \quad (12.20)$$
$$\frac{\delta a_{12}}{\delta K} = \cos\Omega\cos K - \sin\Omega\sin\Phi\sin K = a_{22}$$

etc.

This saves considerable storage and time.

The program now assembles the matrix OBS(I,J), whose dimensions are $(2n+m, 8)$, where n is the number of horizontal points and m is the number of vertical points. The submatrix OBS($2n+m$, $i_{1 \text{ to } 7}$) represents the above defined **A** matrix, while OBS($2n+m$, 8), a column matrix, represents the **L** matrix. The mode of formation of this matrix is quite evident if Eq.

(8.1) is written in the normal linear form and the partials computed according to the previously developed ideas.

Solution steps now closely follow the mathematical outline. However it is appropriate to mention the mechanism by which the solution terminates itself. After some initial experimentation the system used by Tewinkel [97] is adopted as the test that 'convergence' has been reached. This system says that changes in Ω, Φ, or K must be less than 1×10^{-5} rad. Present tests indicate that this is quite satisfactory in guaranteeing convergence for this purpose, as the magnitudes on the dimensioned translations necessary for convergence are dependent on the scale of the work in hand. This restriction does not apply to the undimensioned angular measure.

The Computer Program

A detailed setup of the program is included in the App. C together with a Fortran IV statement listing. Numerous comments cards are included to facilitate easy understanding.

The program has two principal operating modes:

1. Regularized strip triangulation
2. Block triangulation

Mode (1), *regularized strip triangulation,* joins successive models together on the assumption that the number of indicated pass points in the ith model corresponds to the number of such points in the (i+1)th model. Between each model a control card indicating the model number (MDLN), number of horizontal control points (NHC), number of vertical control points (NVC), number of arbitrary points (NARB), and number of pass points (NPASS) must be placed.

To select this mode the heading "STRIP bbbbl" must be punched on the first data card, starting with column 1.

Mode (2), *block triangulation,* has three operating modes selected by the value of the variable ICOUNT indicated on the first card. A value of zero indicates that two strips will be formed prior to entering the block mode, a value of one indicates one strip will be formed, and a value of two indicates that only the block mode will be used. Thus the first datacard is to read "BLOK bbbbbX" for this mode.

In the block mode models are separated by a card listing only the model no. and the number of observed points. The present program does not check if a solution is mathematically feasible.

The advantages of this mode of operation are as follows:

1. The triangulation can proceed to the left or right of the initially absolutely oriented model; thus reducing the "mathematical" length of the

strip (in considering the propagation of errors and in applying the conventional adjustment procedures).

2. Triangulation of blocks of photographs can be undertaken in a logical way by the use of selected patterns in a geometrically strong manner. The most powerful connection mode is the one using the L-mode of connection.

3. Consider a strip of models, warped and distorted in either model or ground space, with each model connection point recorded three times (strip 1 in Fig. 12-7). A second strip is now joined to the first strip so that it is perpendicular to the former. It is likewise, but independently, warped in space and each model connection point is recorded three times (strip 2 in Fig. 12-7). Subsequent strips are now connected to this basic frame, by continuing the L-mode, until the block has been formed. The use of thrice recorded control points along the tying edge forces the new strip to conform closely to the established distortion mode of the old strip which in turn maintains some regularity in the block, which can now be subjected to the adjustment procedure.

4. This L-mode can be used to section large blocks into quarters by using a middle model as the starting model. It must be recognized that it is not essential that this middle model be absolutely oriented (although it remains desirable) as adjustment procedures are able to cope with this problem.

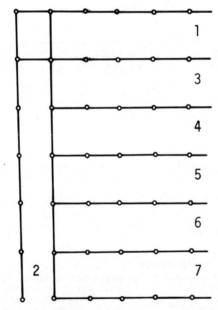

Figure 12-7a. L-mode of Block Formation Suggested When Sidelap Less Than 50%

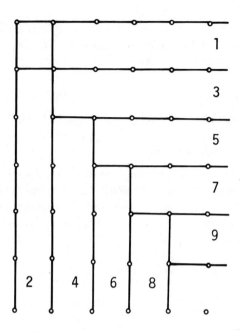

Figure 12-7b. L-mode of Block Formation Suggested When Sidelap More Than 50%

Program Limitations. The program presented is a double precision Fortran IV program written for an IBM 360/75. Translation to any other system should not be laborious.

For the IBM 360/75 the basic program consumes almost 252K bytes (1 byte = 8 bits) of storage. This allows more than 100 points per model to be read. However 99 points is the recommended limit of operation in strip modes and 25 in the block mode since in the block mode tie points are subsequently listed in a multiple manner. Execution time is approximately 4 sec per model, for models containing 20 points. In the block mode of operation it is necessary to store, in core, the tie points. This places the upper limit on the size of block that can be triangulated. Using 504K bytes of storage, available for D size jobs, the arrays STNO, XX, YY, and ZZ can be dimensioned to 10,000. Noting that pass points and tie points are multiple listed, this size will permit the block whose "L" dimensions are 10 × 10 models. It is to be noted that a block can be split into quarters and each sub-block is treated as a unit. This gives a block size of a total of 40 × 40 models in which 25 points have been observed as the upper limit on the size of the triangulated block.

The above sizes are, however, not the only combinations that are possible. Other sizes can be computed from the following rules which apply only to the block mode of operations:

1. A pass point is listed four times.
2. A tie point is listed four times.
3. A pass point also used as a tie point is listed 16 times.
4. A corner point which serves as a pass point for two strips and also ties the strips together is listed 64 times.

Should these multiple listings become over burdensome or too restrictive, program modifications can be made in the following manner: In the "output section of model under consideration" statements numbered 14 to 19 inclusive of horizontal section, and 12 to17 inclusive of vertical section are to be omitted. However, this elimination should be accomplished by carefully reexamining the connection mode and its ability to maintain the distortion of the initial "L" without the addition of further irregular distortion.

In the block mode of operation the program is unable to distinguish between arbitrary points and pass or tie points if these points happen to fall in the common areas. Thus all points lying in the common areas must be treated with the same precision, at the instrument, as pass or tie points. Such is not the case in the strip mode as these points could be defined to be "arbitrary" and hence not influence the model connection process.

Data Input. The first card of all data decks is one which tells the program to select the mode, i.e., either the strip or the block mode. There are two options in the latter, (a) strip formation of part of the block or (b) total block mode of formation. It is possible with this program to switch from one mode to the other but it is not advised due to the fact that no separation of jobs occurs on the disc unit and hence some sorting errors may result from this by the operator when separating the card output deck.

The formation of the input deck is described diagrammatically by Appendix Figs. C-1, C-2, and C-3. The principal features of this technique are the following:

1. Any model having adequate ground control can be the starting one while coorientation and model connections may proceed in any direction, thus giving an enormous flexibility in the program.
2. The program considers repeat observations at each of the points and more than adequate number of control, pass, and tie points can be handled by applying the principles of Least Squares.
3. The technique is not dependent on any particular type of instrument or method for generating data. The program is equally applied to the data

obtained from computationally oriented models with comparator measurements as those from analogically oriented models at a stereoplotting instrument.

4. The program builds up the block, the adjustment of which can be performed by any method separately—the method depending on the requirements and the facilities at the disposal of the user, and can be numerical, mechanical, or graphical.

5. The technique and the mathematical formulation are very simple and can be easily adapted to any computer—thus has promise and is expected to be of considerable help to those small mapping agencies that are concerned with the problems of control extension but can not afford the luxuries of very high speed computers with large cores and costly comparators.

6. This program may be applicable to any type of extension of block, e.g., spatial triangulation around the moon with lunar orbiter photos, etc.

Furthermore, the quality of model connections & coorientations can be improved by considering affine transformation (see Chap. 8), i.e., an improvement on the mathematics. The quality of block formation and accuracy of adjustment can be improved with (a) increased side-lap between strips, (b) use of auxiliary information (see Chap. 11), and (c) arrangement of pass points in an ideal rectangular pattern which is possible with 80 percent forward overlap during the flight.

Further improvement is possible with marked points particularly if the measuring mark is slightly smaller than the point marked and stereoinstruments (rather than monocomparators) are used for data generation.

13

Accuracy and Economic Considerations

In all photogrammetric applications the relationship between obtainable accuracy and corresponding cost is of paramount importance. If the amount of ground control can be reduced while still maintaining a high degree of accuracy, substantial savings in cost can be made. Therefore, for aerotriangulation, the number of control points should be determined so as to yield accuracy commensurate with the application requirements.

Soliman [92] showed that a relationship exists between cost and accuracy so that "decreasing returns (accuracy) accrue with respect to increasing expenditure (control models), and therefore creating a situation of diminishing marginal substitutability . . . as one moves down the mean square error of position curve" (see Fig. 13-1, indicative of the relationships, drawn after Soliman). An optimal balance between cost and accuracy exists, depending on the cost function used.

With respect to the working procedures of any organization, similar relationships between cost and accuracy over certain ranges can be established and will become a useful tool to enhance decision-making capabilities where cost data are not readily available.

13.1 Efficiency

The ultimate goal in any job is efficiency. The determination of efficiency in phototriangulation is complex because of numerous operations and various possibilities. Basically, there are three factors which determine the efficiency of any engineering procedure such as phototriangulation:

1. Attainable accuracy (A)
2. Economy (E)
3. Required time (T)

To a great extent, these factors are interrelated and may some times contradict each other. Therefore, a compromise between them, in order to fulfill the specific requirements, is always necessary. It is important to understand their relative significance, which depends on the mapping organization and the relevant circumstances. For example, accuracy (A) is generally considered more important in research works within a scientific organization, whereas economy (E) is considered as the prime factor in a commercial agency. In a military agency during a period of war, the factor

183

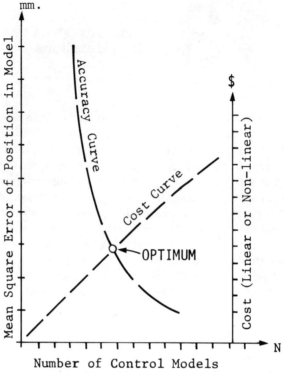

Note: One may question such intersection of two curves with different dimensions in order to obtain the optimum. The scales of such representation for any use in practice, therefore, must be empirically determined.

Figure 13-1. Accuracy—Cost Relationship

time (T) may be of utmost importance. Thus, it may be stated that the degree of efficiency (D) is a function of A, E, and T, i.e.

$$D = f(A,E,T) \tag{13.1}$$

This function is unknown, generally speaking. However, in specific cases, it can be obtained empirically from previous experiences. The function would also change for specific organizations, depending on the time, place and circumstances. There are certain limitations in each factor also. Sometimes, such limitations may be easily specified (e.g., required accuracy or time tolerances), while at other times they can not be. Generally, the limitations in A are specified, predetermined and fairly constant for specific jobs. Limitations in E are fairly narrow particularly for privately owned commercial organizations, in jobs obtained through competitive biddings. Limitations in T are usually very wide. In government agencies (civil or military at peace time) the factor T quite often is less important.

A comprehensive research efforts in this respect initiated by Brandenberger [17] at the Ohio State University has shown that, on an average, the efficiency in phototriangulation can be expressed by the following empirically obtained formula:

$$D = \frac{A^2E}{T} \tag{13.2}$$

where accuracy (A) is considered to be the inverse of standard error (univariate)

economy (E) is considered to be the inverse of cost,

time (T) is considered directly.

Further, E and T are to be considered in terms of some standard unit (e.g., per model).

Equation (13.2) may be used in comparing the effective efficiencies of different phototriangulation procedures. However, the relative benefits of reduced cost, time saved and accuracies obtained can not be always treated by mathematical relationships. None the less, consideration of these factors would assist the photogrammetrist towards a rational method of selecting his triangulation procedure.

Accuracy

Experience has shown that, in general, with standard photography (i.e., wide-angle camera, 60 percent overlap and 20-30 percent sidelap), medium-size blocks (about 40-50 photo, square block) and a first order type stereoinstrument (plotter or comparator), the standard residual error in meters is expected to be of the order of 10^{-5} of the scale factor of the photography. Theoretically, any desired small value of standard error can be obtained by lowering the flight altitude (although it increases the number of photos and therefore needs more time and cost).

In strip triangulation, the attainable accuracy is directly dependent on the flying height and the number of models or photos in the strip. Brandenberger [15] found that the standard residual errors in planimetry (m_p) and in elevation (m_z) for standard photography in strip (aeropolygon) triangulation with a standard distribution of given ground control may be expressed (for strips of medium length, i.e., $5 < N < 25$) by:

$$\left. \begin{aligned} m_p &= h\sqrt{N} \cdot a \\ m_z &= h\sqrt{N} \cdot b \end{aligned} \right\} \tag{13.3}$$

where   h is the flying height in km.

N is the total number of models in the strip

a and b are certain empirical constants, their values depending on various factors.

Further,

$$m_p = \sqrt{m_X^2 + m_Y^2} \\[2mm] m_s = \sqrt{m_X^2 + m_Y^2 + m_Z^2} \qquad\qquad (13.4)$$

and accuracy,

$$A = \frac{1}{m_s}. \qquad (13.5)$$

The application of Eq. (13.3) permits us to establish families of graphs (see Figs. 13-2a and 13-2b, drawn after Brandenberger [15]), from which the attainable accuracy for an adjusted strip triangulation, with a certain number of models and a certain flying height, can be read off. Alternately, such graphs can be used to determine the number of models or the flying height for such triangulations for which a specific accuracy is demanded.

What happens within a strip at different locations also often needs a careful consideration. A distinction can be made between a cantilever extension and a bridging. In cantilever extensions, only the first model is assumed to be completely oriented with the aid of control points. In order to obtain an idea on the accuracy at the end of such a strip, one can use the following general equations (after Soliman [91]):

$$\begin{bmatrix} m_X^2 \\[4mm] m_Y^2 \\[4mm] m_Z^2 \end{bmatrix} = \frac{m_0^2 Z^2}{f^2} \begin{bmatrix} A_1 & B_1 & C_1 & D_1 & E_1 \\[4mm] A_1 & B_2 & C_2 + C_2\dfrac{Z^4}{b^4} & D_2 & E_2 \\[4mm] A_3\dfrac{Z^2}{b^2} & B_3\dfrac{Z^2}{b^2} & C_3\dfrac{Z^2}{b^2} & D_3\dfrac{Z^2}{b^2} & E_3\dfrac{Z^2}{b^2} \end{bmatrix} \begin{bmatrix} 1 \\ N \\ N^2 \\ N^3 \\ N^4 \end{bmatrix}$$

$$(13.6)$$

where m_X m_Y m_Z are the standard errors in X, Y and Z, respectively

m_0 is the standard error of Y-parallax measurements of the model points

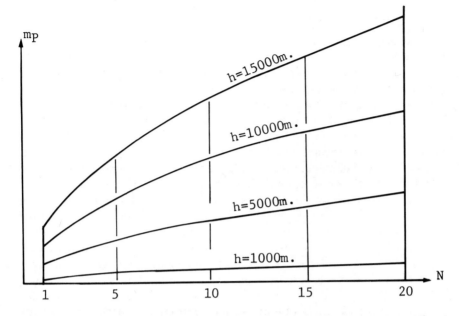

Figure 13-2a. Graphs for Standard Residual Planimetric Errors After Strip Adjustment

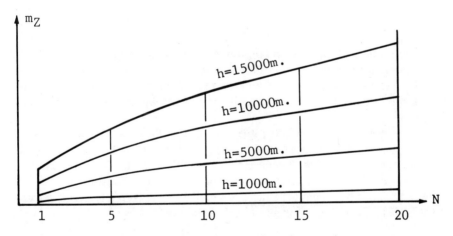

Figure 13-2b. Graphs for Standard Residual Elevation Errors After Strip Adjustment

Z is the projection distance (corresponding to the flying height)

f is the focal length of the camera used

N is the number of the triangulated models

b is the average base length

and A to E are constants.

In such a case, the propagation of the standard errors in the coordinates has a pattern as indicated in Fig. 13-3.

In bridging, the control points are assumed to be available in the first and the last models of the bridged distance. Therefore, the discrepancies between the given (ground) coordinates and the triangulated (model) coordinates at the beginning and the end of the bridging distance are known and, as such, after adjustment, the residual errors at both ends of the bridged distance will be equal to zero. This gives a pattern of propagation of the standard errors of coordinates as is indicated in Fig. 13-4. According to the theory of errors, the value of the standard error of the coordinate at the middle of the bridged distance will be equal to the corresponding value in the case of cantilever extension (M) divided by $\sqrt{2}$; this, assuming that the standard error of the coordinates at the middle of the bridged distance is computed from each end with the same degree of precision. See also Karara [48], Hallert [41], and Soliman [91] in this respect. Soliman also found that the variances of the adjusted coordinates in aerial mapping are directly proportional to N, N^2, N^3 and N^4.

Economy

Economy indications may be obtained from the average cost per model. This should include considerations of the price of instruments (include amortization), salaries of personnel, rental of computers, cost of programming (assuming that the program is already debugged and is in working order).

In a recent paper, Lafferty [60] indicates that the cost of photogrammetric cadastral projects is related to (a) the terrain characteristics, (b) the project area and, (c) the accuracies as specified by the survey engineer. This is equally true for phototriangulation. Some relationship can always be established between these factors which allow reasonably accurate cost estimates as necessary for an effective planning.

Time

In calculating the time factor, one should include the time spent on every operation and this may be expressed in terms of the considered unit (preferably per model).

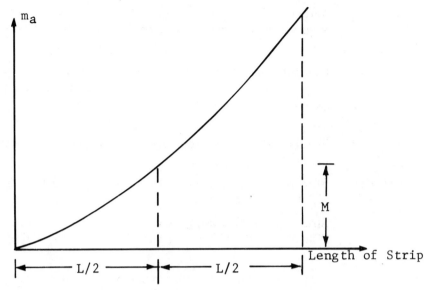

Note: m_a represents m_X, m_Y or m_Z with different scales.

Figure 13-3. Pattern of Propagation of the Standard Error In the Coordinates of Cantilever Extension of a Strip

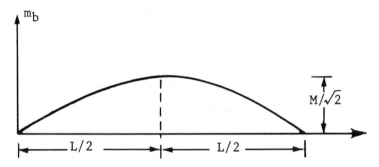

Note: m_b represents m_X, m_Y or m_Z with different scales.

Figure 13-4. Pattern of Propagation of the Standard Error in the Coordinates of Bridging of a Strip.

13.2 Comparative Efficiency

With a view to studying comparative efficiency, six typical phototriangulation systems were studied with actual data obtained from various organizations. Brandenberger [17] is credited for initiating this study:

System Ia: Aeropolygon instrumental strip triangualation with first-order stereoinstruments (e.g., Wild A7, Zeiss C8, Poivilliers B, etc.).

System Ib: Computational (analytical) strip triangulation, both sequential and simultaneous, with stereocomparator (e.g., Zeiss PSK, Wild STK1, etc.) data.

System Ic: Strip triangulation with analytical plotters (e.g., Nistri-Bendix AP-C), both aeropolygon and independent-model methods.

System IIa: Strip triangulation using second-order stereoplotters of Kelsh type (transferring elements of orientation, etc.).

System IIb: Strip triangulation using second-order stereoplotters of Wild A8 type (also by transferring elements of orientation, etc.).

System IIc: Strip triangulation by independent-model method using second-order stereoplotters of Wild A8 type (plus high-speed electronic computer).

Accuracy

The standard errors in these systems, in terms of Eq. (13.3) are as follows:

System	m_P	m_Z	
Ia	$h \cdot \sqrt{N} \cdot 0.10$	$h \cdot \sqrt{N} \cdot 0.06$	
Ib	$h \cdot \sqrt{N} \cdot 0.095$	$h \cdot \sqrt{N} \cdot 0.05$	
Ic	$h \cdot \sqrt{N} \cdot 0.095$	$h \cdot \sqrt{N} \cdot 0.05$	(13.7)
IIa	$h \cdot \sqrt{N} \cdot 0.25$	$h \cdot \sqrt{N} \cdot 0.12$	
IIb	$h \cdot \sqrt{N} \cdot 0.20$	$h \cdot \sqrt{N} \cdot 0.10$	
IIc	$h \cdot \sqrt{N} \cdot 0.105$	$h \cdot \sqrt{N} \cdot 0.08$	

From these, in terms of accuracy (A), the six systems may be compared (considering System Ia as unit):

$$\text{Ia} : \text{Ib} : \text{Ic} : \text{IIa} : \text{IIb} : \text{IIc} = 1 : 1.1 : 1.1 : 0.44 : 0.55 : 0.8 \qquad (13.8)$$

Economy

In the following data on the six systems, consideration of expenses on

(a) aerial photography, (b) field control, and (c) signalization were separated for the sake of fair comparison. The comparative cost rates are:

System	Cost Rates
Ia	X dollars per model
Ib	1.2 · X dollars per model
Ic	1.1 · X dollars per model
IIa	0.7 · X dollars per model
IIb	0.7 · X dollars per model
IIc	0.75 · X dollars per model

$$(13.9)$$

From these, in terms of economy (E), the six systems may be compared (considering Ia as unit):

$$Ia : Ib : Ic : IIa : IIb : IIc = 1 : 0.8 : 0.9 : 1.4 : 1.4 : 1.33 \qquad (13.10)$$

Time

For the comparative study of the six systems, the time spent in the field was not considered. The comparative times are:

System	Times
Ia	Y hours per model
Ib	0.95 · Y hours per model
Ic	0.85 · Y hours per model
IIa	1.20 · Y hours per model
IIb	1.10 · Y hours per model
IIc	0.90 · Y hours per model

$$(13.11)$$

From these, the time (T) of the six systems may be compared:

$$Ia : Ib : Ic : IIa : IIb : IIc = 1 : 0.95 : 0.85 : 1.2 : 1.1 : 0.9 \qquad (13.12)$$

Now, considering Eq. (13.2) and data from Eqs. (13.7), (13.9), and (13.11), one can obtain the comparative degree of efficiency (D) for the six systems studied:

$$\mathbf{Ia : Ib : Ic : IIa : IIb : IIc = 1 : 1.02 : 1.28 : 0.23 : 0.42 : 0.95} \qquad (13.13)$$

One may draw the following conclusions from the above:
The use of the analytical plotters seems to be the most efficient under the present state of the art, whereas the efficiency of phototriangulation with the Kelsh plotter-type instrument (used in the graphical-analogical way) appears to be very low and this should be discouraged. The use of a

second-order-type stereoplotter doubles itself in efficiency if the independent-model method (semianalytical) is utilized. Likewise, the use of a first-order-type instrument by the independent-model method offers excellent possibilities. Note: For efficiency studies, the malfunctioning of the instrument has to be considered also.

13.3 Accuracy Improvements

It has been demonstrated through various researches that the overall accuracy of phototriangulation can be improved with the following considerations:

1. *Sidelap* between strips: In a study comparing sidelap of 20 percent against 60 percent [36] it was observed that the block adjustment is greatly improved when larger sidelap is used. Block triangulation with 60 percent sidelap photography requires less ground control than with the standard procedure using 20 percent sidelap. Alternately, with an equal amount of control, the adjustment is more refined in the case of larger sidelap. Although the planimetric accuracy does not deteriorate seriously with the use of 20-30 percent sidelap instead of 60 percent, the error in elevations increases to the point where the height determinations have little value for topographical mapping. This necessitates the additional elevation control points midway between the flight lines or in the middle of the block. The added side lap offers also a geometric rigor which improves the reliability of the results because of redundant observations (albeit requiring more time and cost).

2. *Auxiliary information (data)*, specifically, horizon photography control. The horizon data were found to have certain advantages over the additional ground control with respect to time, effort and accuracy. The study [36] indicates that with horizon data one would not require additional control in the center of the block. It also provides a powerful alternative for controlling the unavoidable error propagation in block triangulation.

3. *Perimeter control:* Tewinkel [98] reported that aerotriangulation has a remarkably low error propagation if all the photographs of a block having perimeter control are adjusted simultaneously. The error in the center of a block may actually be smaller than at locations on the perimeter between control points. Earlier research reported by Ghosh *et. al* [36] also supports this view.

   The optimum distance between the perimeter control points has not yet been definitely determined but, according to Tewinkel [96], "a separation of three air-bases has proved to be adequate with an occasional separation of four or five air-bases being permissible.''

4. *Arrangements of points* in an almost rectangular pattern whereby points common to adjacent models fall almost along X = constant and Y = constant lines help considerably into forcing the error propagation to produce smooth systematic patterns. This is also desirable from the convenience and economy points of view, in terms of less number of models and less number of pass points to handle. This can be achieved by careful planning and execution of the aerial photography particularly if 80 percent forward overlap is made operational. This helps in selecting models (with 60 percent forward overlap) in each strip with appropriate locations. This is particularly helpful in the L-mode of operation as described earlier (Chap. 12). In this respect, however, natural points of good photographic image quality may not be available always in the ideal locations. In such cases use can be made of marked and transferred points.

5. *Premarking* of ground control points: Premarking (signalizing) of control points is recognized as a necessity in virtually all computational triangulations, particularly when monocomparators are used for measurements. A vertical (elevation) control station need not be premarked but a flat area near the bench mark needs to be selected in the field, identified on the reference photograph and the elevation of the area should be determined by adequate field procedures.

6. *Point marking:* The critical part of the preparation of photographs for aerial triangulation is the selection, marking and transferring of control and pass points. Marking of natural points is faster and should be preferred when available at the proper locations. Research studies indicate that there is no significant difference between natural and artificial points so far as accuracy of pointing is concerned (see Okang [74]). The disadvantage of marking natural points is that the mark may obscure important details, but in stereoscopic work only one photo need be marked and the detail will still appear on the adjacent photograph. For production work, therefore, stereoinstruments, rather than monocomparators, are recommended in such cases.

Okang [74] also observed that for precision in pointing, it is better that the measuring mark is slightly smaller than the point marked. Further, the precision of simultaneous marking on two photographs is of the same order of magnitude as that of the transfer of an already marked point to its conjugate position.

When stereoinstruments are used for measurements, one needs marking only one image on the central of the three photographs in a flight line. However, it is necessary to mark stereoscopically the corresponding point in each of the adjacent strips. If a monocomparator is used for measurements, then all the images must be marked stereoscopically on all the overlapping photographs. The point marking operation constitutes an important source of error in computational photogrammetry and it is estimated that this alone may constitute a random error source as large as 5 to 6 μm.

7. *Precision camera:* Superior image resolution in conjunction with a wide angular field of view would improve the accuracy of the results. Lens calibration data must be available and the camera should be dimensionally stable in operational environment. Réseau cameras would be desirable for further improvement in the accuracy.

8. *Fiducial marks:* Fiducial marks are considered to be an integral part of the camera cone. Studies (e.g., see Keller *et. al* [52]) indicate that eight (as against the standard four) fiducial marks are needed in the aerial camera as criteria for correct compensation of film distortion. Furthermore, if a camera has only four fiducial marks, in order to be effective, they should better be located in the corners than in the sides.

9. *Glass diapositives:* Glass diapositive reproduction of film negatives are required if dimensional changes (which may even occur in film during the measuring process) are to be arrested. Such diapositives should be prepared as early as possible following the processing of the negative. Flatness of the surface of the diapositive is another additional point to consider.

10. *Detection of blunders:* An effective method of detecting and eliminating blunders (gross mistakes) in data handling is needed for a successful performance. The working procedure (computer program in the computational approach) should include tests for such purposes for various steps, e.g., in the identification and marking of common points, image coordinate measurements, key punching of data, etc.

The following data (Table 13-1), collected from various studies made in the Department of Geodetic Science at Ohio State University, would give an idea of the obtainable accuracy in aerial strip triangulation. See Fig. 5-15 for further details on the particular strip.

Table 13-1
Comparative Results in Strip Triangulation[a]

Equipment	Method	Standard Errors (m)			Remarks
		m_X	m_Y	m_Z	
Wild A7	1. Aeropolygon (control in every twelfth model)	2.14	1.94	2.20	Same observation
	2. Aeropolygon (control in every sixth model)			1.88	data used for
	3. Independent Geodetic Control (four bases, approx.)	11.6	4.0		procedures
	4. Independent Geodetic Control (four bases, rigorous)	3.54	2.53	3.11	1,2,3,4
	5. Independent Model (control in every twelfth model)	2.23	4.37	4.03	
	6. Aeroleveling (with statoscope data)	3.27	2.81	4.17	
Wild A8	7. Independent Model (control in every fifth model)	1.90	2.60	4.22	
AP-C	8. Aeropolygon (control in every sixth model)	1.76	1.56	3.53	
	9. Independent Model (control in every sixth model)	1.49	2.37	3.04	With improved
	10. Independent Model (control in every sixth model)	0.98	2.16	1.78	polynomials for adjustment

[a]Technical data: Laufen-Bauma (Swiss) strip (OEEPE). Camera: Wild RC7a; f = 100.26mm, format = 14×14 cm². Number of test points: 163 (mostly targeted, all sketched). Flying height: 6000 m. Photo scale: 1:60,000. Strip length: 110 km. Number of models: 36.

Appendix A
Derivations and Forms of the Matrices of the Linearized Coplanarity Condition Equation

A.1 Partial Derivatives of the Coplanarity Condition Equation with Respect to Observed Photo Coordinates

The coplanarity condition equation as given in Chap. 9 defines $[A_i]$ as (see Eqs. (9.2) and (9.6)):

$$[A_i] = \left[\frac{\partial F_i}{\partial x_{1i}} \quad \frac{\partial F_i}{\partial y_{1i}} \quad \frac{\partial F_i}{\partial x_{2i}} \quad \frac{\partial F_i}{\partial y_{2i}} \right] \qquad (9.7)$$

From the equations of Chap. 9:

$$\frac{\partial F_i}{\partial x_{1i}} = \begin{bmatrix} bx & by & bz \\ m_{11}^1 & m_{12}^1 & m_{13}^1 \\ X_{2i} & Y_{2i} & Z_{2i} \end{bmatrix}$$

$$= \begin{bmatrix} bx & by & bz \\ 1 & 0 & 0 \\ X_{2i} & Y_{2i} & Z_{2i} \end{bmatrix} = (bz \cdot Y_{2i} - by \cdot Z_{2i}) \qquad (A.1)$$

Substituting from Eq. (9.4):

$$\frac{\partial F_i}{\partial x_{1i}} = bz\{x_{2i}(\cos\omega\sin\kappa + \sin\omega\sin\phi\cos\kappa)$$

$$+ y_{2i}(\cos\omega\cos\kappa - \sin\omega\sin\phi\sin\kappa) + f\sin\omega\cos\phi\}$$

$$- by\{x_{2i}(\sin\omega\sin\kappa - \cos\omega\sin\phi\cos\kappa)$$

$$+ y_{2i}(\sin\omega\cos\kappa + \cos\omega\sin\phi\sin\kappa) - f\cos\omega\cos\phi\} \qquad (A.2)$$

Similarly,

$$\frac{\partial F_i}{\partial y_{1i}} = \begin{bmatrix} bx & by & bz \\ m_{21}^1 & m_{22}^1 & m_{23}^1 \\ X_{2i} & Y_{2i} & Z_{2i} \end{bmatrix}$$

$$= \begin{bmatrix} bx & by & bz \\ 0 & 1 & 0 \\ X_{2i} & Y_{2i} & Z_{2i} \end{bmatrix} = (bx \cdot Z_{2i} - bz \cdot X_{2i}) \tag{A.3}$$

$$= bx\{x_{2i}(\sin\omega\sin\kappa - \cos\omega\sin\phi\cos\kappa)$$
$$+ y_{2i}(\sin\omega\cos\kappa + \cos\omega\sin\phi\sin\kappa) - f\cos\omega\cos\phi\}$$
$$- bz\{x_{2i}\cos\phi\cos\kappa - y_{2i}\cos\phi\sin\kappa - f\sin\phi\} \tag{A.4}$$

Furthermore,

$$\frac{\partial F_i}{\partial x_{2i}} = \begin{bmatrix} bx & by & bz \\ X_{1i} & Y_{1i} & Z_{1i} \\ m_{11}^1 & m_{12}^1 & m_{13}^1 \end{bmatrix}$$

$$= \begin{bmatrix} bx & by & bz \\ x_{1i} & y_{1i} & -f \\ \cos\phi\cos\kappa & \cos\omega\sin\kappa & \sin\omega\sin\kappa \\ & +\sin\omega\sin\phi\cos\kappa & -\cos\omega\sin\phi\cos\kappa \end{bmatrix} \tag{A.5}$$

$$= (bx \cdot y_{1i} - by \cdot x_{1i})(\sin\omega\sin\kappa - \cos\omega\sin\phi\cos\kappa)$$
$$+ (bx \cdot f + by \cdot x_{1i})(\cos\omega\sin\kappa + \sin\omega\sin\phi\cos\kappa)$$
$$- (by \cdot f + bz \cdot y_{1i})\cos\phi\cos\kappa \tag{A.6}$$

$$\frac{\partial F_i}{\partial y_{2i}} = \begin{bmatrix} bx & by & bz \\ X_{1i} & Y_{1i} & Z_{1i} \\ m_{21}^2 & m_{22}^2 & m_{23}^2 \end{bmatrix}$$

$$= \begin{bmatrix} bx & by & bz \\ x_{1i} & y_{1i} & -f \\ -\cos\phi\cos\kappa & \cos\omega\sin\kappa & \sin\omega\sin\kappa \\ & -\sin\omega\sin\phi\sin\kappa & +\cos\omega\sin\phi\sin\kappa \end{bmatrix} \tag{A.7}$$

$$= (bx \cdot y_{1i} - by \cdot x_{1i})(\sin\omega\cos\kappa + \cos\omega\sin\phi\sin\kappa)$$
$$+ (bx \cdot f + bz \cdot x_{1i})(\cos\omega\cos\kappa - \sin\omega\sin\phi\sin\kappa)$$
$$+ (by \cdot f + bz \cdot y_{1i})\cos\phi\sin\kappa \tag{A.8}$$

A.2 Partial Derivatives of the Coplanarity Condition Equation with Respect to the Unknown Parameters

$[B_i]$ is defined by Eq. (9.8) as:

$$[B_i] = \left[\frac{\partial F_i}{\partial by_2} \quad \frac{\partial F_i}{\partial bz_2} \quad \frac{\partial F_i}{\partial \omega_2} \quad \frac{\partial F_i}{\partial \phi_2} \quad \frac{\partial F_i}{\partial \kappa_2} \right] \tag{9.8}$$

$$\frac{\partial F_i}{\partial by_2} = - \begin{bmatrix} X_{1i} & Z_{1i} \\ \\ X_{2i} & Z_{2i} \end{bmatrix} \tag{A.9}$$

From equation 9.4

$$\frac{\partial F_i}{\partial by_2} = x_{1i}\{x_{2i}(\cos\omega\sin\phi\cos\kappa - \sin\omega\sin\kappa)$$
$$- y_{2i}(\sin\omega\cos\kappa + \cos\omega\sin\phi\sin\kappa) + f \cdot \cos\omega\cos\phi\}$$
$$- f \cdot \{x_{2i}\cos\phi\cos\kappa - y_{2i}\cos\phi\sin\kappa - f \cdot \sin\phi\} \tag{A.10}$$

Similarly,

$$\frac{\partial F_i}{\partial bz_2} = \begin{bmatrix} X_{1i} & Y_{1i} \\ \\ X_{2i} & Y_{2i} \end{bmatrix}$$

$$= x_{1i}\{x_{2i}(\cos\omega\sin\kappa + \sin\omega\sin\phi\cos\kappa)$$
$$+ y_{2i}(\cos\omega\cos\kappa - \sin\omega\sin\phi\sin\kappa) + f \cdot \sin\omega\cos\phi\}$$
$$- y_{1i}\{x_{2i}\cos\phi\cos\kappa - y_{2i}\cos\phi\sin\kappa - f \cdot \sin\phi\} \tag{A.11}$$

$$\frac{\partial F_i}{\partial \omega_2} = \begin{bmatrix} bx & by & bz \\ X_{1i} & Y_{1i} & Z_{1i} \\ \dfrac{\partial X_{2i}}{\partial \omega_2} & \dfrac{\partial Y_{2i}}{\partial \omega_2} & \dfrac{\partial Z_{2i}}{\partial \omega_2} \end{bmatrix}$$

$$= \begin{bmatrix} bx & by & bz \\ x_{1i} & y_{1i} & -f \\ \dfrac{\partial X_{2i}}{\partial \omega_2} & \dfrac{\partial Y_{2i}}{\partial \omega_2} & \dfrac{\partial Z_{2i}}{\partial \omega_2} \end{bmatrix} \qquad (A.12)$$

From Eq. (9.4):

$$\frac{\partial X_{2i}}{\partial \omega_2} = 0$$

$$\frac{\partial Y_{2i}}{\partial \omega_2} = x_{2i}(\cos\omega\sin\phi\cos\kappa - \sin\omega\sin\kappa)$$
$$- y_{2i}(\sin\omega\cos\kappa + \cos\omega\sin\phi\sin\kappa) + f \cdot \cos\omega\cos\phi$$

and,

$$\frac{\partial Z_{2i}}{\partial \omega_2} = x_{2i}(\cos\omega\sin\kappa + \sin\omega\sin\phi\cos\kappa)$$
$$+ y_{2i}(\cos\omega\cos\kappa - \sin\omega\sin\phi\sin\kappa) + f \cdot \sin\omega\cos\phi$$

Now, substituting values in equation (A.12),

$$\frac{\partial F_i}{\partial \omega_2} = \{bx \cdot y_{1i} - by \cdot x_{2i}\} \{x_{2i}(\cos\omega\sin\kappa + \sin\omega\sin\phi\cos\kappa)$$
$$+ y_{2i}(\cos\omega\cos\kappa - \sin\omega\sin\phi\sin\kappa) + f \cdot \sin\omega\cos\phi\}$$
$$+ \{bx \cdot f + bz \cdot x_{1i}\} \{f \cdot \cos\omega\cos\phi$$
$$+ x_{2i}(\cos\omega\sin\phi\cos\kappa - \sin\omega\sin\kappa)$$
$$- y_{2i}(\sin\omega\cos\kappa + \cos\omega\sin\phi\sin\kappa)\} \qquad (A.13)$$

$$\frac{\partial F_i}{\partial \phi_2} = \begin{bmatrix} bx & by & bz \\ X_{1i} & Y_{1i} & Z_{1i} \\ \dfrac{\partial X_{2i}}{\partial \phi_2} & \dfrac{\partial Y_{2i}}{\partial \phi_2} & \dfrac{\partial Z_{2i}}{\partial \phi_2} \end{bmatrix}$$

$$= \begin{bmatrix} bx & by & bz \\ x_{1i} & y_{1i} & -f \\ \dfrac{\partial X_{2i}}{\partial \phi_2} & \dfrac{\partial Y_{2i}}{\partial \phi_2} & \dfrac{\partial Z_{2i}}{\partial \phi_2} \end{bmatrix} \qquad (A.14)$$

From Eq. (9.4):

$$\frac{\partial X_{2i}}{\partial \phi_2} = -x_{2i}\sin\phi\cos\kappa + y_{2i}\sin\phi\sin\kappa - f \cdot \cos\phi$$

$$\frac{\partial Y_{2i}}{\partial \phi_2} = x_{2i}\sin\omega\cos\phi\cos\kappa - y_{2i}\sin\omega\cos\phi\sin\kappa - f \cdot \sin\omega\sin\phi$$

$$\frac{\partial Z_{2i}}{\partial \phi_2} = -x_{2i}\cos\omega\cos\phi\cos\kappa + y_{2i}\cos\omega\cos\phi\sin\kappa + f \cdot \cos\omega\sin\phi$$

Substituting, now, values into Eq. (A.14),

$$\begin{aligned}
\frac{\partial F_i}{\partial \phi_2} = {}& \{bx{\cdot}y_{1i} - by{\cdot}x_{1i}\}\,\{f. \cos\omega\sin\phi + y_{2i}\cos\omega\cos\phi\sin\kappa \\
& -x_{2i}\cos\omega\cos\phi\cos\kappa\} + \{bx \cdot f + bz{\cdot}x_{1i}\} \\
& .\,\{x_{2i}\sin\omega\cos\phi\cos\kappa - y_{2i}\sin\omega\cos\phi\sin\kappa - f \cdot \sin\omega\sin\phi\} \\
& + \{by{\cdot} f + bz{\cdot}y_{1i}\} \\
& \cdot\{x_{2i}\sin\phi\cos\kappa - y_{2i}\sin\phi\sin\kappa + f \cdot \cos\phi\} \qquad (A.15)
\end{aligned}$$

$$\frac{\partial F_i}{\partial \kappa_2} = \begin{bmatrix} bx & by & bz \\ X_{1i} & Y_{1i} & Z_{1i} \\ \dfrac{\partial X_{2i}}{\partial \kappa_2} & \dfrac{\partial Y_{2i}}{\partial \kappa_2} & \dfrac{\partial Z_{2i}}{\partial \kappa_2} \end{bmatrix}$$

$$= \begin{bmatrix} bx & by & bz \\[2mm] x_{1i} & y_{1i} & -f \\[2mm] \dfrac{\partial X_{2i}}{\partial \kappa_2} & \dfrac{\partial Y_{2i}}{\partial \kappa_2} & \dfrac{\partial Z_{2i}}{\partial \kappa_2} \end{bmatrix} \qquad (A.16)$$

From Eq. (9.4):

$$\frac{\partial X_{2i}}{\partial \kappa_2} = -x_{2i}\cos\phi\sin\kappa - y_{2i}\cos\phi\cos\kappa$$

$$\frac{\partial Y_{2i}}{\partial \kappa_2} = x_{2i}(\cos\omega\cos\kappa - \sin\omega\sin\phi\sin\kappa)$$
$$- y_{2i}(\cos\omega\sin\kappa + \sin\omega\sin\phi\cos\kappa)$$

$$\frac{\partial Z_{2i}}{\partial \kappa_2} = x_{2i}(\sin\omega\cos\kappa + \cos\omega\sin\phi\sin\kappa)$$
$$- y_{2i}(\sin\omega\sin\kappa - \cos\omega\sin\phi\cos\kappa)$$

Now, substituting the values into Eq. (A.16),

$$\frac{\partial F_i}{\partial \kappa_2} = \{bx \cdot y_{1i} - by \cdot x_{1i}\} \{x_{2i}(\sin\omega\cos\kappa + \cos\omega\sin\phi\sin\kappa)$$
$$- y_{2i}(\sin\omega\sin\kappa - \cos\omega\sin\phi\cos\kappa)\} + \{bx \cdot f + bz \cdot x_{1i}\}$$
$$\cdot \{x_{2i}(\cos\omega\cos\kappa - \sin\omega\sin\phi\sin\kappa)$$
$$- y_{2i}(\cos\omega\sin\kappa + \sin\omega\sin\phi\cos\kappa)\}$$
$$+ \{by \cdot f + bz \cdot y_{1i}\} \{x_{2i}\cos\phi\sin\kappa + y_{2i}\cos\phi\cos\kappa\} \qquad (A.17)$$

A.3 Forms and Sizes of the Matrices

Let n = Number of observed values of observable quantities

      u = Number of unknown quantities (= 5, here)

      r = Number of conditon equations where observed quantities and unknown quantities are present

Here, n = 4r, since there are four coordinates for each point. The sizes of the matrices in Eq. (9.6) are, therefore,

$$
(9.6) \qquad \underset{r \; n}{[A]} \quad \underset{n \; 1}{V} \quad + \quad \underset{r \; u}{[B]} \quad \underset{u \; 1}{\Delta} \quad + \quad \underset{r \; 1}{F_o} \quad = \quad \underset{r \; 1}{O}
$$

$$
\underset{r \quad n}{A} \;=\;
\begin{bmatrix}
A_1 & 0 & 0 \ldots 0 \\
0 & A_2 & 0 \ldots 0 \\
0 & 0 & A_3 \ldots 0 \\
\vdots & \vdots & \vdots \\
0 & 0 & 0 \ldots A_r
\end{bmatrix}
$$

$$
=
\begin{bmatrix}
XXXX & & & & \\
& XXXX & & & \\
& & XXXX & & \\
& & & \cdot\cdot & \\
& & & & \cdot\cdot \\
& & & & \cdot\cdot \\
& & & & XXXXX
\end{bmatrix}
\atop{r \times n}
$$

$$
\underset{r \quad u}{B} \;=\;
\begin{bmatrix}
B_1 \\
B_2 \\
B_3 \\
\vdots \\
B_r
\end{bmatrix}
\;=\;
\begin{bmatrix}
X & X & X & X & X \\
X & X & X & X & X \\
 & & & & \\
\vdots & \vdots & \vdots & \vdots & \vdots \\
X & X & X & X & X
\end{bmatrix}
\qquad \text{Full matrix}
$$

$$
r \times 5
$$

$$
\mathbf{F}_o \underset{r \quad 1}{} =
\begin{bmatrix}
F_{o1} \\
F_{o2} \\
\vdots \\
F_{or}
\end{bmatrix}
$$

$$r \times 1$$

$$
\mathbf{\Delta} \underset{u \quad 1}{} =
\begin{bmatrix}
\delta by \\
\delta bz \\
\delta \omega \\
\delta \phi \\
\delta \kappa
\end{bmatrix}
$$

$$5 \times 1$$

$$
\mathbf{V} \underset{n \quad 1}{} =
\begin{bmatrix}
V_1 \\
4 \times 1 \\
V_2 \\
4 \times 1 \\
\vdots \\
V_r \\
4 \times 1
\end{bmatrix}
$$

$$n \times 1$$

Appendix B
Computer
Program—Simultaneous
Block

206

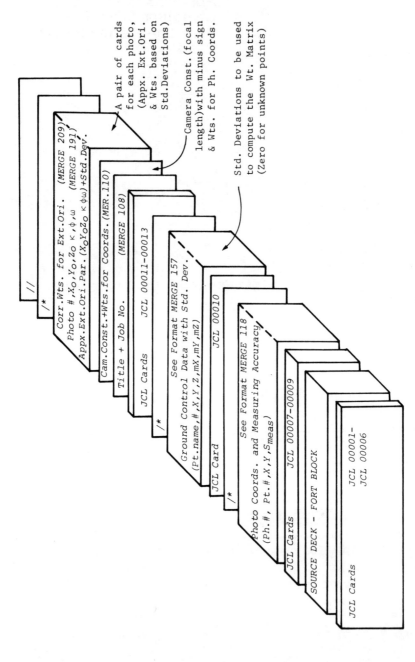

Figure B-1 General Setup for Block (Simultaneous)

```
//    (2500,250),CLASS=C,REGION=252K                                    JCL00001
//STEP1 EXEC PROC=FORTRANG,TIME.CMP=(,20),PARM='MAP,ID'                 JCL00002
//CMP.SYSLIN DD UNIT=SYSDA,SPACE=(CYL,(5,2)),DISP=(MOD,PASS),           JCL00003
// DCB=(RECFM=FB,LRECL=80,BLKSIZE=400)                                  JCL00004
//*     PLACE FORTRAN SOURCE DECK AFTER //CMP.SYSIN DD * CARD           JCL00005
//CMP.SYSIN   DD *                                                     JCL00006
       IMPLICIT REAL*8(A-H,O-Z)                                        BLKTN001
       DIMENSION U1(24),U2(48),PHOTO(4,50),POINT(4,16,23)              BLKTN002
       DIMENSION B12T(24,48),A22T(48,24),DE(24),DS(48)                 BLKTN003
       DIMENSION A11(24,24),A12(24,48),A22(48,48)                      BLKTN004
       DIMENSION  ITITLE(7)                                            BLKTN005
       CALL MERGE (CC,N ,IP,WM,PHOTO,POINT,ITITLE,JOBNUM)              BLKTN006
       K1=3*IP                                                         BLKTN007
       J1=6*N                                                          BLKTN008
       CALL BLKTRN(U1,U2,PHOTO,POINT,B12T,A22T,DE,DS,A11,A12,A22,N,IP,J1,BLKTN009
      *K1,CC,WM,ITITLE,JOBNUM)                                          BLKTN010
       STOP                                                            BLKTN011
       END                                                             BLKTN012
       SUBROUTINE BLKTRN(U1,U2,PHOTO,POINT,B12T,A22T,DE,DS,A11,A12,A22, BLKTN101
      *N,IP,J1,K1,CC,WM,ITITLE,JOBNUM)                                  BLKTN102
C                                                                      BLKTN103
C      BLOCK TRIANGULATION                                             BLKTN104
C                                                                      BLKTN105
       IMPLICIT REAL*8(A-H,O-Z)                                        BLKTN106
       DIMENSION U1(J1),U2(K1),PHOTO(4,50),POINT(4,16,23)              BLKTN107
       DIMENSION B12T(J1,K1),A22T(K1,J1),DE(J1),DS(K1)                 BLKTN108
       DIMENSION A11(J1,J1),A12(J1,K1),A22(K1,K1)                      BLKTN109
       DIMENSION XOE(6),XOEI(6),WE(6,6)                                BLKTN110
       DIMENSION DATA(2),W(2,2),XOS(3),XOSI(3),WS(3,3)                 BLKTN111
       DIMENSION E(2),ATEMP(6,2),B(2,9),R(6),MONTH(12),ITITLE(7)       BLKTN112
       INTEGER PP,P,T,KEY(35)/35*0/                                    BLKTN113
       DATA MONTH(1)/'JAN.'/,MONTH(2)/'FEB.'/,MONTH(3)/'MAR.'/,MONTH(4)/'BLKTN114
      *APR.'/,MONTH(5)/'MAY '/,MONTH(6)/'JUNE'/,MONTH(7)/'JULY'/,MONTH(8)BLKTN115
      */'AUG.'/,MONTH(9)/'SEPT'/,MONTH(10)/'OCT.'/,MONTH(11)/'NOV.'/,MONTBLKTN116
      *H(12)/'DEC.'/                                                    BLKTN117
       WRITE(6,3011)                                                   BLKTN118
       WRITE(6,3012)                                                   BLKTN119
       IOUT=0                                                          BLKTN120
       DF=0.0                                                          BLKTN121
       VDF=0.0                                                         BLKTN122
       ICYCLE=0                                                        BLKTN123
       DO 200 I=1,N                                                    BLKTN125
       P=PHOTO(I,1)                                                    BLKTN127
       DO 201 J=2,7                                                    BLKTN128
  201 PHOTO(I,J+6)=PHOTO(I,J)                                          BLKTN130
       L2=13                                                           BLKTN131
       DO 200 J=1,P                                                    BLKTN136
       POINT(I,J,4)=WM                                                 BLKTN139
       POINT(I,J,5)=0.0                                                BLKTN140
       POINT(I,J,6)=0.0                                                BLKTN141
       POINT(I,J,7)=WM                                                 BLKTN142
       DO 204 K=17,19                                                  BLKTN143
  204 POINT(I,J,K+3)=POINT(I,J,K)                                      BLKTN145
  200 CONTINUE                                                         BLKTN151
C                                                                      BLKTN152
C      CLEAR NORMALS                                                   BLKTN153
C                                                                      BLKTN154
    4 ICYCLE=ICYCLE+1                                                  BLKTN155
       DO 5 I=1,IP                                                     BLKTN156
    5 KEY(I)=0                                                         BLKTN157
    1 DO 2 I=1,J1                                                      BLKTN158
       U1(I)=0.0                                                       BLKTN159
       DO 7 J=1,J1                                                     BLKTN160
    7 A11(I,J)=0.0                                                     BLKTN161
       DO 2 J=1,K1                                                     BLKTN162
    2 A12(I,J)=0.0                                                     BLKTN163
       DO 3 I=1,K1                                                     BLKTN164
       U2(I)=0.0                                                       BLKTN165
       DO 3 J=1,K1                                                     BLKTN166
    3 A22(I,J)=0.0                                                     BLKTN167
C                                                                      BLKTN168
C      LOAD PHOTO DATA                                                 BLKTN169
C                                                                      BLKTN170
       DO 100 J=1,N                                                    BLKTN171
       LOC=13                                                          BLKTN172
       K=PHOTO(J,1)                                                    BLKTN173
       L1=PHOTO(J,50)                                                  BLKTN174
       DO 210 II=2,7                                                   BLKTN175
```

```
      III1=II-1                                                        BLKTN176
      XOE(III1)=PHOTO(J,II)                                            BLKTN177
      XOEI(III1)=PHOTO(J,II+6)                                         BLKTN178
      DO 210 JJ=1,6                                                    BLKTN179
      LOC=LOC+1                                                        BLKTN180
  210 WE(III1,JJ)=PHOTO(J,LOC)                                         BLKTN181
      L=6*(J-1)                                                        BLKTN182
      R(1)=DSIN(XOE(4))                                                BLKTN183
      R(2)=DSIN(XOE(5))                                                BLKTN184
      R(3)=DSIN(XOE(6))                                                BLKTN185
      R(4)=DCOS(XOE(4))                                                BLKTN186
      R(5)=DCOS(XOE(5))                                                BLKTN187
      R(6)=DCOS(XOE(6))                                                BLKTN188
      DO 10 II=1,6                                                     BLKTN189
      LII=L+II                                                         BLKTN190
      IF(WE(II,II).GT.1.0E-15) DF=DF+1.0                               BLKTN191
      VDF=VDF+WE(II,II)*(XOEI(II)-XOE(II))**2                          BLKTN192
      DO 10 JJ=1,6                                                     BLKTN193
      U1(LII)=U1(LII)-WE(II,JJ)*(XOEI(JJ)-XOE(JJ))                     BLKTN194
   10 A11(LII,L+JJ)=A11(LII,L+JJ)+WE(II,JJ)                            BLKTN195
C                                                                      BLKTN196
C     LOAD POINT DATA                                                  BLKTN197
C                                                                      BLKTN198
      DO 100 I=1,K                                                     BLKTN199
      DATA(1)=POINT(J,I,1)                                             BLKTN200
      DATA(2)=POINT(J,I,2)                                             BLKTN201
      P=POINT(J,I,3)                                                   BLKTN202
      LOC=3                                                            BLKTN203
      DO 215 II=1,2                                                    BLKTN204
      DO 215 JJ=1,2                                                    BLKTN205
      LOC=LOC+1                                                        BLKTN206
  215 W(II,JJ)=POINT(J,I,LOC)                                          BLKTN207
      DO 216 II=1,3                                                    BLKTN208
      DO 216 JJ=1,3                                                    BLKTN209
      LOC=LOC+1                                                        BLKTN210
  216 WS(II,JJ)=POINT(J,I,LOC)                                         BLKTN211
      DO 217 II=17,19                                                  BLKTN212
      III1=II-16                                                       BLKTN213
      XOSI(III1)=POINT(J,I,II)                                         BLKTN214
  217 XOSI(III1)=POINT(J,I,II+3)                                       BLKTN215
      DF=DF+2.0                                                        BLKTN216
      LL=3*(P-1)                                                       BLKTN217
C                                                                      BLKTN218
C     OBTAIN PARTIALS                                                  BLKTN219
C                                                                      BLKTN220
      CALL COFEI1(XOS,R,B,XOF,CC,XC,YC)                                BLKTN221
C                                                                      BLKTN222
C     COMPUTE NORMALS                                                  BLKTN223
C                                                                      BLKTN224
      L2=POINT(J,I,23)                                                 BLKTN225
      ITEST=1                                                          BLKTN226
      IF(KEY(P).GT.0) GO TO 12                                         BLKTN227
      KEY(P)=P                                                         BLKTN228
      ITEST=0                                                          BLKTN229
   12 DO 15 II=1,6                                                     BLKTN230
      DO 15 JJ=1,2                                                     BLKTN231
      ATEMP(II,JJ)=0.0                                                 BLKTN232
      DO 15 KK=1,2                                                     BLKTN233
   15 ATEMP(II,JJ)=ATEMP(II,JJ)+B(KK,II)*W(KK,JJ)                      BLKTN234
      E(1)=DATA(1)-XC                                                  BLKTN235
      E(2)=DATA(2)-YC                                                  BLKTN236
      IF(ICYCLE.EQ.1) WRITE(6,3004) L1,L2,POINT(J,I,1),POINT(J,I,2),E(1)BLKTN237
     *,E(2)                                                            BLKTN238
      VDF=VDF+W(1,1)*E(1)**2+W(2,2)*E(2)**2                            BLKTN239
C                                                                      BLKTN240
C     COMPUTE A11                                                      BLKTN241
C                                                                      BLKTN242
      DO 17 II=1,6                                                     BLKTN243
      LII=L+II                                                         BLKTN244
      DO 16 KK=1,2                                                     BLKTN245
   16 U1(LII)=U1(LII)+ATEMP(II,KK)*E(KK)                              BLKTN246
      DO 17 JJ=1,6                                                     BLKTN247
      LJJ=L+JJ                                                         BLKTN248
      DO 17 KK=1,2                                                     BLKTN249
   17 A11(LII,LJJ)=A11(LII,LJJ)+ATEMP(II,KK)*B(KK,JJ)                  BLKTN250
C                                                                      BLKTN251
C     COMPUTE A12                                                      BLKTN252
C                                                                      BLKTN253
```

```
      DO 19 II=1,6                                              BLKTN254
      LII=L+II                                                  BLKTN255
      DO 19 JJ=7,9                                              BLKTN256
      LJJ=LL+JJ-6                                               BLKTN257
      DO 19 KK=1,2                                              BLKTN258
   19 A12(LII,LJJ)=A12(LII,LJJ)+ATEMP(II,KK)*B(KK,JJ)           BLKTN259
C                                                               BLKTN260
C     COMPUTE A22                                               BLKTN261
C                                                               BLKTN262
      DO 23 II=7,9                                              BLKTN263
      II1=II-6                                                  BLKTN264
      DO 23 JJ=1,2                                              BLKTN265
      ATEMP(II1,JJ)=0.0                                         BLKTN266
      DO 23 KK=1,2                                              BLKTN267
   23 ATEMP(II1,JJ)=ATEMP(II1,JJ)+B(KK,II)*W(KK,JJ)             BLKTN268
      DO 100 II=1,3                                             BLKTN269
      M=LL+II                                                   BLKTN270
      DO 26 KK=1,2                                              BLKTN271
      U2(M)=U2(M)+ATEMP(II,KK)*E(KK)                            BLKTN272
      DO 26 JJ=7,9                                              BLKTN273
   26 A22(M,LL+JJ-6)=A22(M,LL+JJ-6)+ATEMP(II,KK)*B(KK,JJ)       BLKTN274
      IF(ITEST.EQ.1) GO TO 100                                  BLKTN275
C                                                               BLKTN276
C     ADDING TERMS DUE TO CONSTRAINT ON SURVEY COORDINATES      BLKTN277
C                                                               BLKTN278
      VDF=VDF+WS(II,II)*(XOSI(II)-XOS(II))**2                   BLKTN279
      IF(WS(II,II).GT.1.0E-15) DF=DF+1.0                        BLKTN280
      DO 28 JJ=1,3                                              BLKTN281
      A22(M,LL+JJ)=A22(M,LL+JJ)+WS(II,JJ)                       BLKTN282
   28 U2(M)=U2(M)-WS(II,JJ)*(XOSI(JJ)-XOS(JJ))                  BLKTN283
  100 CONTINUE                                                  BLKTN284
      CALL MATINV(A22,K1)                                       BLKTN285
      IF(IOUT.EQ.1) GO TO 300                                   BLKTN286
C                                                               BLKTN287
C     FORMING B11                                               BLKTN288
C                                                               BLKTN289
      DO 35 I=1,K1                                              BLKTN290
      DO 35 J=1,J1                                              BLKTN291
      A22T(I,J)=0.0                                             BLKTN292
      DO 35 K=1,K1                                              BLKTN293
   35 A22T(I,J)=A22T(I,J)+A22(I,K)*A12(J,K)                     BLKTN294
      DO 36 I=1,J1                                              BLKTN295
      DO 36 J=1,J1                                              BLKTN296
      DO 36 K=1,K1                                              BLKTN297
   36 A11(I,J)=A11(I,J)-A12(I,K)*A22T(K,J)                      BLKTN298
      CALL MATINV(A11,J1)                                       BLKTN299
C                                                               BLKTN300
C     FORMING B12                                               BLKTN301
C                                                               BLKTN302
      DO 37 I=1,J1                                              BLKTN303
      DO 37 J=1,K1                                              BLKTN304
      B12T(I,J)=0.0                                             BLKTN305
      DO 37 K=1,K1                                              BLKTN306
   37 B12T(I,J)=B12T(I,J)+A12(I,K)*A22(K,J)                     BLKTN307
      DO 38 I=1,J1                                              BLKTN308
      DO 38 J=1,K1                                              BLKTN309
      A12(I,J)=0.0                                              BLKTN310
      DO 38 K=1,J1                                              BLKTN311
   38 A12(I,J)=A12(I,J)-A11(I,K)*B12T(K,J)                      BLKTN312
C                                                               BLKTN313
C     FORMING B22                                               BLKTN314
C                                                               BLKTN315
      DO 39 I=1,K1                                              BLKTN316
      DO 39 J=1,K1                                              BLKTN317
      DO 39 K=1,J1                                              BLKTN318
   39 A22(I,J)=A22(I,J)-A22T(I,K)*A12(K,J)                      BLKTN319
C                                                               BLKTN320
C     SOLVING NORMALS                                           BLKTN321
C                                                               BLKTN322
      DO 40 I=1,J1                                              BLKTN323
      DE(I)=0.0                                                 BLKTN324
      DO 41 J=1,J1                                              BLKTN325
   41 DE(I)=DE(I)-A11(I,J)*U1(J)                                BLKTN326
      DO 40 J=1,K1                                              BLKTN327
   40 DE(I)=DE(I)-A12(I,J)*U2(J)                                BLKTN328
      DO 42 I=1,K1                                              BLKTN329
      DS(I)=0.0                                                 BLKTN330
      DO 43 J=1,K1                                              BLKTN331
```

```
   43 DS(I)=DS(I)-A22(I,J)*U2(J)                                        BLKTN332
      DO 42 J=1,J1                                                      BLKTN333
   42 DS(I)=DS(I)-A12(J,I)*U1(J)                                        BLKTN334
C                                                                       BLKTN335
C     APPLY ALTERATIONS                                                 BLKTN336
C                                                                       BLKTN337
      DO 115 I=1,N                                                      BLKTN338
      II=6*I-7                                                          BLKTN339
      K=PHOTO(I,1)                                                      BLKTN340
      DO 101 IZ=2,7                                                     BLKTN341
  101 PHOTO(I,IZ)=PHOTO(I,IZ)+DE(II+IZ)                                 BLKTN342
      DO 115 J=1,K                                                      BLKTN343
      P=POINT(I,J,3)                                                    BLKTN344
      II=3*P-19                                                         BLKTN345
      DO 115 IZ=17,19                                                   BLKTN346
  115 POINT(I,J,IZ)=POINT(I,J,IZ)+DS(II+IZ)                            BLKTN347
      IF(ICYCLE.LT.3) GO TO 4                                           BLKTN348
      DF=0.0                                                            BLKTN349
      VDF=0.0                                                           BLKTN350
      IOUT=1                                                            BLKTN351
      GO TO 4                                                           BLKTN352
C                                                                       BLKTN353
C     PRINT ROUTINE                                                     BLKTN354
C     ARRAYS XOE,XOEI,XOS, AND XOSI ARE USED FOR TEMPORARY STORAGE      BLKTN355
C                                                                       BLKTN356
  300 CALL MATINV(A11,J1)                                               BLKTN357
      DF=DF-J1-K1                                                       BLKTN358
      VAR=VDF/DF                                                        BLKTN359
      UNSTDR=DSQRT(VAR)                                                 BLKTN360
      CALL IDATIM(IYEAR,IMONTH,IDAY,ITIME)                             BLKTN361
      DO 306 I=1,J1                                                     BLKTN362
      DO 306 J=1,J1                                                     BLKTN363
  306 A11(I,J)=A11(I,J)*VAR                                             BLKTN364
      DO 307 I=1,K1                                                     BLKTN365
      DO 307 J=1,K1                                                     BLKTN366
  307 A22(I,J)=A22(I,J)*VAR                                             BLKTN367
      NDF=DF                                                            BLKTN368
      DO 301 I=1,24                                                     BLKTN369
      IF(ITIME.LT.360000) GO TO 302                                     BLKTN370
  301 ITIME=ITIME-360000                                                BLKTN371
  302 DO 303 J=1,59                                                     BLKTN372
      IF(ITIME.LT.6000) GO TO 304                                       BLKTN373
  303 ITIME=ITIME-6000                                                  BLKTN374
  304 TIME=FLOAT(ITIME)/100.0                                           BLKTN375
      I=I-1                                                             BLKTN376
      J=J-1                                                             BLKTN377
      WRITE(6,3000) ITITLE,JOBNUM,IDAY,MONTH(IMONTH),IYEAR,I,J,TIME,N,NDBLKTN378
     *F,UNSTDR                                                          BLKTN379
      WRITE(3,3003) WM                                                  BLKTN380
      WRITE(3,3012)                                                     BLKTN381
      WRITE(4,3005)                                                     BLKTN382
      WRITE(6,3001)                                                     BLKTN383
      DO 330 I=1,N                                                      BLKTN384
      I6=6*(I-1)                                                        BLKTN385
      DO 305 J=1,6                                                      BLKTN386
      XOE(J)=DSQRT(A11(I6+J,I6+J))                                      BLKTN387
  305 XOEI(J)=PHOTO(I,J+7)-PHOTO(I,J+1)                                 BLKTN388
      L=PHOTO(I,50)                                                     BLKTN389
      WRITE(6,3002) L,(PHOTO(I,J+1),J=1,6),XOE,XOEI,(PHOTO(I,J),J=14,49,BLKTN390
     *7)                                                                BLKTN391
      WRITE(6,3007) ((A11(I6+K,I6+J),J=1,6),K=1,6)                      BLKTN392
      WRITE(6,3009)                                                     BLKTN393
      R(1)=DSIN(PHOTO(I,5))                                             BLKTN394
      R(2)=DSIN(PHOTO(I,6))                                             BLKTN395
      R(3)=DSIN(PHOTO(I,7))                                             BLKTN396
      R(4)=DCOS(PHOTO(I,5))                                             BLKTN397
      R(5)=DCOS(PHOTO(I,6))                                             BLKTN398
      R(6)=DCOS(PHOTO(I,7))                                             BLKTN399
      K=PHOTO(I,1)                                                      BLKTN400
      DO 330 J=1,K                                                      BLKTN401
      P=POINT(I,J,3)                                                    BLKTN402
      KK=3*(P-1)                                                        BLKTN403
      DX=POINT(I,J,17)-PHOTO(I,2)                                       BLKTN404
      DY=POINT(I,J,18)-PHOTO(I,3)                                       BLKTN405
      DZ=POINT(I,J,19)-PHOTO(I,4)                                       BLKTN406
      XT=DX*R(5)*R(4)+DY*(R(6)*R(1)+R(3)*R(2)*R(4))+DZ*(R(3)*R(1)-R(6)*RBLKTN407
     *(2)*R(4))                                                         BLKTN408
      YT=-DX*R(5)*R(1)+DY*(R(6)*R(4)-R(3)*R(2)*R(1))+DZ*(R(3)*R(4)+R(6)*BLKTN409
```

```
        *R(2)*R(1))                                                        BLKTN410
         ZT=DX*R(2)-DY*R(3)*R(5)+DZ*R(6)*R(5)                             BLKTN411
         XC=CC*XT/ZT                                                       BLKTN412
         YC=CC*YT/ZT                                                       BLKTN413
         E(1)=POINT(I,J,1)-XC                                              BLKTN414
         E(2)=POINT(I,J,2)-YC                                              BLKTN415
         LL=POINT(I,J,23)                                                  BLKTN416
         WRITE(3,3004) L,LL,POINT(I,J,1),POINT(I,J,2),E(1),E(2)           BLKTN417
         IF(KEY(P).EQ.0) GO TO 330                                         BLKTN418
         KEY(P)=0                                                          BLKTN419
         DO 320 JJ=1,3                                                     BLKTN420
         XOS(JJ)=DSQRT(A22(KK+JJ,KK+JJ))                                   BLKTN421
  320    XOSI(JJ)=POINT(I,J,JJ+19)-POINT(I,J,JJ+16)                        BLKTN422
         WRITE(4,3006) LL,(POINT(I,J,JJ),JJ=17,19),XOS,XOSI,(POINT(I,J,JJ),BLKTN423
        *JJ=8,16,4)                                                        BLKTN424
         WRITE(4,3008)((A22(KK+II,KK+JJ),JJ=1,3),II=1,3)                   BLKTN425
         WRITE(4,3009)                                                     BLKTN426
         IF(J/2*2.EQ.J) WRITE(4,3010)                                      BLKTN427
  330 CONTINUE                                                             BLKTN428
 3000 FORMAT('1',26(/),T47,7A4,/T53,'JOB NUMBER',I6,/T53,'DATE',I3,1X,A4BLKTN429
        *,I5,/T54,'TIME',I3,':',I2,':',F4.1,/T51,'NUMBER OF PHOTOS = ',I2,/BLKTN430
        *T49,'DEGREES OF FREEDOM =',I5,/T44,'UNIT STANDARD ERROR = ',D12.5)BLKTN431
 3001 FORMAT('1',T58,'RESULTS',/T51,'EXTERIOR ORIENTATION')               BLKTN432
 3002 FORMAT(//,T10,'PHOTO NO. ',I2,T27,'XO (METERS)',T41,'YO (METERS)',BLKTN433
        *T57,'ZO (METERS)',T73,'KAPPA (RAD.)',T91,'PHI (RAD.)',T107,'OMEGA BLKTN434
        *(RAD.)'//T20,3F16.3,3D17.6,//T9,'STD.ERROR',T20,4D16.4,2(1X,D16.4)BLKTN435
        *,//T9,'RESIDUALS',T20,4D16.4,2(1X,D16.4),//T9,'WEIGHTS',T20,6F16.3BLKTN436
        *,//)                                                              BLKTN437
 3003 FORMAT(T58,'RESULTS',/T53,'PHOTO COORDINATES',/T47,'(ALL WEIGHTS TBLKTN438
        *AKEN AS ',F7.1,')')                                               BLKTN439
 3004 FORMAT('0',T30,I2,T44,I3,T50,2F11.3,T73,2D14.4)                     BLKTN440
 3005 FORMAT(T58,'RESULTS',/T52,'SURVEY COORDINATES')                     BLKTN441
 3006 FORMAT(//T31,'POINT NO. ',I3,T52,'X',T68,'Y',T84,'Z',//T42,3F16.3,BLKTN442
        *//T32,'STD. ERROR',T43,3D16.4,//T32,'RESIDUALS',T43,3D16.4,//T32,'BLKTN443
        *WEIGHT',4X,3F16.3,//)                                            BLKTN444
 3007 FORMAT('0',T48,'VARIANCE/COVARIANCE MATRIX'//(T16,6E15.5,/))        BLKTN445
 3008 FORMAT('0',T48,'VARIANCE/COVARIANCE MATRIX'//(T36,3E15.5,/))        BLKTN446
 3009 FORMAT('0',//)                                                       BLKTN447
 3010 FORMAT('1',/)                                                        BLKTN448
 3011 FORMAT('1',T29,'THE PHOTO COORDINATE RESIDUALS PRIOR TO THE FIRST BLKTN449
        *CYCLE ADJUSTMENT ARE:',/)                                        BLKTN450
 3012 FORMAT(//T27,'PHOTO NO.',T41,'POINT NO.',T55, 'X (MM)',T66,'Y (MM)BLKTN451
        *',T78,'VX (MM)',T92,'VY (MM)',/)                                 BLKTN452
  500 FORMAT(2F10.5)                                                       BLKTN453
  501 FORMAT(6F10.5)                                                       BLKTN454
  502 FORMAT(2F10.4)                                                       BLKTN455
  504 FORMAT(3F10.3)                                                       BLKTN456
  511 FORMAT( F10.4)                                                       BLKTN457
  603 FORMAT(2F5.0)                                                        BLKTN458
         RETURN                                                            BLKTN459
         END                                                               BLKTN461
         SUBROUTINE COFEI1(D,R,B,XO,CC,XC,YC)                              COFEI101
C                                                                          COFEI102
C        COMPUTES B FOR EXTERIOR AND INTERIOR ELEMENTS INCLUDING CC        COFEI103
C        REQUIRED ORDER (X,Y,Z,K,P,W)                                      COFEI104
C        N=NUMBER OF POINT WHOSE COEFFICIENTS ARE BEING CALCULATED         COFEI105
C        CAMERA CONSTANT TAKEN NEGATIVE                                    COFEI106
C        R= MATRIX(SK,SP,SW,CK,CP,CW)                                      COFEI107
C        DATA= MATRIX(PT,X,Y,MX,MY,X,Y,Z)                                  COFEI108
C                                                                          COFEI109
         IMPLICIT REAL*8(A-H,O-Z)                                          COFEI110
         DIMENSION R(6),D(3),XO(6),B(2,9)                                  COFEI111
         SK=R(1)                                                           COFEI112
         SP=R(2)                                                           COFEI113
         SW=R(3)                                                           COFEI114
         CK=R(4)                                                           COFEI115
         CP=R(5)                                                           COFEI116
         CW=R(6)                                                           COFEI117
         DX=D(1)-XO(1)                                                     COFEI118
         DY=D(2)-XO(2)                                                     COFEI119
         DZ=D(3)-XO(3)                                                     COFEI120
         DO 110 L=1,6                                                      COFEI121
         B(1,L)=0.0                                                        COFEI122
  110    B(2,L)=0.0                                                        COFEI123
         XT=DX*CP*CK+DY*(CW*SK+SW*SP*CK)+DZ*(SW*SK-CW*SP*CK)              COFEI124
         YT=-DX*CP*SK+DY*(CW*CK-SW*SP*SK)+DZ*(SW*CK+CW*SP*SK)            COFEI125
         ZT=DX*SP-DY*SW*CP+DZ*CW*CP                                        COFEI126
         COZ=CC*(1.0/ZT**2)                                                COFEI127
```

```
      B(1,1)   =-COZ*(ZT*CP*CK-XT*SP)                                    COEFI128
      B(1,2)   =-COZ*(ZT*(CW*SK+SW*SP*CK)+XT*SW*CP)                      COEFI129
      B(1,3)   =-COZ*(ZT*(SW*SK-CW*SP*CK)-XT*CW*CP)                      COEFI130
      B(1,4)   =COZ*(-DX*CP*SK+DY*(CW*CK-SW*SP*SK)+DZ*(SW*CK+CW*SP*SK)   COEFI131
     1)*ZT                                                               COEFI132
      B(1,5)   =COZ*(ZT*(-DX*SP*CK+DY*SW*CP*CK-DZ*CW*CP*CK)-XT*(DX*      COEFI133
     1CP+DY*SW*SP-DZ*CW*SP))                                             COEFI134
      B(1,6)   =COZ*(ZT*(DY*(CW*SP*CK-SW*SK)+DZ*(CW*SK+SW*SP*CK))+       COEFI135
     1XT*(DY*CW*CP+DZ*SW*CP))                                            COEFI136
      XC=CC*XT*(1.0/ZT)                                                  COEFI137
      B(2,1)   =COZ*(ZT*CP*SK+YT*SP)                                     COEFI138
      B(2,2)   =-COZ*(ZT*(CW*CK-SW*SP*CK)+YT*SW*CP)                      COEFI139
      B(2,3)   =-COZ*(ZT*(SW*CK+CW*SP*SK)-YT*CW*CP)                      COEFI140
      B(2,4)   =COZ*(ZT*(-DX*CP*CK-DY*(CW*SK+SW*SP*CK)+DZ*(CW*SP*CK      COEFI141
     1-SW*SK)))                                                          COEFI142
      B(2,5)   =COZ*(ZT*(DX*SP*SK-DY*SW*CP*SK        +DZ*CW*CP*         COEFI143
     1SK)-YT*(DX*CP+DY*SP-DZ*CW*SP))                                     COEFI144
      B(2,6)   =COZ*(ZT*(-DY*(SW*CK+CW*SP*SK)+DZ*(CW*CK-SW*SP*SK))+      COEFI145
     1YT*(DY*CW*CP+DZ*SW*CP))                                            COEFI146
      YC=CC*YT*(1.0/ZT)                                                  COEFI147
      DO 126 I=1,3                                                       COEFI148
      B(1,I+6)=B(1,I)                                                    COEFI149
  126 B(2,I+6)=B(2,I)                                                    COEFI150
      DO 125 I=1,2                                                       COEFI151
      DO 125 J=1,6                                                       COEFI152
  125 B(I,J)=(-1.0)*B(I,J)                                               COEFI153
  150 CONTINUE                                                           COEFI154
      RETURN                                                             COEFI155
      END                                                               COEFI156
      SUBROUTINE MATINV(A,N)                                             MATINV01
      IMPLICIT REAL*8(A-H,O-Z)                                          MATINV02
      DIMENSION A(N,N),B(140),C(140)                                     MATINV03
      M=N-1                                                              MATINV04
      A(1,1)=1.0/A(1,1)                                                  MATINV05
      IF(M) 2900,2906,2900                                              MATINV06
 2900 DO 2905 I=1,M                                                      MATINV07
      L=I+1                                                              MATINV08
      DO 2901 J=1,I                                                      MATINV09
      B(J)=0.0                                                           MATINV10
 2901 C(J)=0.0                                                           MATINV11
      DO 2902 J=1,I                                                      MATINV12
      DO 2902 K=1,I                                                      MATINV13
      B(J)=B(J)-A(K,J)*A(L,K)                                            MATINV14
 2902 C(K)=C(K)-A(K,J)*A(J,L)                                            MATINV15
      D=A(L,L)                                                           MATINV16
      DO 2903 J=1,I                                                      MATINV17
 2903 D=D+C(J)*A(L,J)                                                    MATINV18
      D=1.0/D                                                            MATINV19
      DO 2904 J=1,I                                                      MATINV20
      A(J,L)=C(J)*D                                                      MATINV21
      A(L,J)=B(J)*D                                                      MATINV22
      DO 2904 K=1,I                                                      MATINV23
 2904 A(J,K)=A(J,K)+B(K)*C(J)*D                                          MATINV24
 2905 A(L,L)=D                                                           MATINV25
 2906 RETURN                                                             MATINV26
      END                                                               MATINV27
      SUBROUTINE MERGE (CC,NF,JP,WM,PH,PT,ITITLE,JOBNUM)                 MERGE101
      REAL*8 PH(4,50),PT(4,16,23)                                        MERGE102
      DIMENSIONCP(2),FOTO(16,20,6),SURVEY(16,20,9),UNQP(135),XO(6)       MERGE103
      DIMENSION  ITITLE(7)                                               MERGE104
      REAL   WE(6,6)/36*0.0/,WS(3,3)/9*0.0/,NAME(3),MX,MY,MZ             MERGE105
      INTEGER PTCNT(45),PTCNTS(45)                                       MERGE106
      READ(5,510) ITITLE,JOBNUM                                          MERGE107
  510 FORMAT(7A4,2X,I4)                                                  MERGE108
      READ (5,101)CC,WM                                                  MERGE109
  101 FORMAT(2F10.3)                                                     MERGE110
      NF=1                                                               MERGE111
      JP=0                                                               MERGE112
      DIV=0.0                                                            MERGE113
      IP=0                                                               MERGE114
      IFTMP=0                                                            MERGE115
      IUNQP=0                                                            MERGE116
    5 READ(1,1000,END=30) PHOTO,POINT,(CP(I),I=1,2),TEMP                 MERGE117
 1000 FORMAT(2F5.0,3F10.4)                                               MERGE118
      IF(DIV.EQ.0.0) GO TO 15                                            MERGE119
      IF(PHOTO.EQ.FOTO(IF,1,1)) GO TO 20                                 MERGE120
      PTCNT(IF)=IP                                                       MERGE121
      IP=0                                                               MERGE122
```

```
      IFTMP=IF                                          MERGE123
      DO 10 I=1,NF                                       MERGE124
      IF(PHOTO.NE.FOTO(I,1,1)) GO TO 10                 MERGE125
      IP=PTCNT(I)                                        MERGE126
      IF=I                                               MERGE127
      GO TO 20                                           MERGE128
   10 CONTINUE                                           MERGE129
      NF=NF+1                                            MERGE130
   15 IF=IFTMP+1                                         MERGE131
   20 DIV=DIV+1.0                                        MERGE132
      DO 25 I=1,IP                                       MERGE133
      IF(POINT.NE.FOTO(IF,I,2)) GO TO 25                MERGE134
      FOTO(IF,I,4)=(FOTO(IF,I,4)+CP(1))/2.0             MERGE135
      FOTO(IF,I,5)=(FOTO(IF,I,5)+CP(2))/2.0             MERGE136
      FOTO(IF,I,6)=(FOTO(IF,I,6)+TEMP)/2.0              MERGE137
      GO TO 5                                            MERGE138
   25 CONTINUE                                           MERGE139
      IP=IP+1                                            MERGE140
      FOTO(IF,IP,1)=PHOTO                                MERGE141
      FOTO(IF,IP,2)=POINT                                MERGE142
      FOTO(IF,IP,4)=CP(1)                                MERGE143
      FOTO(IF,IP,5)=CP(2)                                MERGE144
      FOTO(IF,IP,6)=TEMP                                 MERGE145
      GO TO 5                                            MERGE146
   30 PTCNT(IF)=IP                                       MERGE147
      DO33 I=1,NF                                        MERGE148
      PTCNTS(I)=0                                        MERGE149
      IP=PTCNT(I)                                        MERGE150
      DO 33 J=1,IP                                       MERGE151
   33 FOTO(I,J,3)=0.0                                    MERGE152
C                                                        MERGE153
C     READ SURVEY DATA                                   MERGE154
C                                                        MERGE155
   35 READ(2,1001,END=50) (NAME(I),I=1,3),DNO,X,Y,Z,MX,MY,MZ  MERGE156
 1001 FORMAT(2A4,A2,F4.0,6F11.3)                         MERGE157
      DO 38 J=1,IUNOP                                    MERGE158
      IF(UNOP(J).EQ.DNO) GO TO 997                      MERGE159
   38 CONTINUE                                           MERGE160
      IUNOP=IUNOP+1                                      MERGE161
      UNOP(IUNOP)=DNO                                    MERGE162
      IFOUND=0                                           MERGE163
      JP=JP+1                                            MERGE164
      DO 45 I=1,NF                                       MERGE165
      IP=PTCNT(I)                                        MERGE166
      DO 40 J=1,IP                                       MERGE167
      IF(DNO.NE.FOTO(I,J,2)) GO TO 40                   MERGE168
      SURVEY(I,J,1)=NAME(1)                              MERGE169
      SURVEY(I,J,2)=NAME(2)                              MERGE170
      SURVEY(I,J,3)=NAME(3)                              MERGE171
      SURVEY(I,J,4)=X                                    MERGE172
      SURVEY(I,J,5)=Y                                    MERGE173
      SURVEY(I,J,6)=Z                                    MERGE174
      SURVEY(I,J,7)=MX                                   MERGE175
      SURVEY(I,J,8)=MY                                   MERGE176
      SURVEY(I,J,9)=MZ                                   MERGE177
      FOTO(I,J,3)=JP                                     MERGE178
      PTCNTS(I)=PTCNTS(I)+1                              MERGE179
      IFOUND=1                                           MERGE180
      GO TO 45                                           MERGE181
   40 CONTINUE                                           MERGE182
   45 CONTINUE                                           MERGE183
      IF(IFOUND) 35,999,35                              MERGE184
   50 WRITE(6,2008)                                      MERGE185
 2008 FORMAT('0INPUT FOR THE FORTRAN BLOCK',//)         MERGE186
      WRITE(6,2000) CC,NF,JP                             MERGE187
      WRITE(6,2000)WM                                    MERGE188
 2000 FORMAT(F10.3,2I5)                                  MERGE189
   55 READ(5,1003,END=150) PHOTO,(XO(I),I=1,6)          MERGE190
 1003 FORMAT(F4.0,6F11.3)                                MERGE191
      DO 60 I=1,NF                                       MERGE192
      IPHOTO=FOTO(I,1,1)                                 MERGE193
      IF(PHOTO.EQ.FLOAT(IPHOTO)) GO TO 65               MERGE194
   60 CONTINUE                                           MERGE195
      GO TO 998                                          MERGE196
   65 IF(PTCNTS(I).EQ.0) GO TO 996                      MERGE197
      IP=PTCNTS(I)                                       MERGE198
      PH(I,1)=IP                                         MERGE199
      PH(I,50)=IPHOTO                                    MERGE200
```

```
   70 WRITE(6,2001) IP,IPHOTO                                      MERGE201
 2001 FORMAT(2I5)                                                   MERGE202
      DO 75 J=1,6                                                   MERGE203
      IJ=J+1                                                        MERGE204
      PH(I,IJ)=XO(J)                                                MERGE205
   75 WRITE(6,2002) XO(J)                                           MERGE206
 2002 FORMAT(F11.3)                                                 MERGE207
      READ(5,1004) (WE(J,J),J=1,6)                                  MERGE208
 1004 FORMAT(6F10.3)                                                MERGE209
      L1=13                                                         MERGE210
      DO 80 J=1,6                                                   MERGE211
      IF(WE(J,J).EQ.0.0) WE(J,J)=1.0D25                             MERGE212
      WE(J,J)=1.0/WE(J,J)**2                                        MERGE213
      DO 200 L=1,6                                                  MERGE214
      L1=L1+1                                                       MERGE215
  200 PH(I,L1)=WE(J,L)                                              MERGE216
   80 WRITE(6,2003) (WE(J,L),L=1,6)                                 MERGE217
 2003 FORMAT(6F10.3)                                                MERGE218
      DO 100 J=1,IP                                                 MERGE219
      IPOINT=FOTO(I,J,2)                                            MERGE220
      IF(FOTO(I,J,3).EQ.0.0) GO TO 995                              MERGE221
      IPSUDO=FOTO(I,J,3)                                            MERGE222
      PT(I,J,1)=FOTO(I,J,4)                                         MERGE223
      PT(I,J,2)=FOTO(I,J,5)                                         MERGE224
      PT(I,J,3)=IPSUDO                                              MERGE225
      PT(I,J,23)=IPOINT                                             MERGE226
      WRITE(6,2004) (FOTO(I,J,L),L=4,5)                             MERGE227
   85 WRITE(6,2005) IPSUDO,IPOINT,(SURVEY(I,J,L),L=1,3)             MERGE228
 2004 FORMAT(2F10.3)                                                MERGE229
 2005 FORMAT(2I5,2X,2A4,A2)                                         MERGE230
      DO 90 L=4,6                                                   MERGE231
      K=13+L                                                        MERGE232
  201 PT(I,J,K)=SURVEY(I,J,L)                                       MERGE233
   90 WRITE(6,2006) SURVEY(I,J,L)                                   MERGE234
 2006 FORMAT(F11.3)                                                 MERGE235
      DO 95 L=7,9                                                   MERGE236
      IF(SURVEY(I,J,L).EQ.0.0) SURVEY(I,J,L)=1.0D25                 MERGE237
      WS(L-6,L-6)=1.0/SURVEY(I,J,L)**2                              MERGE238
      KL=7+3*(L-7)                                                  MERGE239
      DO 94 N=1,3                                                   MERGE240
      K=KL+N                                                        MERGE241
   94 PT(I,J,K)=WS(L-6,N)                                           MERGE242
 2007 FORMAT(3F10.3)                                                MERGE243
   95 WRITE(6,2007) (WS(L-6,N),N=1,3)                               MERGE244
      GO TO 100                                                     MERGE245
  995 WRITE(6,9003) IPOINT                                          MERGE246
 9003 FORMAT(' POINT NUMBER ',I5,' HAS NO CORRESPONDING SURVEY COORDINATMERGE247
     *E DATA')                                                      MERGE248
  100 CONTINUE                                                      MERGE249
      GO TO 55                                                      MERGE250
  996 WRITE(6,9004) IPHOTO                                          MERGE251
 9004 FORMAT(' PHOTO NUMBER ',I5,' HAS NO OBJECT SPACE POINTS FOR WHICH MERGE252
     *SURVEY DATA WAS INPUT')                                       MERGE253
      GO TO 55                                                      MERGE254
  997 IPOINT=DNO                                                    MERGE255
      WRITE(6,9002) IPOINT                                          MERGE256
 9002 FORMAT(' SURVEY POINT NUMBER ',I5,' HAS BEEN ENCOUNTERED PREVIOUSLMERGE257
     *Y -- SUBSEQUENT ENCOUNTERS ARE IGNORED')                     MERGE258
      GO TO 35                                                      MERGE259
  998 IPHOTO=PHOTO                                                  MERGE260
      WRITE(6,9001) IPHOTO                                          MERGE261
 9001 FORMAT(' PHOTO NUMBER ',I5,' HAS NO CORRESPONDING PHOTO NUMBER IN MERGE262
     *THE PHOTO COORDINATE DATA')                                   MERGE263
      READ(5,1004) (WE(J,J),J=1,6)                                  MERGE264
      GO TO 55                                                      MERGE265
  999 IPOINT=DNO                                                    MERGE266
      JP=JP-1                                                       MERGE267
      WRITE(6,9000) IPOINT                                          MERGE268
 9000 FORMAT(' POINT NUMBER ',I5,' HAS NO CORRESPONDING POINT NUMBER IN MERGE269
     *THE PHOTO COORDINATE DATA')                                   MERGE270
      GO TO 35                                                      MERGE271
  150 RETURN                                                        MERGE272
      END                                                           MERGE274
/*
```

```
//STEP2 EXEC PROC=RUNFORT,TIME.LKED=(,20),TIME.GO=(1,20),REGION.GO=252K  JCL00007
//LKED.SYSLIN DD DSN=*.STEP1.CMP.SYSLIN,DISP=(OLD,DELETE)                JCL00008
//GO.FT01F001 DD *                                                       JCL00009
     20    7   105.6856     61.4963
     20    8   107.9901     63.4393
     20    9     7.1071    -27.4812
     20   10     8.8981      7.8185
     21    1    73.9109     91.7115      .010
     21    2    85.0789    -44.8377      .010
     21    3    69.8560     -8.2889      .010
     21    7    -0.5324     53.0685
     21    8    -0.6009     54.6293
     21    9   -98.2175    -33.8200
     21   10   -95.7196      1.3921
     22    6   -98.2121     90.1087      .010
     21    4    12.0727     24.5224      .010
     22    4   -89.9721     12.9013      .010
     21    5    37.6479    -58.4897      .010
     21    6    14.2475    102.2505      .010
     22    5   -64.3277    -70.1343      .010
     22    1   -29.1931     80.4293      .010
     22    2   -16.5971    -56.3155      .010
     22    3   -32.1743    -19.6246      .010
     22    7  -102.7578     41.2395
     22    8  -106.1120     42.6030
/*
//GO.FT02F001 DD *                                                       JCL00010
ARPS        1 10949.064   10051.131 229.454        0.01        0.01      0.01
BKR         2 10915.382    9545.662 225.837        0.01        0.01      0.01
HAG         3 10879.676    9688.487 226.949
3           4 10000.0     10000.0   228.577                              0.01
PAS1        5 12000.0      8300.0   230.0
PAS2        6 12400.0     14000.0   230.0
ABGR        7 10690.0      9850.0   230.0
ABTP        8 10690.0      9850.0   250.0
PSSS        9 10200.0      9700.0   220.0
PUMP       10 10274.919    9818.564 220.0          0.01        0.01
/*
//GO.FT03F001 DD SYSOUT=A,DCB=(RECFM=FBA,LRECL=133,BLKSIZE=665)          JCL00011
//GO.FT04F001 DD SYSOUT=A,DCB=(RECFM=FBA,LRECL=133,BLKSIZE=665)          JCL00012
//GO.SYSIN DD *                                                          JCL00013
        GEO SCI                    1
   -152.010 1000.000
     20 10246.0      9760.0       800.0

     21 10630.84     9758.37      791.6     -0.15223  -0.00455   -0.0004

     22 11014.98     9737.46      787.91    -0.15678   0.01166    0.0074358

/*
//
```

Appendix C
Computer
Program—Independent
Model Block

218

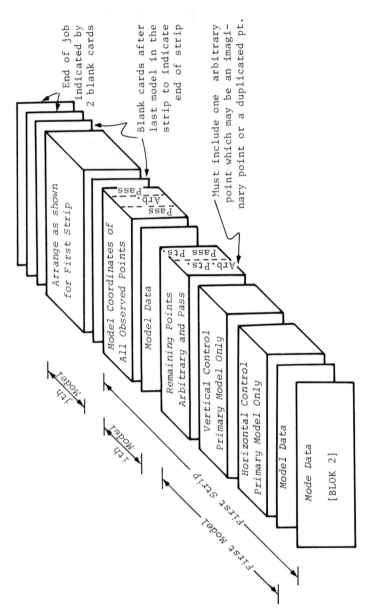

Figure C-1 General Setup for Strips

219

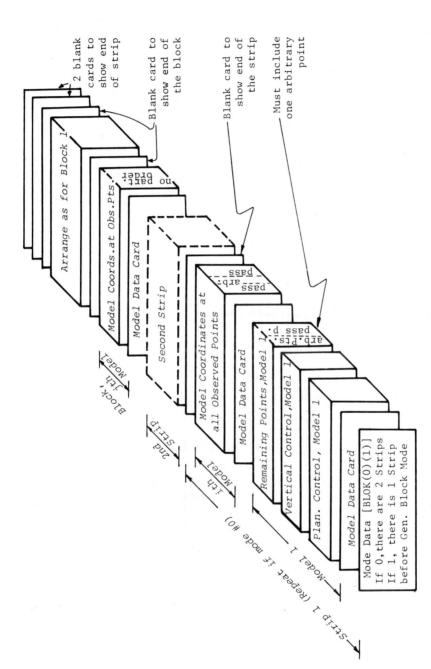

Figure C-2 General Setup for Block Using Strips to form the basic "L"

220

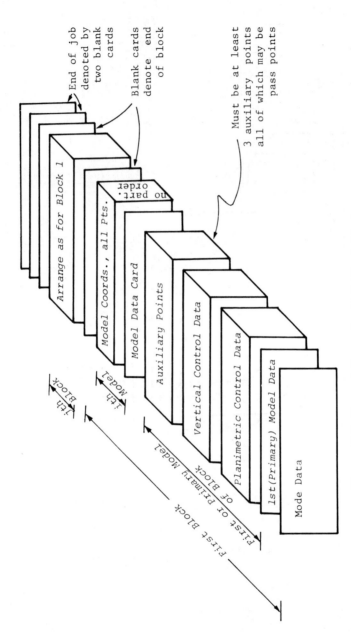

Figure C-3 General Setup for Full Block Mode

```
//          (2000,500),CLASS=C,MSGLEVEL=(0,0)
//COMPILE    EXEC PGM=IEYFORT,
//              PARM='LOAD,SOURCE,MAP,ID',                              &
//              REGION=126K,                                           &
//              TIME=(,10)
//SYSPRINT   DD SYSOUT=A
//SYSPUNCH   DD SYSOUT=B
//SYSLIN     DD DSNAME=&LOADSET,                                       &
//              UNIT=SYSDA,                                            &
//              DCB=(RECFM=FB,LRECL=80,BLKSIZE=400),                   &
//              DISP=(NEW,PASS),                                       &
//              SPACE=(CYL,(1,1))
//SYSIN      DD *
C***************************************************************************************
C
C PHOTO TRIANGULATION WITH INDEPENDANT MODELS.
C PROGRAM IS SUITED FOR IBM 360/75 OF COMPUTER CENTRE AND IS IN DOUBLE PRECISION
C METHOD IS THAT OF USCGS
C***************************************************************************************
C
      IMPLICIT REAL *8 (A-H,O-Z)
      REAL *8  KAP,NORM,LDX,LDY,ID
      INTEGER *4 CHCD,CVCD,COBS,ROBS,STOPIT,RNORM,CDATA
C     DIMENSION  HCD(150,6),VCD(150,5),OBS(150,8),NORM(56,8),T1(10),T(2)
C    1,DATA(150,4),P(10),STNO(1500),XX(1500),YY(1500),ZZ(1500)
      DIMENSION  HCD(250,6),VCD(250,5),OBS(250,8),NORM(56,8),T1(10),T(2)
     1,DATA(250,4),P(10),STNO(2500),XX(2500),YY(2500),ZZ(2500)
      REAL *8  NORMM(7,7),U(7),NORMIN(7,7), ANS(7)
      DIMENSION NAME(5)
      DATA ITEST1/'BLOK'/
      DO 2 I=1,1000
      STNO(I)=0.
      XX(I)=0.
      YY(I)=0.
      ZZ(I)=0.
    2 CONTINUE
      INPTS=0
C
C
   10 COBS =8
      CHCD =6
      CVCD =5
      RNORM=7
      CDATA=4
      CONV = 180.D0/3.1415926536
C     READ CARD WHICH TELL PROGRAM WHICH OPPERATING MODE TO USE
      READ (5,150) ITEST4,ICOUNT,NAME(1),NAME(2),NAME(3),NAME(4),NAME(5)
C***************************************************************************************
C
C     READ STATEMENT FOR FIRST MODEL NUMBER,NUMBER OF HORIZONTAL CONTROL POINTS,
C     NUMBER OF VERTICAL CONTROL POINTS,NUMBER OF ARBITARY POINTS,AND NUMBER OF
C     PASS POINTS
   11 IJK=0
      READ(5,101) MDLN,NHC,NVC,NARB,NPASS
      IF(NARB.EQ.0) GO TO 50
      WRITE(6,104) NAME(1),NAME(2),NAME(3),NAME(4),NAME(5)
C     NOW READ IN HORIZONTAL CONTROL FOR FIRST MODEL. DATA ORDER IS: ID, GROUND-
C     X, GROUND-Y, MODEL-X, MODEL-Y, MODEL-Z.
      DO 200 I=1,NHC
      READ(5,102) (HCD(I,J),J=1,6)
  200 CONTINUE
C     NOW READ IN VERTICAL CONTROL FOR FIRST MODEL. DATA ORDER IS: ID, GROUND-Z,
C     MODEL-X, MODEL-Y, MODEL-Z
      DO 201 I=1,NVC
      READ(5,103) (VCD(I,J),J=1,5)
  201 CONTINUE
   35 NITS =0
      STOPIT =0
C     END BASIC INPUT AND SET UP SECTION
C***************************************************************************************
C
C     NOW START SECTION DEALING WITH INITIAL OR APPROXIMATE VALUES
C
C     NEXT 5 STATEMENTS COMPUTE APPROX SCALE BETWEEN MODEL AND GROUND
      SDX = HCD(1,4)  - HCD(2,4)                                        1
      SDY = HCD(1,5)  - HCD(2,5)                                        2
      LDX = HCD(1,2)  - HCD(2,2)                                        3
```

```
           LDY = HCD(1,3) - HCD(2,3)                                              4
           S = DSORT((SDX**2+SDY**2)/(LDX**2+LDY**2))                             5
C     NOW FIND APPROXIMATE KAPPA OF MODEL
           KAP=DATAN2(LDY,LDX)-DATAN2(SDY,SDX)
C          KAP=DATAN2(SDY,SDX)-DATAN2(LDY,LDX)
C     NEXT 5 STATEMENTS COMPUTE APPROXIMATE TRANSLATIONS BETWEEN THIS MODEL
C     SYSTEM AND GROUND SYSTEM
           SKAP = DSIN(KAP)                                                       1
           CKAP = DCOS(KAP)                                                       2
           TX  = HCD( 1,4) - S*(HCD(1,2)*CKAP +HCD(1,3)* SKAP)                    3
           TY  = HCD( 1,5) - S*(-HCD(1,2)*SKAP+HCD(1,3)* CKAP)                    4
           TZ  = VCD( 1,5) - S*VCD(1,2)                                           5
C     INITIAL APPROXIMATIONS FOR PHI AND OMEGA ARE ENTERED
           PHI  = 0.D0
           OMG  = 0.D0
C
C************************************************************************************
C
C     THIS BEGIN ITTERATIVE SECTION OF FORMING MATRIX PARTIALS
C     NEXT 6 STATEMENTS  SINES AND COSINES OF ORIENTATION MATRIX
        12 SOMG=DSIN(OMG)
           COMG = DCOS(OMG)                                                       2
           SPHI = DSIN(PHI)                                                       3
           CPHI = DCOS(PHI)                                                       4
           SKAP = DSIN(KAP)                                                       5
           CKAP = DCOS(KAP)                                                       6
C     NEXT 9 STATEMENTS COMPUTE ELEMENTS OF ORIENTATION MATRIX
           A11 =CPHI * CKAP                                                       1
           A12 =COMG * SKAP + SOMG * SPHI * CKAP                                  2
           A13 = SOMG * SKAP - COMG * SPHI * CKAP                                 3
           A21 =-CPHI* SKAP                                                       4
           A22 =COMG * CKAP - SOMG * SPHI * SKAP                                  5
           A23 =SOMG * CKAP + COMG * SPHI * SKAP                                  6
           A31 =SPHI                                                              7
           A32 =-SOMG*CPHI                                                        8
           A33 =COMG * CPHI                                                       9
C     IF THIS IS FINAL COMPUTATION OF ORIENTATION MATRIX TRANSFER
           IF(STOPIT.EQ.1) GO TO 49
C     NEXT  9 STATEMENTS COMPUTES PARTIALS OF ORIENTATION MATRIX WITH RESPECT TO
C     PHI
           PA11 = -SPHI * CKAP                                                    1
           PA12 =  SOMG * CPHI * CKAP                                             2
           PA13 = -COMG * CPHI * CKAP                                             3
           PA21 =  SPHI * SKAP                                                    4
           PA22 = -SOMG * CPHI * SKAP                                            5
           PA23 =  COMG * CPHI * SKAP                                            6
           PA31 =  CPHI                                                           7
           PA32 =  SOMG * SPHI                                                    8
           PA33 = -COMG * SPHI                                                    9
C
C************************************************************************************
C     THE OBSERVATION EQUATION SECTION
C     STATE COMPUTATION OF X AND Y OBSERVATION EQUATION FOR THIS MODEL 21
C     STATEMENTS ENVOLVED
           DO 48 I=1,NHC                                                          1
           J = I*2-1                                                              2
           Z = (1.D0/S) * (A13*(HCD(I,4)-TX)+ A23*(HCD(I,5)-TY) + A33*(HCD(I,     3
          16)- TZ))
           OBS(J,1) = S* (-A13 * HCD(I,3) + A12 * Z )                             4
           OBS(J,2) = S * (PA11 * HCD(I,2) +PA12 * HCD(I,3) + PA13 * Z )          5
           OBS(J,3) = S * ( A21 * HCD(I,2) + A22 * HCD(I,3) +  A23 * Z )          6
           OBS(J,4) =     ( A11 * HCD(I,2) + A12 * HCD(I,3) +  A13 * Z )          7
           OBS(J,5) = 1.D0                                                        8
           OBS(J,6) = 0.D0                                                        9
           OBS(J,7) = 0.D0                                                        10
           OBS(J,8) =-S * OBS(J,4) - TX + HCD(I,4)                                11
           K = J+1                                                                12
           OBS(K,1) = S * (-A23 * HCD(I,3) + A22 * Z )                            13
           OBS(K,2) = S * (PA21 * HCD(I,2) +PA22 * HCD(I,3) + PA23 * Z )          14
           OBS(K,3) = S * (-A11 * HCD(I,2) - A12 * HCD(I,3) -  A13 * Z )          15
           OBS(K,4) =     ( A21 * HCD(I,2) + A22 * HCD(I,3) +  A23 * Z )          16
           OBS(K,5) = 0.D0                                                        17
           OBS(K,6) = 1.D0                                                        18
           OBS(K,7) = 0.D0                                                        19
           OBS(K,8) =-S * OBS(K,4) - TY + HCD(I,5)                                20
        48 CONTINUE                                                               21
C     NEXT 13 STATEMENTS USED TO COMPUTE Z OBSERVATION EQUATIONS FOR MODEL
           DO 47 I =1, NVC                                                        1
```

```
      J = K+I                                                                     2
      X =(1.DO/S) * ( A11*(VCD(I,3)-TX) + A21*(VCD(I,4)-TY) + A31*(VCD(I           3
     1,5) - TZ) )
      Y =(1.DO/S) * ( A12*(VCD(I,3)-TX) + A22*(VCD(I,4)-TY) + A32*(VCD(I           4
     1,5) - TZ) )
      OBS(J,1) = S * (-A33 * Y  +  A32* VCD(I,2))                                  5
      OBS(J,2) = S * (PA31 * X  +  PA32* Y  +  PA33* VCD(I,2))                     6
      OBS(J,3) = 0.DO                                                             7
      OBS(J,4) =          A31 * X   +   A32* Y  +   A33* VCD(I,2)                  8
      OBS(J,5) = 0.DO                                                             9
      OBS(J,6) = 0.DO                                                             10
      OBS(J,7) = 1.DO                                                             11
      OBS(J,8) =-S * OBS(J,4) - TZ +VCD(I,5)                                      12
   47 CONTINUE                                                                    13
C
C
C*********************************************************************************
C
C     NOW ENTER NORMAL EQUATION STAGE
C     COMPUTE NUMBER OF OBSERVATION EQUATIONS
      ROBS =2*NHC+NVC
C     CLEAR NORMAL MATRIX AS SOME ELEMENTS MAY BE ZERO
      DO 46 I = 1, RNORM
      DO 46 J=I,COBS
   46 NORM(I,J) = 0.DO
C     FORM NORMAL EQUATIONS IN NEXT 4 STATEMENTS
      DO 45 I =1,COBS                                                             1
      DO 45 J =I,COBS                                                             2
      DO 45 K =1,ROBS                                                             3
   45 NORM(I,J) = NORM(I,J)+ OBS(K,I)* OBS(K,J)                                   4
C     FORM LOWER TRIANGULAR PART OF NORMAL EQUATIONS NEXT 4 STATEMENTS
      DO 44 I =1, COBS
      DO 44 J =I, COBS
      NORM(J,I) = NORM(I,J)
   44 CONTINUE
C     INVERT NORMAL EQUATION MATRIX AND FORM SOLUTION VECTOR.10 STATEMENTS
      DO 215 I=1,7                                                                1
      U(I)=NORM(8,I)                                                              2
      DO 215 J=1,7                                                                3
      NORMM(I,J)=NORM(I,J)                                                        4
  215 CONTINUE                                                                    5
      CALL VERSOL (NORMM,NORMIN,7,7)                                              6
      CALL AMAMPY (NORMIN,U,ANS,7,7,1 )                                           7
      DO 216 I=1,7                                                                8
      NORM(I,8)= ANS(I)                                                           9
  216 CONTINUE                                                                    10
C     THERE IS NO SINGULARITY CHECK HERE.
C     INSERT HERE SINGULARITY CHECK IF DESIRED
      IERROR =0
      IF(IERROR.GT.0) GO TO 43
C     COMPUTE  ADJUSTED PARAMETERS  NEXT 7 STATEMENTS
      OMG = OMG + NORM(1,8)                                                       1
      PHI = PHI + NORM(2,8)                                                       2
      KAP = KAP + NORM(3,8)                                                       3
      S   = S   + NORM(4,8)                                                       4
      TX  = TX  + NORM(5,8)                                                       5
      TY  = TY  + NORM(6,8)                                                       6
      TZ  = TZ  + NORM(7,8)                                                       7
C     COUNT ITTERATIONS
      NITS=NITS + 1
C     TEST CONVERGENCE OF SOLUTION  7STATEMENTS
      A   =DABS(NORM(1,8))                                                        1
      B=DABS(NORM(2,8))                                                           2
      C=DABS(NORM(3,8))                                                           3
      D=1.D-05                                                                    4
      IF( A.GT.D .OR. B.GT.D .OR. C.GT.D ) GO TO 12                               5
   32 STOPIT =1                                                                   6
      GO TO 12                                                                    7
C
C*********************************************************************************
C
C     ENTER OUTPUT SECTION OF PROGRAM FOR MODEL UNDER CONSIDERATION
C
C
   49 OMG =OMG * CONV
      PHI =PHI * CONV
      KAP =KAP * CONV
C     WRITE OUTPUT FOR THIS MODEL- ORIENTATION DATA ONLY
```

```
      WRITE(6,105) MDLN,NITS,OMG,PHI,KAP,S,TX,TY,TZ
C     NEXT 14-STATEMENTS COMPUTE CO-ORDINATES OF HORIZONTAL CONTROL,COMPUTE
C     ERRORS,AND WRITE RESULTS
      WRITE(6,106)                                                         1
      DO 39 I=1,NHC                                                        2
      A = HCD(I,4)-TX                                                      3
      B = HCD(I,5)-TY                                                      4
      C = HCD(I,6)-TZ                                                      5
      D = 1.D0/S                                                           6
      X = D*(A11*A+A21*B+A31*C)                                           7
      Y = D*(A12*A+A22*B+A32*C)                                           8
      Z = D*(A13*A+A23*B+A33*C)                                           9
      LDX = X - HCD(I,2)                                                  10


      WRITE(1)      HCD(I,1),                    X,Y,Z                     13
      IJK=IJK+1
      IF (ITEST1.NE.ITEST4 ) GO TO 39
      STNO(IJK+INPTS) = HCD(I,1)
        XX(IJK+INPTS) = X
        YY(IJK+INPTS) = Y
        ZZ(IJK+INPTS) = Z
   39 CONTINUE
C     NEXT 12 STATEMENTS COMPUTE CO-ORDINATES OF VERTICAL CONTROL,COMPUTE
C     ERRORS,AND WRITE RESULTS
      WRITE(6,108)                                                        1
      DO 38 I=1,NVC                                                        2
      A   =  VCD(I,3) -TX                                                  3
      B   =  VCD(I,4) -TY                                                  4
      C   =  VCD(I,5) -TZ                                                  5
      X   =  D * (A11*A +A21*B +A31*C)                                     6
      Y   =  D * (A12*A +A22*B +A32*C)                                     7
      Z   =  D * (A13*A +A23*B +A33*C)                                     8
      DZ  =  Z - VCD(I,2)                                                  9
      WRITE(6,109) VCD(I,1),VCD(I,2),X,Y,Z,DZ                             10
      WRITE(1)      VCD(I,1),          X,Y,Z                              11
      IJK=IJK+1
      IF (ITEST1.NE.ITEST4 ) GO TO 38
      STNO( IJK + INPTS ) = VCD(I,1)
        XX( IJK + INPTS ) = X
        YY( IJK + INPTS ) = Y
        ZZ( IJK + INPTS ) = Z
   38 CONTINUE
C     NEXT 21 STATEMENTS READ MODEL CO-ORDINATES OF REMAINING POINTS IN THIS
C     MODEL,COMPUTE AND WRITE GROUND CO-ORDINATES,AND TRANSFER GROUND
C     CO-ORDINATES OF THE PASS POINTS TO TEMPORARY STORAGE
      K =      0                                                          1
      IF(ITEST1.NE.ITEST4. OR.ICOUNT.LE.1) GO TO 206
      NPASS=0
      NARB=IPTS
      NPTS=IPTS
      GO TO 207
  206 NPTS = NARB +NPASS                                                  2
      DO 202 I=1,NPTS                                                     4A
      READ(5,111) (DATA(I,J), J=1,4)                                      4
  202 CONTINUE                                                            4B
  207 WRITE(6,110)                                                        3
      DO 37 I= 1,NPTS                                                     5
      A =  DATA(I,2) -TX                                                  6
      B =  DATA(I,3) -TY                                                  7
      C =  DATA(I,4) -TZ                                                  8
      X = D*( A11*A +A21*B +A31*C)                                        9
      Y = D*( A12*A +A22*B +A32*C)                                       10
      Z = D*( A13*A +A23*B +A33*C)                                       11
      IF (I.LE.NARB) GO TO 34                                            12
      K = K+1                                                            13
      HCD(K,1) = DATA(I,1)                                               14
      HCD(K,2) = X                                                       15
      HCD(K,3) = Y                                                       16
      VCD(K,1) = DATA(I,1)                                               17
      VCD(K,2) = Z                                                       18
   34 WRITE(6,112)  DATA(I,1),X,Y,Z                                      19
      WRITE(1)      DATA(I,1),X,Y,Z                                      20
      IJK=IJK+1
      IF ( ITEST1.NE.ITEST4) GO TO 37
      STNO( IJK + INPTS ) = DATA(I,1)
        XX( IJK + INPTS ) = X
```

```
             YY( IJK + INPTS ) = Y
             ZZ( IJK + INPTS ) = Z
       37 CONTINUE
C        NEXT CARD SWITCHES MODE OF COMPUTATIONS FROM STRIP TO BLOCK
         IF(ICOUNT.GT.1.AND.ITEST1.EQ.ITEST4) GO TO 800
C
C**********************************************************************************
C
C        NOW ENTER SECTION THAT PICKS UP NEXT MODEL AND TRANSFERS CONTROL
C
C        NEXT STATEMENT READS THE NEXT MODEL NUMBER,NUMBER OF HORIZONTAL AND
C        VERTICAL CONTROLS (WHICH ARE BOTH EQUAL TO THE NUMBER OF PASS POINTS
C        IN THE PRECEDING MODEL), THE NUMBER OF ARBITARY POINTS,AND THE NUMBER
C        OF PASS POINTS TO THE NEXT MODEL
         READ(5,101) MDLN,NHC,NVC,NARB,NPASS
         IF (NHC.EQ.0) GO TO 51
C        NEXT 6 STATEMENTS READ MODEL CO-ORDINATES OF POINTS CONNECTING THIS
C        MODEL TO THE PREVIOUS MODEL AND STORE THEM WITH THE PREVIOUSLY COMPUTED
C        GROUND CO-ORDINATES
         DO 36 I=1, NHC
         READ(5,111) ID,HCD(I,4),HCD(I,5),HCD(I,6)
         IF( ID.NE.HCD(I,1))GO TO 52
         VCD(I,3) = HCD(I,4)
         VCD(I,4) = HCD(I,5)
       36 VCD(I,5) = HCD(I,6)
         GO  TO 35
C        THIS REPRESENTS THE END OF A STRIP.  MUST RE-ENTER THE STRIP MODE
C        OR THE BLOCK MODE EVEN IF ONLY ONE STRIP IS BEING INVESTIGATED
       51 WRITE(6,113)
         INPTS=INPTS+IJK
         IJK=0
         IF (ITEST1.NE.ITEST4) GO TO 11
         ICOUNT=ICOUNT +1
         IF ( ICOUNT.GT.1 ) GO TO 800
         GO TO 11
       52 WRITE(6,114)
         GO TO 53
       43 WRITE(6,115)
         GO TO  53
       50 WRITE(6,116)
       53 CONTINUE
         REWIND 1
         WRITE(6,601) INPTS
C        NOW WRITE OUT THE DISC RECORDS
         DO 602 I=1,INPTS
         READ(1) AA,AB,AC,AD
         WRITE(6,603) AA,AB,AC,AD
         WRITE(7,606) AA,AB,AC,AD
      602 CONTINUE
         CALL EXIT
C        INSERT HERE THE BLOCK PICK UP MODE
C
      800 INPTS=INPTS+IJK
         IJK=0
         READ (5,155) MDLN,IPTS
         IF (IPTS .EQ. 0 ) GO TO 11
C        READ IN THE OBSERVED MODEL COORDINATES OF THE NEXT MODEL
         DO 1500 I=1,IPTS
         READ (5,111) (DATA(I,J),J=1,4 )
     1500 CONTINUE
C        NEXT 19 STATEMENTS CONDUCT SEARCH OF ARRAYS HOLDING BLOCK DATA FOR
C        SUITABLE POINTS TO ACT AS CONTROL POINTS  IF A POINT NUMBER APPEARS
C        MORE THAN ONCEIN THE  BLOCK ARRAY THEN IT IS USED AS A MULTIPLE POINT
C        IN THE LEAST SQUARES SOLUTION.
         IJ=0
         DO 1501 I=1,IPTS
         NUMBER= DATA(I,1)
         DO 1502 I1=1,INPTS
         IF (NUMBER.NE.STNO(I1)) GO TO 1502
         IJ=IJ+1
         HCD(IJ,1) =  DATA(I,1)
         HCD(IJ,2) = XX(I1)
         HCD(IJ,3) = YY(I1)
         HCD(IJ,4) = DATA(I,2)
         HCD(IJ,5) = DATA(I,3)
         HCD(IJ,6) = DATA(I,4)
         VCD(IJ,1)  = DATA(I,1)
```

```
       VCD(IJ,2)   = ZZ(I1)
       VCD(IJ,3)   = DATA(I,2)
       VCD(IJ,4)   = DATA(I,3)
       VCD(IJ,5)   = DATA(I,4)
1502 CONTINUE
1501 CONTINUE
     NHC=IJ
     NVC=IJ
     GO TO 35
C  53 CALL EXIT
C     FORMAT STATEMENTS
C
C*************************************************************************
C*************************************************************************
C*************************************************************************
C
C
 101 FORMAT (I6,2X,I2,3X,I2,3X,I2,3X,I2)
 102 FORMAT (F6.0,4X,5(F10.3,2X))
 103 FORMAT (F6.0,16X,4(F10.3,2X))
 104 FORMAT(1H1,///////////////////,1X,35X,52(1H*),/,36X,1H*,50X,1H*,
    1/,36X,1H*,50X,1H*,/,36X,1H*,50X,1H*,/,36X,1H*,50X,1H*,/,36X,1H*,5X
    2,41H      INDEPENDENT MODEL TRIANGULATION      ,4X,1H*,/, 36X,1H*,5X
    3,41H      ----------------------------      ,4X,1H*,/, 36X,1H*,50
    4X,1H*,/,36X,1H*,50X,1H*,/,36X,1H*,15X,5A4,15X,1H*,/,36X,1H*,50X,1H
    5*,/,36X,1H*,50X,1H*,/,36X,52(1H*)   )
 105 FORMAT(1H1,//,10X,6HMODEL ,I6,                ///,15X,39HABSOLUTE
    1 ORIENTATION WAS ACHIEVED WITH ,I3,11H ITERATIONS,//,15X,22HORIENT
    2ATION DATA ARE -,//,28X,8HOMEGA = ,D17.8,8H DEGREES,/,30X,6HPHI =
    3,D17.8,8H DEGREES,/,28X,8HKAPPA = ,D17.8,8H DEGREES,/,21X,15HSCALE
    4 FACTOR = ,D17.8,/,20X,16HX-TRANSLATION = ,D16.8,3H MM,/,20X,16HY-
    5TRANSLATION = ,D16.8,3H MM,/,20X,16HZ-TRANSLATION = ,D16.8,3H,MM )
 106 FORMAT(/////,15X,33HPOINTS USED AS HORIZONTAL CONTROL,//,15X,6HIDE
    1NT.,6X,7HGIVEN-X,5X,7HGIVEN-Y,7X,34HCOMPUTED-X  COMPUTED-Y  COMPUT
    2ED-Z,6X,17HX-ERROR   Y-ERROR)
 107 FORMAT(/,14X,F7.0,3X,2(F11.3,1X),4X,3(F11.3,1X),4X,2(F8.3,2X))
 108 FORMAT(/////,15X,31HPOINTS USED AS VERTICAL CONTROL,//,15X,6HIDENT
    1.,6X,7HGIVEN-Z,19X,34HCOMPUTED-X  COMPUTED-Y  COMPUTED-Z,6X,7HZ-ER
    2ROR)
 109 FORMAT(/,14X,F7.0,3X,F11.3,17X,3(F11.3,1X),4X,F8.3)
 110 FORMAT(/////,15X, 40HCOMPUTED COORDINATES OF REMAINING POINTS,//,1
    15X,6HIDENT.,9X,1HX,11X,1HY,11X,1HZ )
 111 FORMAT ( F6.0,28X,3(F10.3,2X))
 112 FORMAT (/,14X,F7.0,3X,3(F11.3,1X))
 113 FORMAT (//////////,5X,18H***END OF STRIP***)
 114 FORMAT (//////,5X,52HTHE PASS POINTS ARE NOT GIVEN IN THE PROPER SE
    1QUENCE)
 115 FORMAT (//////,5X,85HTHE MATRIX OF THE NEXT MODEL IS SINGULAR OR AN
    1 OVERFLOW HAS OCCURRED DURING INVERSION )
 116 FORMAT (////,5X,35HALL COMPUTATION HAVE BEEN COMPLETED)
 150 FORMAT (A4,1X,I5 ,5A4 )
 155 FORMAT (I6,12X,I2)
 603 FORMAT (10X,4G20.10 )
 601 FORMAT (1H1,10X, 'NUMBER OF RECORDS ON DISC IS ',I5,/////)
 606 FORMAT(F10.0,10X,3G20.10)
     RETURN
     END
C*************************************************************************
C*************************************************************************
C
C     MATRIX SUBROUTINE SUPPORT PACKAGE:DOUBLE PRECISION VERSION
C
C*************************************************************************
     SUBROUTINE VERSOL ( A,B,I,M)
     IMPLICIT REAL *8 (A-H,O-Z)
     DIMENSION  A(I,M),B(I,M),P(100)
     N=I-1
     MI=M-1
     DO 1 J=1,I
     DO 1 K=1,I
   1 B(J,K) =A(J,K)
     DO 5 K= 1,I
     DO 2 J= 1,MI
   2 P(J) = B(1,J+1)/B(1,1)
     P(M) = 1.DO /B(1,1)
     DO 4 L =1,N
     DO 3 J =1,MI
```

```
    3 B(L,J) = B(L+1,J+1)- B(L+1,1)*P(J)
    4 B(L,M) =-B(L+1, 1 )*P(M)
      DO 5 J =1,M
    5 B(I,J) = P(J)
      RETURN
      END
      SUBROUTINE MATAD(A,B,C,I,J)
      IMPLICIT REAL *8 (A-H,O-Z)
      DIMENSION A(I,J),B(I,J),C(I,J)
      DO 1 L=1,J
      DO 1 M=1,I
    1 C(M,L) = A(M,L) +B(M,L)
      RETURN
      END
      SUBROUTINE MATSB (A,B,C,I,J)
      IMPLICIT REAL *8 (A-H,O-Z)
      DIMENSION A(I,J),B(I,J),C(I,J)
      DO 1 L=1,J
      DO 1 M=1,I
    1 C(M,L) = A(M,L) -B(M,L)
      RETURN
      END
      SUBROUTINE TRANS(A,B,I,J)
      IMPLICIT REAL *8 (A-H,O-Z)
      DIMENSION  A(I,J),B(J,I)
      DO 1 K=1,J
      DO 1 L=1,I
    1 B(K,L) =A(L,K)
      RETURN
      END
      SUBROUTINE AMAMPY (A,B,C,I,J,K)
      IMPLICIT REAL *8 (A-H,O-Z)
      DIMENSION  A(I,J),B(J,K),C(I,K)
      DO 1 M=1,K
      DO 1 L=1,I
      C(L,M) = O.DO
      DO 1 N =1,J
    1 C(L,M) = C(L,M)+A(L,N)*B(N,M)
      RETURN
      END
/*
//LINKEDIT    EXEC PGM=IEWL,                                            &
//            PARM='LIST,XREF,LET',                                     &
//            REGION=126K,                                             &
//            TIME=(,10)
//SYSLMOD     DD DSNAME=&GOSET(MAIN),                                   &
//            UNIT=SYSDA,                                               &
//            DCB=(RECFM=U,BLKSIZE=3072),                              &
//            DISP=(NEW,PASS),                                         &
//            SPACE=(CYL,(1,1,1))
//SYSLIB      DD DSNAME=SYS1.FORTLIB,DISP=SHR
//            DD DSNAME=SYS2.FORTSSP,DISP=SHR
//SYSUT1      DD UNIT=SYSDA,                                            &
//            SPACE=(CYL,(2,2))
//SYSPRINT    DD SYSOUT=A
//SYSLIN      DD DSNAME=&LOADSET,                                       &
//            DISP=(OLD,DELETE)
//GO          EXEC PGM=*.LINKEDIT.SYSLMOD,                              &
//*           TIME=1,REGION=126K
//            TIME=3,REGION=252K
//FT06F001    DD SYSOUT=A
//FT01F001    DD UNIT=SYSDA,SPACE=(CYL,(5,1)),                          &
//            DCB=(LRECL=151,RECFM=VS,BLKSIZE=755),                     &
//            DISP=(NEW,DELETE)
//SYSUDUMP    DD SYSOUT=A
//FT07F001    DD SYSOUT=B
//FT05F001    DD *
```

Bibliography

1. Ackermann, F., "Experience with Block-Triangulation by Independent Models." Paper presented at the 1972 Annual Meeting of the American Society of Photogrammetry, March, 1972.
2. Ackermann, F., "Experience with Applications of Block Adjustment for Large Scale Surveys," *Photogrammetric Record*, Vol. 7, No. 41, April, 1973.
3. Ackermann, F., H. Ebner, and H. Klein, "Block Triangulation with Independent Models," *Photogrammetric Engineering*, Vol. 39, No. 9, Sept., 1973.
4. Amer, F., "Digital Block Adjustment," *Photogrammetric Record*, Vol. 4, No. 19, April, 1962.
5. American Society of Photogrammetry, *Manual of Photogrammetry*, 3d ed., 1966.
6. Anderson, James M., "Analytical Aerotriangulation Using Triplets." Ph.D. thesis, Cornell University, 1964.
7. Anderson, James M., "Coordinate Transformation for Basic Unit Assembly in Sequential System of Analytic Aerotriangulation," *ISP Archives*, Vol. 17, part 8 (paper presented at Commission III, 1969).
8. Anderson, James M. and A. J. McNair, "Analytic Aerotriangulation: Triplets and Sub-Blocks," *Photogrammetria*, Vol. 21, No. 6, Dec., 1966.
9. Anderson, James M. and Everett H. Ramey, "Analytic Block Adjustment," *Photogrammetric Engineering*, Vol. 39, No. 10, Oct., 1973.
10. Atkinson, P. C., "Early Experiment with Aerodist," S and M Provisional Reports, Dept. of Mines and Technical Surveys, Ottawa, Canada, June, 1964.
11. Bachmann, W. K., "Théorie des Erreurs et Compensation des Triangulations Aeriennes." Thèse, Ecole de'Ingénieurs de Lausanne, Switzerland, 1946.
12. Ball, William E., Jr., "A Tensor Approach to Block Triangulation," *Photogrammetric Engineering*, Vol. 39, No. 1, Jan., 1973.
13. Bertram, S., "Atmospheric Refraction," *Photogrammetric Engineering*, Vol. 32, No. 1, Jan., 1966.
14. Brandenberger, A. J., *The Practice of Spatial Aerial Triangulation*, Photogrammetric Institute, Federal Institute of Technology, Zurich, 1951.
15. Brandenberger, A. J., "Some Considerations about Error Propaga-

tion in Strip Triangulations; Attainable Accuracy," *Photogrammetria*, Vol. 14, No. 2, 1957-8.

16. Brandenberger, A. J., "Strip Triangulation with Independent Geodetic Controls; Triangulation of Strip Quadrangles," Publication of the Institute of Geodesy, Photogrammetry, and Cartography, No. 9, Ohio State University, 1959.

17. Brandenberger, A. J., "The Economical Significance of Aerial Triangulation Using Auxiliary Data," *Photogrammetria*, Vol. 22, No. 6, Sept., 1967.

18. Brown, Duane C., "A Solution to the General Problem of Multiple Station Analytical Stereotriangulation." RCA Data Reduction Report No. 43, Feb., 1958.

19. Brown, Duane C., "Accuracies of Analytical Triangulation in Applications to Cadastral Surveying," *Surveying and Mapping*, Vol. 33, No. 3, Sept., 1973.

20. Brown, Duane C., Ronald G. Davis, and Frederick C. Johnson, "The Practical and Rigorous Adjustment of Large Photogrammetric Nets." Technical documentary report No. RADC-TDR-64-353; RADC, Griffis Air Force Base, New York, Oct., 1964.

21. Case, James B., "The Utilization of Constraints in Analytical Photogrammetry," *Photogrammetric Engineering*, Vol. 27, No. 5, Dec., 1961.

22. Clark, David and James Clendinning, *Plane and Geodetic Surveying*, Constable and Company, Ltd., London, 1956.

23. Colcord, J. E., "Aerial Triangulation Strip Adjustment with Independent Geodetic Control," *Photogrammetric Engineering*, Vol. 27, No. 1, March, 1961.

24. Das, Gouri B., "Aerotriangulation with Independent Models Using Affine Transformation." ISP, XII Congress, Ottawa, Canada, 1972.

25. Davis, Ronald G., "Advanced Techniques for the Rigorous Analytical Adjustment of Large Photogrammetric Nets," *Photogrammetria*, Vol. 22, No. 5, July, 1967.

26. Doyle, Frederick J., "Multiple Station Analytical Triangulation Program." Technical report submitted to U.S. Army Engineer GIMRADA from Raytheon Company, Dec., 1965.

27. Dresden, A., *Solid Analytical Geometry and Determinants*, John Wiley & Sons, Inc., New York, 1948.

28. Ebner, H., "Theoretical Accuracy Models for Block Triangulation." Paper at Commission III, International Congress of Photogrammetry, Ottawa, Canada, 1972.

29. Elassal, Atef A., "Analytical Aerial Triangulation Through Silmultaneous Relative Orientation of Multiple Cameras." Civil Engineering Studies, Photogrammetry Series, No. 2, University of Illinois, Oct., 1965.

30. Eshbach, Ovid W., *Handbook of Engineering Fundamentals*, John Wiley & Sons, Inc., New York, 1957.

31. Fereday, D. L., "Perspective Center Co-ordinates: A Study of Calculation Methods," *Photogrammetric Record*, Vol. 7, No. 41, April, 1973.

32. Ghosh, Sanjib K., "Strip Triangulation with Independent Geodetic Control," *Photogrammetric Engineering*, Vol. 28, No. 5, Nov., 1962.

33. Ghosh, Sanjib K., "Global (Total) Adjustment of Aerotriangulation with AP/C to Control Models in Kelsh Plotter." A paper presented to ISP Commission III, June, 1968.

34. Ghosh, Sanjib K., "Strip Triangulation with Independent Models," *Photogram* (Journal of the Roorkee University Photogrammetric Society, India), Vol. 1, No. 1, Oct., 1968.

35. Ghosh, Sanjib K., *Theory of Stereophotogrammetry*, 2d ed., Ohio State University, Columbus, Ohio, July, 1972.

36. Ghosh, Sanjib K., John F. Kenefick, and Arthur S. Brown, "Analytical Block Triangulation with Fictitous Data," Report No. 103, Department of Geodetic Science, Ohio State University, Feb., 1968.

37. Ghosh, Sanjib K. and Peter J. Morgan, "A Method of Block Triangulation with Independent Models," Report No. 128, Department of Geodetic Science, Ohio State University, July, 1970.

38. Gracie, Gordon, "A Statistical Investigation of the Propagation of Random Errors in Analog Aerotriangulation." Civil Engineering Studies, Photogrammetry Series, No. 3, University of Illinois, Oct., 1963.

39. Gracie, Gordon, "An Index to Publications in the English Language Pertaining to Aerotriangulation in Space," *Photogrammetric Engineering*, Vol. 30, No. 2, March, 1964.

40. Gracie, Gordon, "Analytical Block Triangulation with Sequential Independent Models," *Photogrammetria*, Vol. 22, No. 5, July, 1967.

41. Hallert, B., "A Theoretical Investigation of Aerial Triangulation as a Problem of Maxima and Minima," *Photogrammetric Engineering*, Vol. 24, No. 5, Dec., 1958.

42. Hallert, B., *Photogrammetry*, McGraw-Hill Book Company, New York, 1960.

43. Harris, W. D., G. C. Tewinkel, and C. A. Whitten, "Analytic Aero-

triangulation," Technical Bulletin No. 21 (corrected), U.S. Department of Commerce, Coast and Geodetic Survey, July, 1963.

44. Holden, G. J. F. and L. Berlin, "Independent Models and Calculators," *Photogrammetric Engineering*, Vol. 40, No. 5, May, 1974.

45. Inghilleri, G. and R. Galetto, "Further Developments of the Methods of Aerotriangulation by Independent Models," *Photogrammetria*, Vol. 22, No. 1, Jan. 1967.

46. Jaksic, Z., "Solution of Aerial Triangulation Problems Using the NRC Analytical Plotter," *Photogrammetria*, Vol. 22, No. 2, Feb., 1967.

47. Jerie, H. G., "Theoretical Height Accuracy of the Strip and Block Triangulation with and without Use of Auxiliary Data," *Photogrammetria*, Vol. 23, No. 1, Jan., 1968.

48. Karara, H. M., "Maximum Bridging Distance in Spatial Aerotriangulation," *Photogrammetric Engineering*, Vol. 28, No. 4, Sept., 1961.

49. Karara, H. M., "Studies in Spatial Aerotriangulation." University of Illinois Engineering Experimental Station Technical Report No. 5, 1963.

50. Karara, H. M., "Mono Versus Stereo Analytical Photogrammetry—Theoretical Considerations and Experimental Results," *Photogrammetria*, Vol. 22, No. 3, March, 1967.

51. Keller, M. and G. C. Tewinkel, "Aerotriangulation Strip Adjustment," Technical Bulletin No. 23, U.S. Department of Commerce, ESSA, Coast and Geodetic Survey, 1964.

52. Keller, M. and G. C. Tewinkel, "Aerotriangulation, Image Coordinate Refinement," Technical Bulletin No. 25, U.S. Department of Commerce, March, 1965.

53. Keller, M. and G. C. Tewinkel, "Three-photo Aerotriangulation," Technical Bulletin No. 29, U.S. Department of Commerce, Coast and Geodetic Survey, Feb., 1966.

54. Keller, M. and G. C. Tewinkel, "Block Analytic Aerotriangulation," Technical Bulletin No. 35, U.S. Department of Commerce, ESSA, Coast and Geodetic Survey, Nov., 1967.

55. Kenefick, John F., "60 Percent vs. 20 Percent Sidelap," *Photogrammetric Engineering*, Vol. 34, No. 6, June, 1968.

56. Kenefick, John F. Personal communications from John F. Kenefick Photogrammetric Consultant, Inc., Satellite Beach, FL, Oct., 1973.

57. Konecny, G., "Analytical Aerial Triangulation with Convergent Photography," *Photogrammetria*, Vol. 22, No. 2, Feb., 1967.

58. Kratky, V., "On the Solution of Analytical Aerotriangulation by

Means of an Iterative Procedure," *Photogrammetria*, Vol. 22, No. 5, July, 1967.

59. Kubik, K., E. R. Bosman, and D. Eckhardt, "Systematic Image Errors in Aerial Triangulation," *Photogrammetria*, Vol. 29, No. 4, Sept., 1973.

60. Lafferty, Maurice E., "Accuracy/Cost with Analytics," *Photogrammetric Engineering*, Vol. 39, No. 5, May, 1973.

61. Ligterink, G. H., "Aerial Triangulation by Independent Models —The Coordinates of the Perspective Center and Their Accuracy," *Photogrammetria*, Vol. 26, No. 1, June, 1970.

62. Livingston, Robert G., "Airborne Mapping Equipment Quality Development," *Photogrammetric Engineering*, Vol. 32, No. 3, May, 1966.

63. Maarek, A., "New Math Model for Independent-Model Triangulation," *Photogrammetric Engineering*, Vol. 39, No. 10, Oct., 1973.

64. Mahoney, W. C., "Proposal, Development and Testing of a System of Analytical Triangulation for Medium Scale Digital Computers." Ph.D. dissertation, Ohio State University, 1961.

65. Mark, Rolf-Peter, "The Influence of Systematic Errors in Block-Triangulation with Particular Consideration of Systematic Comparator Errors," *Vermessungs Informationen* (Surveying News), No. 25, Jenoptik, Jena GmbH, 1972.

66. Matos, Robert A., "Multiple-Station Analytical Triangulation," *Photogrammetric Engineering*, Vol. 37, No. 2, Feb., 1971.

67. McKenzie, Morris, L. and Robert C. Eller, "Computational Methods in the U.S.G.S.," *Photogrammetric Engineering*, Vol. 31, No. 5, Sept., 1965.

68. McNair, Arthur J. and Guirguis F. Yassa, "Optimizing Flight Altitude and Bridging Distance for Aerial Triangulation." Paper presented at the ASP San Francisco Convention, Sept., 1971.

69. Mikhail, Edward M., "A New Approach to Analytical Aerotriangulation: Two Directional Triplets in Sub-block." Ph.D. thesis, Cornell University, 1963.

70. Mikhail, Edward M., "Silmultaneous Three-Dimensional Transformation of Higher Degree," *Photogrammetric Engineering*, Vol. 30, No. 4, 1964.

71. Mikhail, Edward M., "Horizontal Aerotriangulation by Independent Models Using Horizon Camera Photography," *Photogrammetria*, Vol. 23, No. 5, Sept., 1968.

72. Morgan, Peter, "Rigorous Adjustment of Strips," *Photogrammetric Engineering*, Vol. 37, No. 12, Dec., 1971.

73. Nanayakkara, Christopher, "A Study on Spatial Triangulation Round a Globe in Close-Range Photogrammetry." M.Sc. thesis, Ohio State University, 1970.

74. Okang, Joseph P., "Comparative Study of Point-Marking Devices and Their Suitability for Photogrammetric Problems." Ph.D. dissertation, Ohio State University, 1972.

75. Philip, Aldwyn, "Independent Model Aerial Triangulation Refinement and Error Studies." Ph.D. dissertation, Ohio State University, 1973.

76. Pope, A. J., "Some Pitfalls to Be Avoided in the Iterative Adjustment of Nonlinear Problems." Paper presented at the Annual Convention, American Society of Photogrammetry, March, 1972.

77. Powell, Richard W., "AN/USQ 28 Verticality Verification Test." Paper presented at the 1972 ASP Fall Convention, Columbus, Ohio, Oct., 1972.

78. Prescott, W. G. and S. K. Ghosh, "Global Adjustment of Aerial Triangulation," Report No. 69, Department of Geodetic Science, Ohio State University, March, 1966.

79. Reolofs, R., "Thompson's Method of Aerial Triangulation by Independent Models: Two Extensions," *Photogrammetria*, Vol. 23, No. 4, July, 1968.

80. Saastamoinen, J., "Refraction," *Photogrammetric Engineering*, Vol. 38, No. 8, Aug., 1972.

81. Santoni, E., "Aerial Triangulation Using the Solar Periscope," *Photogrammetria*, Vol. 14, No. 1, 1957.

82. Scarpace, Frank L. and Paul R. Wolf, "Atmospheric Refraction," *Photogrammetric Engineering*, Vol. 39, No. 5, May, 1973.

83. Schenk, Anton, "Fortran Program for Photogrammetric Block Triangulation with the Bundles Method," Institute für Geodasie und Photogrammetrie, E.T.H., Zurich, Switzerland, 1972.

84. Schmid, Hellmut H., "A General Analytical Solution to the Problem of Photogrammetry," U.S. Ballistic Research Laboratories Report No. 1065, July, 1959.

85. Schut, G. H., "Development of Programs for Strip and Block Adjustment at the National Research Council of Canada," *Photogrammetric Engineering*, Vol. 30, No. 2, March, 1964.

86. Schut, G. H., "Formation of Strips from Independent Models," National Research Council of Canada, July, 1967.

87. Schut, G. H., "Polynomial Transformation of Strips Versus Linear Transformation of Models: A Theory and Experiments," *Photogrammetria*, Vol. 22, No. 6, Sept., 1967.

88. Schut, G. H., "Photogrammetric Refraction," *Photogrammetric Engineering*, Vol. 35, No. 1, Jan., 1969.

89. Schut, G. H., "Similarity Transformation and Least Squares," *Photogrammetric Engineering*, Vol. 39, No. 6, June, 1973.

90. Smithsonian Institute, *Smithsonian Meteorological Tables*, (5th printing), Smithsonian Institute Press, Washington, D.C., 1971.

91. Soliman, Affifi H., "Standard Error in Strip Adjustment," *Photogrammetric Engineering*, Vol. 35, No. 1, Jan., 1969.

92. Soliman, Affifi H., "Accuracy and Application," *Photogrammetric Engineering*, Vol. 37, No. 8, Aug., 1971.

93. Stewart, R. A., "Aerodist Controlled Photography for Topographic Mapping." Ph.D. dissertation, Ohio State University, 1973.

94. Stewart, W. S. and S. H. Hull, "Analytical Aerial Triangulation in the Ordinance Survey," ISP Archives, International Society of Photogrammetry, 1968-9.

95. Strahle, John A., "Comparison of Semi-analytical and Aeropolygon Stereo-triangulation on the Analytical Stereoplotter AP/C." M.Sc. thesis, Ohio State University, 1971.

96. Tewinkel, G. C., "Analytic Absolute Orientation in Photogrammetry," Technical Bulletin No. 19, U.S. Department of Commerce, Coast and Geodetic Survey, 1962.

97. Tewinkel, G. C., "Accuracy of Block Triangulation." Paper presented at the 1970 ACSM-ASP Technical Conference in Denver, Oct., 1970.

98. Tewinkel, G. C., "Aerotriangulation for Control Surveys," *Surveying and Mapping*, Vol. 32, No. 1, March, 1972.

99. Thompson, E. H., "Aerial Triangulation by Independent Models," *Photogrammetria*, Vol. 19, No. 7, 1962-4.

100. Thompson, E. H., "Review of Methods of Independent Model Aerial Triangulation," *Photogrammetric Record*, Vol. 5, No. 26, Oct., 1965.

101. Umbach, Melvin J., "Aerotriangulation: Transformation of Surveying and Mapping Coordinate Systems," Technical Bulletin No. 34, U.S. Department of Commerce, ESSA, Coast and Geodetic Survey, Aug., 1967.

102. Uotila, Urho A., "Introduction to Adjustment Computations with Matrices." Lecture notes, Department of Geodetic Science, Ohio State University, 1969.

103. U. S. Standard Atmosphere Supplements, U. S. Government Printing Office, 1966.

104. Veress, S. A. and M. Nasu, "Triangulation with Santoni Stereo-

simplex IIC," *Photogrammetric Engineering*, Vol. 39, No. 11, Nov., 1973.

105. Weissman, Simha, "Horizon Controlled Analytical Strip Triangulation." Ph.D. dissertation, Ohio State University, 1967.

106. Williams, V. A. and H. H. Brazier, "Aerotriangulation by Independent Models: A Comparison with Other Methods," *Photogrammetria*, Vol. 21, No. 3, June, 1966.

107. Wong, K. W. and G. Elphingstone, "Aerotriangulation by SAPGO," *Photogrammetric Engineering*, Vol. 38, No. 8, Aug., 1972.

108. Wood, R., "Analytical Aerial Triangulation with Angular Measurements," *Photogrammetric Record*, Vol. 6, No. 36, Oct., 1970.

109. Zarzycki, J. M., "The Use of Horizon Camera, Doppler Navigation, and Statoscope in Aerial Triangulation," ISP, *International Archives of Photogrammetry*, Vol. XV, Part 5, Com. III, 1965.

110. Zeller, M., *Text Book of Photogrammetry*, H. K. Lewis and Co., Ltd., London, 1952.

Index

Index

About the Author

Sanjib K. Ghosh was educated in India, the Netherlands, and the United States. He received the Ph.D. from Ohio State University, where he is now an associate professor of geodetic science and civil engineering. He has also been a surveyor for the Survey of India, and a United Nations fellow. The author of numerous journal articles and one book, *Theory of Stereophotogrammetry,* Professor Ghosh's research interests include the geometry and calibration of conventional and nonconventional photogrammetric systems and their applications in measurements.